What's New!

Burberry
My Burberry Blush
1.0 oz EDP Sp $ 68.00
Your Price : _____
1.6 oz EDP Sp $ 90.00
Your Price : _____
3.0 oz EDP Sp $ 120.00
Your Price : _____

Calvin Klein
CK One Gold
3.4 oz EDT Sp $ 58.00
Your Price : _____

Calvin Klein
Obsessed
1.0 oz EDP Sp $ 56.00
Your Price : _____
1.7 oz EDP Sp $ 75.00
Your Price : _____
3.4 oz EDP Sp $ 94.00
Your Price : _____

Carolina Herrera
Good Girl
1.7 oz EDP Sp $ 90.00
Your Price : _____
2.7 oz EDP Sp $ 115.00
Your Price : _____

Christian Dior
Poison Girl
1.7 oz EDP Sp $ 95.00
Your Price : _____
3.4 oz EDP Sp $ 125.00
Your Price : _____

Coach
New York
1.7 oz EDP Sp $ 75.00
Your Price : _____
3.0 oz EDP Sp $ 95.00
Your Price : _____

Creed
Aventus
1.0 oz EDP Sp $ 270.00
Your Price : _____

Dolce & Gabbana
Dolce Rosa Excelsa
1.0 oz EDP Sp $ 76.00
Your Price : _____
1.6 oz EDP Sp $ 94.00
Your Price : _____
2.5 oz EDP Sp $ 117.00
Your Price : _____

Elizabeth Taylor
White Diamonds Night
3.3 oz EDP Sp $ 68.00
Your Price : _____

Escada
Aqua Del Sol
1.0 oz EDT Sp $ 48.00
Your Price : _____
3.3 oz EDT Sp $ 68.00
Your Price : _____

Giorgio Armani
Sky Di Gioia
1.0 oz EDP Sp $ 50.00
Your Price : _____
1.7 oz EDP Sp $ 72.00
Your Price : _____
3.4 oz EDP Sp $ 92.00
Your Price : _____

Guerlain
Mon Guerlain
1.0 oz EDP Sp $ 66.00
Your Price : _____
1.7 oz EDP Sp $ 94.00
Your Price : _____
3.4 oz EDP Sp $ 124.00
Your Price : _____

Jimmy Choo
Illicit Flower
2.0 oz EDT Sp $ 78.00
Your Price : _____
3.4 oz EDT Sp $ 98.00
Your Price : _____

Jimmy Choo
L'Eau
2.0 oz EDT Sp $ 78.00
Your Price : _____
3.0 oz EDT Sp $ 98.00
Your Price : _____

Juicy Couture
Viva La Juicy Sucre
1.7 oz EDP Sp $ 76.00
Your Price : _____
3.4 oz EDP Sp $ 96.00
Your Price : _____

Juicy Couture
Viva La Juicy Glace
1.7 oz EDP Sp $ 76.00
Your Price : _____
3.4 oz EDP Sp $ 96.00
Your Price : _____

Marc Jacobs
Daisy Dream Kiss
1.7 oz EDT Sp $ 80.00
Your Price : _____

Marc Jacobs
Daisy Eau So Fresh Kiss
2.5 oz EDT Sp $ 96.00
Your Price : _____

Marc Jacobs
Daisy Kiss
1.7 oz EDT Sp $ 80.00
Your Price : _____

Marc Jacobs
Decadence
1.7 oz EDP Sp $ 99.00
Your Price : _____
3.4 oz EDP Sp $ 122.00
Your Price : _____

Marc Jacobs
Divine Decadence
1.7 oz EDP Sp $ 99.00
Your Price : _____
3.4 oz EDP Sp $ 122.00
Your Price : _____

Miu Miu
L'Eau Bleue
1.0 oz EDP Sp $ 68.00
Your Price : _____
1.7 oz EDP Sp $ 90.00
Your Price : _____
3.4 oz EDP Sp $ 118.00
Your Price : _____

Miu Miu
Miu Miu
1.0 oz EDP Sp $ 68.00
Your Price : _____
1.7 oz EDP Sp $ 90.00
Your Price : _____
3.4 oz EDP Sp $ 118.00
Your Price : _____

Moschino
Fresh Couture
1.0 oz EDT Sp $ 45.00
Your Price : _____
1.7 oz EDT Sp $ 62.00
Your Price : _____
3.4 oz EDT Sp $ 82.00
Your Price : _____

Moschino
Fresh Couture Pink
1.0 oz EDT Sp $ 45.00
Your Price : _____
1.7 oz EDT Sp $ 62.00
Your Price : _____
3.4 oz EDT Sp $ 82.00
Your Price : _____

Narciso Rodriguez
Fleur Musk
1.6 oz EDP Sp $ 97.00
Your Price : _____
3.3 oz EDP Sp $ 124.00
Your Price : _____

Prada
Candy Gloss
1.0 oz EDT Sp $ 58.00
Your Price : _____
1.7 oz EDT Sp $ 76.00
Your Price : _____
2.7 oz EDT Sp $ 96.00
Your Price : _____

Prada
Candy Kiss
1.7 oz EDP Sp $ 90.00
Your Price : _____
2.7 oz EDP Sp $ 120.00
Your Price : _____

Ralph Lauren
Tender Romance
1.7 oz EDP Sp $ 76.00
Your Price : _____
3.4 oz EDP Sp $ 96.00
Your Price : _____

Ralph Lauren
Woman
1.0 oz EDP Sp $ 64.00
Your Price : _____
1.7 oz EDP Sp $ 84.00
Your Price : _____

Thierry Mugler
Angel Muse
1.0 oz EDP Sp $ 70.00
Your Price : _____
1.7 oz EDP Sp $ 95.00
Your Price : _____

Tommy Hilfigher
The Girl
1.7 oz EDT Sp $ 45.00
Your Price : _____
3.4 oz EDT Sp $ 57.00
Your Price : _____

Tory Burch
Jolie Fleur Bleue
1.7 oz EDP Sp $ 96.00
Your Price : _____
3.4 oz EDP Sp $ 126.00
Your Price : _____

Tiry Burch
Jolie Fleur Rose
1.7 oz EDP Sp $ 96.00
Your Price : _____
3.4 oz EDP Sp $ 126.00
Your Price : _____

Tory Burch
Jolie Fleur Verte
1.7 oz EDP Sp $ 96.00
Your Price : _____
3.4 oz EDP Sp $ 126.00
Your Price : _____

Tory Burch
Love Relentlessly
1.7 oz EDP Sp $ 88.00
Your Price : _____
3.4 oz EDP Sp $ 118.00
Your Price : _____

Valentino
Donna
1.7 oz EDP Sp $ 97.00
Your Price : _____
3.4 oz EDP Sp $ 133.00
Your Price : _____

Valentino
Valentina Poudre
1.7 oz EDP Sp $ 89.00
Your Price : _____
2.7 oz EDP Sp $ 120.00
Your Price : _____

YSL
Black Opium Nuit Blanche
1.0 oz EDP Sp $ 69.00
Your Price : _____
1.7 oz EDP Sp $ 90.00
Your Price : _____
3.4 oz EDP Sp $ 115.00
Your Price : _____

Yves Saint Laurent
Mon Paris
1.7 oz EDP Sp $ 92.00
Your Price : _____
3.0 oz EDP Sp $ 122.00
Your Price : _____

What's New!

Azzaro
Chrome Intense
3.4 oz EDT Sp $ 87.00
Your Price : _____

Azzaro
Wanted
1.7 oz EDT Sp $ 65.00
Your Price : _____
3.4 oz EDT Sp $ 85.00
Your Price : _____

Burberry
Brit Splash
1.7 oz EDT Sp $ 65.00
Your Price : _____
3.4 oz EDT Sp $ 82.00
Your Price : _____

Burberry
Mr Burberry
1.6 oz EDT Sp $ 68.00
Your Price : _____
3.3 oz EDT Sp $ 88.00
Your Price : _____
5.0 oz EDT Sp $ 115.00
Your Price : _____

Burberry
Mr Burberry
1.6 oz EDP Sp $ 75.00
Your Price : _____
3.3 oz EDP Sp $ 95.00
Your Price : _____
5.0 oz EDP Sp $ 130.00
Your Price : _____

Calvin Klein
Ck2
1.0 oz EDT Sp $ 40.00
Your Price : _____
1.7 oz EDT Sp $ 55.00
Your Price : _____
3.4 oz EDT Sp $ 75.00
Your Price : _____

Calvin Klein
Eternity Now
1.0 oz EDT Sp $ 42.00
Your Price : _____
3.4 oz EDT Sp $ 79.00
Your Price : _____

Calvin Klein
Obsessed
2.5 oz EDT Sp $ 64.00
Your Price : _____
4.2 oz EDT Sp $ 80.00
Your Price : _____

Cartier
L'Envol De Cartier
1.6 oz EDP Sp $ 82.00
Your Price : _____
2.7 oz EDP Sp $ 115.00
Your Price : _____
3.3 oz EDP Sp $ 132.00
Your Price : _____

Cartier
Pasha Noire Sport
3.3 oz EDT Sp $ 110.00
Your Price : _____
5.1 oz EDT Sp $ 140.00
Your Price : _____

Christian Dior
Sauvage
2.0 oz EDT Sp $ 74.00
Your Price : _____
3.4 oz EDT Sp $ 92.00
Your Price : _____
6.8 oz EDT Sp $ 145.00
Your Price : _____

Davidoff
Horizon
1.7 oz EDT Sp $ 59.00
Your Price : _____
3.4 oz EDT Sp $ 89.00
Your Price : _____

Dolce & Gabbana
Light Blue Intense
1.6 oz EDP Sp $ 68.00
Your Price : _____
3.3 oz EDP Sp $ 86.00
Your Price : _____
6.7 oz EDP Sp $ 125.00
Your Price : _____

Emporio Armani
Acqua Di Gio Profumo
2.5 oz EDP Sp $ 95.00
Your Price : _____
4.2 oz EDP Sp $ 130.00
Your Price : _____
6.1 oz EDP Sp $ 150.00
Your Price : _____

Giorgio Armani
Armani Code Profumo
2.0 oz EDP Sp $ 90.00
Your Price : _____
3.7 oz EDP Sp $ 110.00
Your Price : _____
6.7 oz EDP Sp $ 135.00
Your Price : _____

Givenchy
Gentleman Only Intense
1.7 oz EDT Sp $ 71.00
Your Price : _____
3.3 oz EDT Sp $ 93.00
Your Price : _____
5.0 oz EDT Sp $ 115.00
Your Price : _____

Givenchy
PI Extreme
3.4 oz EDT Sp $ 89.00
Your Price : _____

Gucci
Guilty Absolute
3.0 oz EDP Sp $ 99.00
Your Price : _____
5.0 oz EDP Sp $ 125.00
Your Price : _____

Gucci
Intense Oud
1.7 oz EDP Sp $ 99.00
Your Price : _____
3.0 oz EDP Sp $ 137.00
Your Price : _____

Hugo Boss
Boss The Scent Intense
1.7 oz EDP Sp $ 76.00
Your Price : _____
3.3 oz EDP Sp $ 94.00
Your Price : _____
6.7 oz EDP Sp $ 130.00
Your Price : _____

Jimmy Choo
Man Ice
1.7 oz EDT Sp $ 68.00
Your Price : _____
3.3 oz EDT Sp $ 88.00
Your Price : _____

John Varvatos
Dark Rebel
2.5 oz EDT Sp $ 69.00
Your Price : _____
4.2 oz EDT Sp $ 89.00
Your Price : _____

Kenneth Cole
Black Bold
3.4 oz EDP Sp $ 80.00
Your Price : _____

Kenneth Cole
Mankind Hero
1.7 oz EDT Sp $ 60.00
Your Price : _____
3.4 oz EDT Sp $ 80.00
Your Price : _____

Lacoste
Eau Magnetic
3.3 oz EDT Sp $ 75.00
Your Price : _____
5.9 oz EDT Sp $ 92.00
Your Price : _____

Mont Blanc
Legend Spirit
1.7 oz EDT Sp $ 68.00
Your Price : _____
3.3 oz EDT Sp $ 88.00
Your Price : _____
6.7 oz EDT Sp $ 110.00
Your Price : _____

Paco Rabanne
Invictus Intense
1.7 oz EDT Sp $ 70.00
Your Price : _____
3.4 oz EDT Sp $ 93.00
Your Price : _____

Paco Rabanne
One Million Prive
1.7 oz EDP Sp $ 66.00
Your Price : _____
3.4 oz EDP Sp $ 90.00
Your Price : _____

Sean John
Sean John
3.4 oz EDT Sp $ 70.00
Your Price : _____

Thierry Mugler
A *Men Pure Tonka
3.4 oz EDT Sp $ 89.00
Your Price : _____

Tom Ford
Soleil Blanc
1.7 oz EDP Sp $ 230.00
Your Price : _____
3.4 oz EDP Sp $ 312.00
Your Price : _____

Versace
Dylan Blue
1.7 oz EDT Sp $ 67.00
Your Price : _____
3.4 oz EDT Sp $ 86.00
Your Price : _____

Victor & Rolph
Spicebomb Fresh
3.04 oz EDT Sp $ 98.00
Your Price : _____
5.0 oz EDT Sp $ 125.00
Your Price : _____

Vince Camuto
Eterno
1.7 oz EDT Sp $ 60.00
Your Price : _____
3.4 oz EDT Sp $ 77.00
Your Price : _____

Vince Camuto
Oud
1.7 oz EDT Sp $ 60.00
Your Price : _____
3.4 oz EDT Sp $ 77.00
Your Price : _____

Vince Camuto
Solare
1.7 oz EDT Sp $ 60.00
Your Price : _____
3.4 oz EDT Sp $ 77.00
Your Price : _____

Yves Saint Laurent
L'Homme Le Parfum Ultime
2.0 oz EDP Sp $ 80.00
Your Price : _____
3.3 oz EDP Sp $ 104.00
Your Price : _____
6.7 oz EDP Sp $ 140.00
Your Price : _____

Abbreviations Used in the Catalog

1. EDT = Eau de Toilette

2. EDP = Eau de Parfum

3. COL = Cologne

4. Sp = Spray

5. Printed Prices = Approximate Retail Prices

6. $ = US Dollar

7. Sizes = 1.6 oz or 1.7 oz is 50ml
   Sizes = 3.3 oz or 3.4 oz is   100ml

Note : Items and Prices Displayed in this catalog are for reference purpose only. Their accuracy is not guaranteed.

Adidas
Floral Dream
1.7 oz EDT Sp $ 37.00
Your Price : _____
3.4 oz EDT Sp $ 59.00
Your Price : _____

Adidas
Free Emotion
1.7 oz EDT Sp $ 37.00
Your Price : _____
3.4 oz EDT Sp $ 59.00
Your Price : _____

Adidas
Natural Vitality
1.7 oz EDT Sp $ 37.00
Your Price : _____
3.4 oz EDT Sp $ 59.00
Your Price : _____

Adidas
Pure Lightness
1.7 oz EDT Sp $ 37.00
Your Price : _____
3.4 oz EDT Sp $ 59.00
Your Price : _____

Adrienne Vittadini
Adrienne Vittadini
1.7 oz EDT Sp $ 55.00
Your Price : _____
3.4 oz EDT Sp $ 70.00
Your Price : _____

Adrienne Vittadini
AV
1.0 oz EDT Sp $ 39.00
Your Price : _____
1.7 oz EDT Sp $ 54.00
Your Price : _____
3.0 oz EDT Sp $ 74.00
Your Price : _____

Adrienne Vittadini
Capri
1.0 oz EDT Sp $ 49.00
Your Price : _____
3.4 oz EDT Sp $ 74.00
Your Price : _____

Agent Provocateur
Agent Provocateur
1.7 oz EDP Sp $ 80.00
Your Price : _____
3.3 oz EDP Sp $ 105.00
Your Price : _____

Agent Provocateur
Maitresse
1.7 oz EDP Sp $ 85.00
Your Price : _____
3.4 oz EDP Sp $ 112.00
Your Price : _____

Alessandro
Alessandro Del Acqua
1.7 oz EDT Sp $ 65.00
Your Price : _____
3.4 oz EDT Sp $ 112.00
Your Price : _____

Alexander Julian
McQueen
1.6 oz EDT Sp $ 40.00
Your Price : _____
3.3 oz EDT Sp $ 59.00
Your Price : _____

Alfred Sung
Forever
2.5 oz EDP Sp $ 63.00
Your Price : _____
4.2 oz EDP Sp $ 78.00
Your Price : _____

Alfred Sung
Jewel
1 oz EDP Sp $ 40.00
Your Price : _____
1.7 oz EDP Sp $ 59.00
Your Price : _____
3.4 oz EDP Sp $ 78.00
Your Price : _____

Alfred Sung
Paradise
1 oz EDP Sp $ 40.00
Your Price : _____
1.7 oz EDP Sp $ 59.00
Your Price : _____
3.4 oz EDP Sp $ 78.00
Your Price : _____

Alfred Sung
Sha
1.7 oz EDT Sp $ 59.00
Your Price : _____
3.4 oz EDT Sp $ 73.00
Your Price : _____

Altred Sung
Shi
1.6 oz EDT Sp $ 59.00
Your Price : _____
3.4 oz EDT Sp $ 73.00
Your Price : _____

Alfred Sung
Sung
1.7 oz EDT Sp $ 59.00
Your Price : _____
3.4 oz EDT Sp $ 73.00
Your Price : _____

Alfred Sung
Pure
1.7 oz EDP Sp $ 59.00
Your Price : _____
3.4 oz EDP Sp $ 73.00
Your Price : _____

Angel Schlesser
Angel Schlesser
1.6 oz EDP Sp $ 58.00
Your Price : _____
3.4 oz EDP Sp $ 78.00
Your Price : _____

Angel Schlesser
Essential
1.7 oz EDP Sp $ 58.00
Your Price : _____
3.4 oz EDP Sp $ 78.00
Your Price : _____

Animale
Animale
1.7 oz EDP Sp $ 50.00
Your Price : _____
3.4 oz EDP Sp $ 70.00
Your Price : _____

Animale
Animale Animale
1.7 oz EDP Sp $ 50.00
Your Price : _____
3.4 oz EDP Sp $ 70.00
Your Price : _____

Animale
Chaleur D' Animale
1.7 oz EDP Sp $ 65.00
Your Price : _____
3.4 oz EDP Sp $ 80.00
Your Price : _____

Animale
Temptation
1.7 oz EDP Sp $ 63.00
Your Price : _____
3.4 oz EDP Sp $ 83.00
Your Price : _____

Anna Sui
Anna Sui
1.0 oz EDT Sp $ 45.00
Your Price : _____
1.7 oz EDT Sp $ 62.00
Your Price : _____
3.4 oz EDT Sp $ 78.00
Your Price : _____

Anna Sui
Dolly Girl
1.7 oz EDT Sp $ 55.00
Your Price : _____
3.4 oz EDT Sp $ 75.00
Your Price : _____

Anna Sui
Dolly Girl Bon jour
L'amour
1.6 oz EDT Sp $ 60.00
Your Price : _____
3.4 oz EDT Sp $ 75.00
Your Price : _____

Anna Sui
Magic Romance
1.7 oz EDT Sp $ 62.00
Your Price : _____
2.5 oz EDT Sp $ 78.00
Your Price : _____

Anna Sui
Dolly Girl On The Beach
1.0 oz EDT Sp $ 50.00
Your Price : _____
1.7 oz EDT Sp $ 60.00
Your Price : _____

Anna Sui
Dolly Girl OOH LA LOVE
1.7 oz EDT Sp $ 60.00
Your Price : _____
3.4 oz EDT Sp $ 78.00
Your Price : _____

Anna Sui
Secret Wish
1.7 oz EDT Sp $ 45.00
Your Price : _____
2.5 oz EDT Sp $ 60.00
Your Price : _____

Anucci
Femme
1.6 oz EDT Sp $ 48.00
Your Price : _____
3.3 oz EDT Sp $ 60.00
Your Price : _____

Anucci
Princess
1.6 oz EDT Sp $ 47.00
Your Price : _____
3.3 oz EDT Sp $ 55.00
Your Price : _____

Aramis
Havana Pour Elle
1.7 oz EDP Sp $ 65.00
Your Price : _____
3.4 EDP Sp $ 75.00
Your Price : _____

Ariana Grande
Sweet Like Candy
1.7 oz EDP Sp $ 49.00
Your Price : _____
3.4 oz EDP Sp $ 59.00
Your Price : _____

Ariana Grande
Ari
1.7 oz EDP Sp $ 49.00
Your Price : _____
3.4 oz EDP Sp $ 59.00
Your Price : _____

Azzaro
Now
1.7 oz EDP Sp $ 55.00
Your Price : _____
3.4 oz EDP Sp $ 75.00
Your Price : _____

Azzaro
Oh La La
1.7 oz EDP Sp $ 45.00
Your Price : _____
3.4 oz EDP Sp $ 69.00
Your Price : _____

Azzaro
Eau Belle
1.7 oz EDP Sp $ 55.00
Your Price : _____
3.4 oz EDP Sp $ 75.00
Your Price : _____

Azzaro
Azzura
1.7 oz EDT Sp $ 63.00
Your Price : _____
3.4 oz EDT Sp $ 78.00
Your Price : _____

Azzaro
Visit
1.7 oz EDP Sp $ 45.00
Your Price : _____
3.4 oz EDP Sp $ 60.00
Your Price : _____

Baby Phat
Fabulosity
1.7 oz EDT Sp $ 45.00
Your Price : _____
3.4 oz EDT Sp $ 73.00
Your Price : _____

Baby Phat
Goddess
1.6 oz EDT Sp $ 48.00
Your Price : _____
3.4 oz EDT Sp $ 73.00
Your Price : _____

Baby Phat
Golden Goddess
1.6 oz EDT Sp $ 49.00
Your Price : _____
3.4 oz EDT Sp $ 73.00
Your Price : _____

Balenciaga Paris
Florabotanica
1.7 oz EDP Sp $ 105.00
Your Price : _____
3.4 oz EDP Sp $ 134.00
Your Price : _____

Balenciaga Paris
Rosabotanica
1.7 oz EDP Sp $ 105.00
Your Price : _____
3.4 oz EDP Sp $ 134.00
Your Price : _____

Balenciaga Paris
Balenciaga Paris
1.7 oz EDP Sp $ 115.00
Your Price : _____
2.5 oz EDP Sp $ 148.00
Your Price : _____

Banana Republic
Rose wood
1.7 oz EDP Sp $ 48.00
Your Price : _____
3.4 oz EDP Sp $ 75.00
Your Price : _____

BCBGMAXAZRIA
BCBGMAXAZRIA
1.7 oz EDP Sp $ 55.00
Your Price : _____
3.4 oz EDP Sp $ 75.00
Your Price : _____

BCBGMAXAZRIA
BCBGIRLS Nature
1.7 oz EDT Sp $ 60.00
Your Price : _____

BCBGMAXAZRIA
BCBGirls Sexy
1.7 oz EDT Sp $ 60.00
Your Price : _____

BCBGMAXAZRIA
Bon Genre
1.7 oz EDP Sp $ 55.00
Your Price : _____
3.4 oz EDP Sp $ 75.00
Your Price : _____

BCBGMAXAZRIA
Bon Chic
1.7 oz EDP Sp $ 55.00
Your Price : _____
3.4 oz EDP Sp $ 75.00
Your Price : _____

Bebe
Bebe
1.6 oz EDP Sp $ 48.00
Your Price : _____
3.4 oz EDP Sp $ 58.00
Your Price : _____

Bebe
Desire
1.6 oz EDP Sp $ 45.00
Your Price : _____
3.4 oz EDP Sp $ 58.00
Your Price : _____

Bebe
Gold
1.6 oz EDP Sp $ 49.00
Your Price : _____
3.4 oz EDP Sp $ 58.00
Your Price : _____

Bebe
Love
1.6 oz EDP Sp $ 48.00
Your Price : _____
3.4 oz EDP Sp $ 58.00
Your Price : _____

Bebe
Noveau Chic
1.6 oz EDP Sp $ 45.00
Your Price : _____
3.4 oz EDP Sp $ 58.00
Your Price : _____

Bebe
Sheer
1.6 oz EDP Sp $ 48.00
Your Price : _____
3.4 oz EDP Sp $ 58.00
Your Price : _____

Bebe
Wishes & Dreams
1.6 oz EDP Sp $ 45.00
Your Price : _____
3.4 oz EDP Sp $ 58.00
Your Price : _____

Benetton
B-United
1.6 oz EDT Sp $ 47.00
Your Price :
3.4 oz EDT Sp $ 59.00
Your Price :

Benetton
Hot
1.7 oz EDT Sp $ 40.00
Your Price :
3.4 oz EDT Sp $ 59.00
Your Price :

Benetton
Sport Pure
1.6 oz EDT Sp $ 39.00
Your Price :
3.3 oz EDT Sp $ 50.00
Your Price :

Benetton
Colors
1.7 oz EDT Sp $ 40.00
Your Price :
3.4 oz EDT Sp $ 59.00
Your Price :

Benetton
Funtastic
1.6 oz EDT Sp $ 29.00
Your Price :
3.3 oz EDT Sp $ 35.00
Your Price :

Benetton
Tribu
1.7 oz EDT Sp $ 50.00
Your Price :
3.4 oz EDT Sp $ 65.00
Your Price :

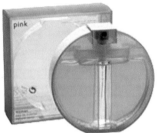

Benetton
Inferno Paradiso
1.7 oz EDT Sp $ 40.00
Your Price :
3.4 oz EDT Sp $ 59.00
Your Price :

Benetton
Sport
1.6 oz EDT Sp $ 39.00
Your Price :
3.3 oz EDT Sp $ 50.00
Your Price :

Betsey Johnson
Betsey Johnson
1.6 oz EDP Sp $ 75.00
Your Price :
3.4 oz EDP Sp $ 95.00
Your Price :

Betsey Johnson
Too Too
1.6 oz EDP Sp $ 55.00
Your Price :
3.3 oz EDP Sp $ 65.00
Your Price :

Beyonce
Heat
1.6 oz EDP Sp $ 49.00
Your Price :
3.4 oz EDP Sp $ 59.00
Your Price :

Beyonce
Heat Mrs Carter
1.6 oz EDP Sp $ 49.00
Your Price :
3.4 oz EDP Sp $ 59.00
Your Price :

Beyonce
Heat Rush
1.6 oz EDP Sp $ 49.00
Your Price :
3.4 oz EDP Sp $ 59.00
Your Price :

Beyonce
Heat Wild Orchid
1.6 oz EDP Sp $ 49.00
Your Price :
3.4 oz EDP Sp $ 59.00
Your Price :

Beyonce
Midnight Heat
1.6 oz EDP Sp $ 49.00
Your Price :
3.4 oz EDP Sp $ 59.00
Your Price :

Beyonce
Pulse
1.6 oz EDP Sp $ 49.00
Your Price :
3.4 oz EDP Sp $ 59.00
Your Price :

Beyonce
Pulse Nyc
1.6 oz EDP Sp $ 49.00
Your Price :
3.4 oz EDP Sp $ 59.00
Your Price :

Beyonce
Rise
1.6 oz EDP Sp $ 49.00
Your Price :
3.4 oz EDP Sp $ 59.00
Your Price :

Bijan
1.7 oz EDT Sp $ 49.00
Your Price :
2.5 oz EDT Sp $ 69.00
Your Price :

Bijan
Black
1.6 oz EDT Sp $ 59.00
Your Price :
2.5 oz EDT Sp $ 69.00
Your Price :

Bijan
DNA
1.6 oz EDT Sp $ 63.00
Your Price :
3.3 oz EDP Sp $ 75.00
Your Price :

Bijan
Nude
1.7 oz EDP Sp $ 59.00
Your Price :
2.5 oz EDP Sp $ 69.00
Your Price :

Bijan
Style
1.7 oz EDT Sp $ 49.00
Your Price :
2.5 oz EDT Sp $ 69.00
Your Price :

Bijan
Wicked
1.6 oz EDT Sp $ 59.00
Your Price :
2.5 oz EDT Sp $ 69.00
Your Price :

Bijan
With a Twist
1.7 oz EDP Sp $ 48.00
Your Price :
3.4 oz EDP Sp $ 90.00
Your Price :

Bijan
VIP
1.6 oz EDT Sp $ 49.00
Your Price :
2.5 oz EDT Sp $ 59.00
Your Price :

Bijan
Light
1.6 oz EDT Sp $ 49.00
Your Price :
2.5 oz EDT Sp $ 59.00
Your Price :

Bill Blass
1.0 oz EDT Sp $ 30.00
Your Price :
1.7 oz EDT Sp $ 45.00
Your Price :
3.4 oz EDT Sp $ 70.00
Your Price :

Bill Blass
Amazing
1.7 oz EDP Sp $ 45.00
Your Price :
3.4 oz EDP Sp $ 70.00
Your Price :

Bill Blass
Hot
1.7 oz EDT Sp $ 45.00
Your Price :
3.4 oz EDT Sp $ 70.00
Your Price :

Bill Blass
New
1.3 oz EDP Sp $ 70.00
Your Price :
2.7 oz EDP Sp $ 100.00
Your Price :

Bill Blass
Nude
1.7 oz COL Sp $ 54.00
Your Price :
3.4 oz COL Sp $ 64.00
Your Price :

Bob Mackie
Perhaps
1.6 oz EDP Sp $ 63.00
Your Price :
3.4 oz EDP Sp $ 75.00
Your Price :

Bob Mackie
Mackie
1.7 oz EDT Sp $ 59.00
Your Price :
3.4 oz EDT Sp $ 75.00
Your Price :

Bob Mackie
Masquerade
1.7 oz EDP Sp $ 54.00
Your Price :
3.4 oz EDP Sp $ 75.00
Your Price :

Bond No. 9 NYC
Astor Place
1.7 oz EDP Sp $ 220.00
Your Price :
3.4 oz EDP Sp $ 315.00
Your Price :

Bond No. 9 NYC
B9
1.7 Oz EDP Sp $ 280.00
Your Price :
3.3 Oz EDP Sp $ 340.00
Your Price :

Bond No. 9 NYC
Bleecker Street
1.7 Oz EDP Sp $ 230.00
Your Price :
3.3 Oz EDP Sp $ 320.00
Your Price :

Bond No. 9 NYC
Broadway Nite
1.7 oz EDP Sp $ 200.00
Your Price :
3.3 oz EDP Sp $ 280.00
Your Price :

Bond No. 9 NYC
Brooklyn
1.7 Oz EDP Sp $ 215.00
Your Price :
3.3 Oz EDP Sp $ 295.00
Your Price :

Bond No. 9 NYC
Bryant Park
1.7 oz EDP Sp $ 215.00
Your Price : _____
3.3 oz EDP Sp $ 300.00
Your Price : _____

Bond No. 9 NYC
Central Park West
1.7 oz EDP Sp $ 230.00
Your Price : _____
3.3 oz EDP Sp $ 300.00
Your Price : _____

Bond No. 9 NYC
Chelsea Flowers
1.7 oz EDP Sp $ 215.00
Your Price : _____
3.4 oz EDP Sp $ 300.00
Your Price : _____

Bond No. 9 NYC
Chinatown
1.7 oz EDP Sp $ 220.00
Your Price : _____
3.3 oz EDP Sp $ 310.00
Your Price : _____

Bond No. 9 NYC
Central Park South
1.7 oz EDP Sp $ 230.00
Your Price : _____
3.3 oz EDP Sp $ 330.00
Your Price : _____

Bond No. 9 NYC
Fashion Avenue
1.7 oz EDP Sp $ 200.00
Your Price : _____
3.4 oz EDP Sp $ 280.00
Your Price : _____

Bond No. 9 NYC
Harrods For Her
1.7 oz EDP Sp $ 170.00
Your Price : _____
3.4 oz EDP Sp $ 250.00
Your Price : _____

Bond No. 9 NYC
High Line
1.7 oz EDP Sp $ 220.00
Your Price : _____
3.4 oz EDP Sp $ 320.00
Your Price : _____

Bond No. 9 NYC
Hudson Yards
1.7 oz EDP Sp $ 230.00
Your Price : _____
3.3 oz EDP Sp $ 330.00
Your Price : _____

Bond No. 9 NYC
I Love NY (Mother's Day)
1.7 oz EDP Sp $ 170.00
Your Price : _____
3.4 oz EDP Sp $ 250.00
Your Price : _____

Bond No. 9 NYC
Little Italy
1.7 oz EDP Sp $ 200.00
Your Price : _____
3.4 oz EDP Sp $ 265.00
Your Price : _____

Bond No. 9 NYC
Madison Soiree
1.7 oz EDP Sp $ 200.00
Your Price : _____
3.4 oz EDP Sp $ 280.00
Your Price : _____

Bond No. 9 NYC
Madison Square Park
1.7 oz EDP Sp $ 230.00
Your Price : _____
3.4 oz EDP Sp $ 330.00
Your Price : _____

Bond No. 9 NYC
New York Fling
1.7 oz EDP Sp $ 200.00
Your Price : _____
3.4 oz EDP Sp $ 280.00
Your Price : _____

Bond No. 9 NYC
Nolita
3.4 oz EDP Sp $ 350.00
Your Price : _____

Bond No. 9 NYC
Nuits De Noho
1.7 oz EDP Sp $ 215.00
Your Price : _____
3.4 oz EDP Sp $ 300.00
Your Price : _____

Bond No. 9 NYC
Park Avenue
1.7 oz EDP Sp $ 200.00
Your Price : _____
3.4 oz EDP Sp $ 280.00
Your Price : _____

Bond No. 9 NYC
Park Avenue South
1.7 oz EDP Sp $ 230.00
Your Price : _____
3.4 oz EDP Sp $ 330.00
Your Price : _____

Bond No. 9 NYC
Perfumista Avenue
1.7 oz EDP Sp $ 300.00
Your Price : _____
3.3 oz EDP Sp $ 410.00
Your Price : _____

Bond No. 9 NYC
Saks En Rose
1.7 oz EDP Sp $ 200.00
Your Price : _____
3.4 oz EDP Sp $ 295.00
Your Price : _____

Bond No. 9 NYC
So New York
1.7 oz EDP Sp $ 200.00
Your Price : _____
3.4 oz EDP Sp $ 280.00
Your Price : _____

Bond No. 9 NYC
The Scent of Peace
1.7 Oz EDP Sp $ 230.00
Your Price : _____
3.3 Oz EDP Sp $ 320.00
Your Price : _____

Bond No. 9 NYC
Union Square
1.7 oz EDP Sp $ 215.00
Your Price : _____
3.3 oz EDP Sp $ 300.00
Your Price : _____

Bond No. 9 NYC
Washington Square
1.7 oz EDP Sp $ 215.00
Your Price : _____
3.4 oz EDP Sp $ 315.00
Your Price : _____

Bond No. 9 NYC
West Side
1.7 oz EDP Sp $ 220.00
Your Price : _____
3.4 oz EDP Sp $ 300.00
Your Price : _____

Bottega Veneta
Essence Aromatique
1.7 oz EDT Sp $ 95.00
Your Price : _____

Bottega Veneta
Eau Legere
1.7 oz EDT Sp $ 100.00
Your Price : _____
2.5 oz EDT Sp $ 125.00
Your Price : _____

Bottega Veneta
Eau Sensuelle
1.7 oz EDP Sp $ 120.00
Your Price : _____
2.5 oz EDP Sp $ 155.00
Your Price : _____

Bottega Veneta
Bottega Veneta
1.7 oz EDP Sp $ 120.00
Your Price : _____
2.5 oz EDP Sp $ 155.00
Your Price : _____

Bottega Veneta
Knot
1.7 oz EDP Sp $ 125.00
Your Price : _____
2.5 oz EDP Sp $ 160.00
Your Price : _____

Boucheron
1.0 oz EDP Sp $ 95.00
Your Price : _____
1.6 oz EDP Sp $ 106.00
Your Price : _____
3.0 oz EDP Sp $ 136.00
Your Price : _____

Boucheron
1.7 oz EDT Sp $ 76.00
Your Price : _____
3.3 oz EDT Sp $ 116.00
Your Price : _____

Boucheron
B de Bouchron
1.6 oz EDP Sp $ 76.00
Your Price : _____
3.3 oz EDP Sp $ 165.00
Your Price : _____

Boucheron
Eau Legere
1.6 oz EDT Sp $ 78.00
Your Price : _____
3.3 oz EDT Sp $ 96.00
Your Price : _____

Boucheron
Initial
1.7 oz EDT Sp $ 75.00
Your Price : _____
3.4 oz EDT Sp $ 115.00
Your Price : _____

Boucheron
Jaipur
1.7 oz EDT Sp $ 75.00
Your Price : _____
3.4 oz EDT Sp $ 115.00
Your Price : _____

Boucheron
Jaipur Bracelet
1.6 oz EDT Sp $ 93.00
Your Price : _____
3.3 oz EDT Sp $ 110.00
Your Price : _____

Boucheron
Jaipur Saphir
1.6 oz EDT Sp $ 75.00
Your Price : _____
3.4 oz EDT Sp $ 115.00
Your Price : _____

Boucheron
Miss Boucheron
1.6 oz EDT Sp $ 96.00
Your Price : _____
3.3 oz EDT Sp $ 110.00
Your Price : _____

Boucheron
Trouble
1.7 oz EDP Sp $ 75.00
Your Price : _____
3.4 oz EDP Sp $ 115.00
Your Price : _____

Boucheron
Trouble Eau Legere
1.7 oz EDP Sp $ 75.00
Your Price : _____
3.4 oz EDP Sp $ 115.00
Your Price : _____

Boucheron
Trouble Joaillier
1.6 oz EDP Sp $ 93.00
Your Price : _____
3.4 oz EDP Sp $ 115.00
Your Price : _____

Bourjois
Soir De Paris
1.7 oz EDP Sp $ 55.00
Your Price : _____
3.4 oz EDP Sp $ 68.00
Your Price : _____

Britney Spears
Believe
1.7 oz EDP Sp $ 48.00
Your Price : _____
3.3 oz EDP Sp $ 58.00
Your Price : _____

Britney Spears
Curious
1.7 oz EDP Sp $ 49.00
Your Price : _____
3.3 oz EDP Sp $ 59.00
Your Price : _____

Britney Spears
Circus Fantasy
1.7 oz EDP Sp $ 48.00
Your Price : _____
3.3 oz EDP Sp $ 58.00
Your Price : _____

Britney Spears
Curious In Control
1.6 oz EDP Sp $ 49.00
Your Price : _____
3.3 oz EDP Sp $ 59.00
Your Price : _____

Britney Spears
Cosmic Radiance
1.7 Oz EDP Sp $ 55.00
Your Price : _____
3.3 Oz EDP Sp $ 65.00
Your Price : _____

Britney Spears
Fantasy
1.7 oz EDP Sp $ 45.00
Your Price : _____
3.4 oz EDP Sp $ 55.00
Your Price : _____

Britney Spears
Fantasy The Naughty Remix
3.3 Oz EDP Sp $ 65.00
Your Price : _____

Britney Spears
Fantasy The Nice Remix
3.3 Oz EDP Sp $ 65.00
Your Price : _____

Britney Spears
Hidden Fantasy
1.7 oz EDP Sp $ 45.00
Your Price : _____
3.3 oz EDP Sp $ 55.00
Your Price : _____

Britney Spears
Island Fantasy
1.7 oz EDP Sp $ 45.00
Your Price : _____
3.3 oz EDP Sp $ 55.00
Your Price : _____

Britney Spears
Midnight Fantasy
1.0 oz EDP Sp $ 38.00
Your Price : _____
1.7 oz EDP Sp $ 49.00
Your Price : _____
3.3 oz EDP Sp $ 59.00
Your Price : _____

Britney Spears
Radiance
1.7 oz EDP Sp $ 55.00
Your Price : _____
3.4 oz EDP Sp $ 65.00
Your Price : _____

Brosseau
Ombre Rose
1.0 oz EDP Sp $ 50.00
Your Price : _____
1.7 oz EDP Sp $ 65.00
Your Price : _____
3.4 oz EDP Sp $ 80.00
Your Price : _____

Burberry
Baby Touch
1.7 oz EDT Sp $ 55.00
Your Price : _____
3.3 oz EDT Sp $ 75.00
Your Price : _____

Burberry
Body
1.3 oz EDP Sp $ 62.00
Your Price : _____
2.0 oz EDP Sp $ 85.00
Your Price : _____
2.8 oz EDP Sp $ 105.00
Your Price : _____

Burberry
Body
1.3 oz EDT Sp $ 56.00
Your Price : _____
2.0 oz EDT Sp $ 75.00
Your Price : _____
2.8 oz EDT Sp $ 95.00
Your Price : _____

Burberry
Body Intense
2.0 oz EDP Sp $ 90.00
Your Price : _____
2.8 oz EDP Sp $ 115.00
Your Price : _____

Burberry
Brit
1.7 oz EDP Sp $ 84.00
Your Price : _____
3.4 oz EDP Sp $ 105.00
Your Price : _____

Burberry
Brit
1.7 oz EDT Sp $ 74.00
Your Price : _____
3.4 oz EDT Sp $ 94.00
Your Price : _____

Burberry
Brit Gold
1.7 oz EDP Sp $ 85.00
Your Price : _____
3.4 oz EDP Sp $ 95.00
Your Price : _____

Burberry
Brit Red
1.7 oz EDP Sp $ 85.00
Your Price : _____
3.4 oz EDP Sp $ 95.00
Your Price : _____

Burberry
Brit Rhythm
1.0 oz EDT Sp $ 56.00
Your Price : _____
1.6 oz EDT Sp $ 75.00
Your Price : _____
3.0 oz EDT Sp $ 95.00
Your Price : _____

Burberry
Brit 'Sheer'
1.0 oz EDT Sp $ 55.00
Your Price : _____
1.7 oz EDT Sp $ 74.00
Your Price : _____
3.3 oz EDT Sp $ 96.00
Your Price : _____

Burberry
Brit Summer
1.6 oz EDT Sp $ 70.00
Your Price : _____
3.0 oz EDT Sp $ 90.00
Your Price : _____

Burberry
Burberry
1.0 oz EDP Sp $ 58.00
Your Price : _____
1.7 oz EDP Sp $ 75.00
Your Price : _____
3.4 oz EDP Sp $ 95.00
Your Price : _____

Burberry
London (Fabric)
1.0 oz EDP Sp $ 58.00
Your Price : _____
1.7 oz EDP Sp $ 75.00
Your Price : _____
3.4 oz EDP Sp $ 95.00
Your Price : _____

Burberry
My Burberry
1.6 oz EDP Sp $ 95.00
Your Price : _____
3.0 oz EDP Sp $ 125.00
Your Price : _____

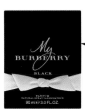

Burberry
My Burberry Black
1.6 oz EDP Sp $ 95.00
Your Price : _____
3.0 oz EDP Sp $ 125.00
Your Price : _____

Burberry
Sport
1.7 oz EDP Sp $ 63.00
Your Price : _____
2.5 oz EDP Sp $ 75.00
Your Price : _____

Burberry
Summer
1.7 oz EDT Sp $ 55.00
Your Price : _____
3.4 oz EDT Sp $ 75.00
Your Price : _____

Burberry
The Beat
1.7 oz EDP Sp $ 75.00
Your Price : _____
2.5 oz EDP Sp $ 90.00
Your Price : _____

Burberry
Touch
1.0 oz EDP Sp $ 58.00
Your Price : _____
1.7 oz EDP Sp $ 75.00
Your Price : _____
3.4 oz EDP Sp $ 95.00
Your Price : _____

Burberry
Weekend
1.0 oz EDP Sp $ 50.00
Your Price : _____
1.7 oz EDP Sp $ 72.00
Your Price : _____
3.4 oz EDP Sp $ 92.00
Your Price : _____

Bvlgari
Au The Rouge (Red Tea)
1.4 oz EDP Sp $ 67.00
Your Price : _____
2.5 oz EDP Sp $ 120.00
Your Price : _____

Bvlgari
Aqua Divina
3.4 oz EDP Sp $ 85.00
Your Price : _____

Bvlgari
Black
1.3 oz EDT Sp $ 52.00
Your Price : _____
2.5 oz EDT Sp $ 80.00
Your Price : _____

Bvlgari
BLV
2.5 oz EDP Sp $ 85.00
Your Price : _____
3.4 oz EDP Sp $ 120.00
Your Price : _____

Bvlgari
BLV II
2.5 oz EDP Sp $ 79.00
Your Price : _____

Bvlgari
BLV Absolute
1.3 oz EDP Sp $ 62.00
Your Price : _____
3.4 oz EDP Sp $ 120.00
Your Price : _____

Bvlgari
Blv Notte
1.4 oz EDP Sp $ 70.00
Your Price : _____
2.5 oz EDP Sp $ 90.00
Your Price : _____

Bvlgari
Eau Parfumee Au The Blanc
1.7 oz EDP Sp $ 81.00
Your Price : _____
2.5 oz EDP Sp $ 97.00
Your Price : _____
5.0 oz EDP Sp $ 160.00
Your Price : _____

Bvlgari
Eau Parfumee Au The Vert
1.7 oz EDP Sp $ 81.00
Your Price : _____
2.5 oz EDP Sp $ 97.00
Your Price : _____
5.0 oz EDP Sp $ 160.00
Your Price : _____

Bvlgari
Extreme
1.7 oz EDT Sp $ 81.00
Your Price : _____
3.4 oz EDT Sp $ 120.00
Your Price : _____

Bvlgari
Green Tea
1.4 oz EDP Sp $ 67.00
Your Price : _____
3.4 oz EDP Sp $ 120.00
Your Price : _____

Bvlgari
Jasmin Noir
1.7 oz EDP Sp $ 98.00
Your Price : _____
3.4 oz EDP Sp $ 148.00
Your Price : _____

Bvlgari
Mon Jasmin Noir
1.0 oz EDP Sp $ 68.00
Your Price : _____
1.7 oz EDP Sp $ 83.00
Your Price : _____
2.5 oz EDP Sp $ 105.00
Your Price : _____

Bvlgari
Omnia
1.35 oz EDP Sp $ 67.00
Your Price : _____
2.2 oz EDP Sp $ 87.00
Your Price : _____

Bvlgari
Omnia Indian Garnet
1.3 oz EDT Sp $ 66.00
Your Price : _____
2.2 oz EDT Sp $ 82.00
Your Price : _____

Bvlgari
Omnia Amethyste
1.35 oz EDT Sp $ 66.00
Your Price : _____
2.2 oz EDT Sp $ 82.00
Your Price : _____

Bvlgari
Omnia Paraiba
1.3 oz EDT Sp $ 66.00
Your Price : _____
2.2 oz EDT Sp $ 82.00
Your Price : _____

Bvlgari
Omnia Coral
1.35 oz EDT Sp $ 66.00
Your Price : _____
2.2 oz EDP Sp $ 82.00
Your Price : _____

Bvlgari
Omnia Crystalline
1.35 oz EDT Sp $ 66.00
Your Price : _____
2.2 oz EDT Sp $ 82.00
Your Price : _____

Bvlgari
Omnia Green Jade
1.35 oz EDT Sp $ 66.00
Your Price : _____
2.2 oz EDT Sp $ 82.00
Your Price : _____

Bvlgari
Petits Et Mamans
1.6 oz EDP Sp $ 65.00
Your Price : _____
3.3 oz EDP Sp $ 95.00
Your Price : _____

Bvlgari
Pour Femme
1.7 oz EDP Sp $ 95.00
Your Price : _____
3.4 oz EDP Sp $ 140.00
Your Price : _____

Bvlgari
Rose Essentielle
1.7 oz EDP Sp $ 95.00
Your Price : _____
3.4 oz EDP Sp $ 140.00
Your Price : _____

Bvlgari
Rose Goldea
1.7 oz EDP Sp $ 112.00
Your Price : _____
3.4 oz EDP Sp $ 155.00
Your Price : _____

Bvlgari
Voile De Jasmin
1.7 oz EDT Sp $ 75.00
Your Price : _____
3.4 oz EDT Sp $ 110.00
Your Price : _____

Cacharel
Amor Amor
1.7 oz EDT Sp $ 55.00
Your Price : _____
3.4 oz EDT Sp $ 75.00
Your Price : _____

Cacharel
Anais Anais
1.7 oz EDT Sp $ 52.00
Your Price : _____
3.4 oz EDT Sp $ 62.00
Your Price : _____

Cacharel
Eden
1.0 oz EDP Sp $ 50.00
Your Price : _____
3.4 oz EDP Sp $ 90.00
Your Price : _____

Cacharel
Liberte
1.7 oz EDT Sp $ 70.00
Your Price : _____
2.5 oz EDT Sp $ 80.00
Your Price : _____

Cacharel
Noa
1.0 oz EDT Sp $ 50.00
Your Price : _____
1.7 oz EDT Sp $ 65.00
Your Price : _____
3.3 oz EDT Sp $ 90.00
Your Price : _____

Cacharel
Noa Fleur
1.7 oz EDT Sp $ 65.00
Your Price : _____
3.4 oz EDT Sp $ 90.00
Your Price : _____

Cacharel
Promesse
1.7 oz EDT Sp $ 65.00
Your Price : _____
3.3 oz EDT Sp $ 90.00
Your Price : _____

Cacharel
Scarlett
1.7 oz EDT Sp $ 65.00
Your Price : _____
3.3 oz EDT Sp $ 90.00
Your Price : _____

Caesars
Caesars Women
3.3 oz EDC Sp $ 60.00
Your Price : _____

Café
Café
3.0 oz EDT Sp $ 55.00
Your Price : _____

Café
Café Café
3.0 oz EDT Sp $ 55.00
Your Price : _____

Calvin Klein
Beauty
1.7 oz EDP Sp $ 65.00
Your Price : _____
3.4 oz EDP Sp $ 85.00
Your Price : _____

Calvin Klein
Beauty Sheer Essence
1.7 oz EDT Sp $ 65.00
Your Price : _____
3.4 oz EDT Sp $ 85.00
Your Price : _____

Calvin Klein
CK Be
1.7 oz EDT Sp $ 40.00
Your Price : _____
3.4 oz EDT Sp $ 50.00
Your Price : _____
6.7 oz EDT Sp $ 64.00

Calvin Klein
CK IN2U
1.7 oz EDT Sp $ 45.00
Your Price : _____
3.4 oz EDT Sp $ 55.00
Your Price : _____
5.0 oz EDT Sp $ 68.00

Calvin Klein
CK One
1.7 oz EDT Sp $ 49.00
Your Price : _____
3.4 oz EDT Sp $ 58.00
Your Price : _____
6.7 oz EDT Sp $ 72.00
Your Price : _____

Calvin Klein
CK One Summer
1.7 oz EDT Sp $ 45.00
Your Price : _____
3.4 oz EDT Sp $ 54.00
Your Price : _____

Calvin Klein
Contradiction
1.7 oz EDP Sp $ 60.00
Your Price : _____
3.4 oz EDP Sp $ 75.00
Your Price : _____

Calvin Klein
Escape
1.7 oz EDP Sp $ 49.00
Your Price : _____
3.4 oz EDP Sp $ 75.00
Your Price : _____

Calvin Klein
Eternity
1.7 oz EDP Sp $ 68.00
Your Price : _____
3.4 oz EDP Sp $ 86.00
Your Price : _____
6.7 oz EDP Sp $ 125.00
Your Price : _____

Calvin Klein
Eternity Aqua
1.7 oz EDP Sp $ 60.00
Your Price : _____
3.4 oz EDP Sp $ 78.00
Your Price : _____

Calvin Klein
Eternity Moment
1.7 oz EDP Sp $ 65.00
Your Price : _____
3.4 oz EDP Sp $ 78.00
Your Price : _____

Calvin Klein
Eternity Air
1.7 oz EDP Sp $ 71.00
Your Price : _____
3.4 oz EDP Sp $ 88.00
Your Price : _____

Calvin Klein
Euphoria
1.7 oz EDP Sp $ 72.00
Your Price : _____
3.4 oz EDP Sp $ 92.00
Your Price : _____
5.5 oz EDP Sp $ 112.00
Your Price : _____

Calvin Klein
Euphoria Blossom
1.7 oz EDP Sp $ 60.00
Your Price : _____
3.3 oz EDP Sp $ 90.00
Your Price : _____

Calvin Klein
Euphoria Crystalline
1.7 oz EDP Sp $ 78.00
Your Price : _____
3.4 oz EDP Sp $ 90.00
Your Price : _____

Calvin Klein
Euphoria Forbidden
1.7 oz EDP Sp $ 64.00
Your Price : _____
3.4 oz EDP Sp $ 85.00
Your Price : _____

Calvin Klein
Euphoria Lustre
1.7 oz EDP Sp $ 60.00
Your Price : _____
3.3 oz EDP Sp $ 90.00
Your Price : _____

Calvin Klein
Eternity Summer 2011
1.7 oz EDP Sp $ 65.00
Your Price : _____
3.4 oz EDP Sp $ 78.00
Your Price : _____

Calvin Klein
Eternity Summer 2013
1.7 oz EDP Sp $ 65.00
Your Price : _____
3.4 oz EDP Sp $ 78.00
Your Price : _____

Calvin Klein
Obsession
1.7 oz EDP Sp $ 68.00
Your Price : _____
3.4 oz EDP Sp $ 86.00
Your Price : _____

Calvin Klein
Obsession Night
1.7 oz EDP Sp $ 68.00
Your Price : _____
3.4 oz EDP Sp $ 86.00
Your Price : _____

Calvin Klein
Secret Obsession
1.7 oz EDP Sp $ 59.00
Your Price : _____
3.4 oz EDP Sp $ 75.00
Your Price : _____

Calvin Klein
Truth
1.7 oz EDP Sp $ 49.00
Your Price : _____
3.4 oz EDP Sp $ 75.00
Your Price : _____

Calvin Klein
CK One Red
3.4 oz EDT Sp $ 54.00
Your Price : _____

Calvin Klein
CK One Shock
3.4 oz EDT Sp $ 54.00
Your Price : _____

Calvin Klein
Euphoria Gold
1.7 Oz EDP Sp $ 68.00
Your Price : _____
3.4 Oz EDP Sp $ 88.00
Your Price : _____

Calvin Klein
Euphoria Essence
1.7 oz EDP Sp $ 69.00
Your Price : _____
3.4 oz EDP Sp $ 89.00
Your Price : _____

Calvin Klein
Eternity Now
1.0 oz EDP Sp $ 48.00
Your Price : _____
1.7 oz EDP Sp $ 68.00
Your Price : _____
3.4 oz EDP Sp $ 86.00
Your Price : _____

Calvin Klein
Eternity Purple Orchid
3.4 oz EDP Sp $ 75.00
Your Price : _____

Calvin Klein
Euphoria Endless
1.4 oz EDP Sp $ 65.00
Your Price : _____
2.5 oz EDP Sp $ 74.00
Your Price : _____
4.0 oz EDP Sp $ 94.00
Your Price : _____

Calvin Klein
Eternity Night
3.4 oz EDP Sp $ 80.00
Your Price : _____

Calvin Klein
Deep Euphoria
1.7 oz EDP Sp $ 72.00
Your Price : _____
3.4 oz EDP Sp $ 92.00
Your Price : _____

Calvin Klein
Beauty Sheer
1.7 oz EDP Sp $ 65.00
Your Price : _____
3.4 oz EDP Sp $ 85.00
Your Price : _____

Carlos Santana
1.7 oz EDP Sp $ 50.00
Your Price : _____
3.4 oz EDP Sp $ 70.00
Your Price : _____

Carolina Herrera
212
2.0 oz EDT Sp $ 78.00
Your Price : _____
3.4 oz EDT Sp $ 102.00
Your Price : _____

Carolina Herrera
212 Sexy
2.0 oz EDP Sp $ 78.00
Your Price : _____
3.4 oz EDP Sp $ 102.00
Your Price : _____

Carolina Herrera
212 Splash
2.0 oz EDT Sp $ 70.00
Your Price : _____
3.4 oz EDT Sp $ 90.00
Your Price : _____

Carolina Herrera
212 White
2.0 oz EDT Sp $ 69.00
Your Price : _____
3.4 oz EDT Sp $ 79.00
Your Price : _____

Carolina Herrera
CH L' EAU
1.7 oz EDT Sp $ 85.00
Your Price : _____
3.4 oz EDT Sp $ 105.00
Your Price : _____

Carolina Herrera
212 VIP
1.7 oz EDP Sp $ 78.00
Your Price : _____
2.7 oz EDP Sp $ 102.00
Your Price : _____

Carolina Herrera
Carolina Herrera
1.0 oz EDT Sp $ 40.00
Your Price : _____
1.7 oz EDT Sp $ 65.00
Your Price : _____
3.4 oz EDT Sp $ 90.00
Your Price : _____

Carolina Herrera
Carolina Herrera
1.0 oz EDP Sp $ 56.00
Your Price : _____
1.7 oz EDP Sp $ 78.00
Your Price : _____
3.4 oz EDP Sp $ 107.00
Your Price : _____

Carolina Herrera
CH
1.7 oz EDT Sp $ 86.00
Your Price : _____
3.4 oz EDT Sp $ 107.00
Your Price : _____

Carolina Herrera
Chic
1 oz EDP Sp $ 49.00
Your Price : _____
1.7 oz EDP Sp $ 65.00
Your Price : _____
2.7 oz EDP Sp $ 90.00
Your Price : _____

Carolina Herrera
Flore
1.7 oz EDP Sp $ 78.00
Your Price : _____
3.4 oz EDP Sp $ 90.00
Your Price : _____

Carolina Herrera
CH Sublime
1.7 oz EDP Sp $ 75.00
Your Price : _____
2.7 oz EDP Sp $ 95.00
Your Price : _____

Carolina Herrera
212 Summer
2.0 oz EDT Sp $ 68.00
Your Price : _____

Carolina Herrera
212 VIP Rose
1.7 Oz EDP Sp $ 78.00
Your Price : _____
2.7 Oz EDP Sp $ 102.00
Your Price : _____

Carolina Herrera
Good Girl
1.7 Oz EDP Sp $ 90.00
Your Price : _____
2.7 Oz EDP Sp $ 115.00
Your Price : _____

Cartier
Baiser Vole
1.6 oz EDP Sp $ 106.00
Your Price : _____
3.3 oz EDP Sp $ 150.00
Your Price : _____

Cartier
Delices De Cartier
1.6 oz EDT Sp $ 75.00
Your Price : _____
3.3 oz EDT Sp $ 105.00
Your Price : _____

Cartier
Delices De Cartier
Eau Fruitee
1.6 oz EDT Sp $ 85.00
Your Price : _____
3.3 oz EDT Sp $ 105.00
Your Price : _____

Cartier
De Lune
1.5 oz EDT Sp $ 75.00
Your Price : _____
2.5 oz EDT Sp $ 98.00
Your Price : _____
4.2 oz EDT Sp $ 125.00
Your Price : _____

Cartier
Eau De Cartier
1.6 oz EDT Sp $ 75.00
Your Price : _____
3.3 oz EDT Sp $ 95.00
Your Price : _____
6.75 oz EDT Sp $ 127.00
Your Price : _____

Cartier
Eau De Cartier Essence
D' Orange
1.6 oz EDT Sp $ 75.00
Your Price : _____
3.3 oz EDT Sp $ 95.00
Your Price : _____
6.75 oz EDT Sp $ 127.00
Your Price : _____

Cartier
Must De Cartier
1.6 oz EDT Sp $ 90.00
Your Price : _____
3.3 oz EDT Sp $ 130.00
Your Price : _____

Cartier
Must De Cartier
Eau Fine
5.0 oz EDT Sp $ 105.00
Your Price : _____

Cartier
La Panthere
1.0 oz EDP Sp $ 77.00
Your Price : _____
1.6 oz EDP Sp $ 110.00
Your Price : _____
2.5 oz EDP Sp $ 140.00
Your Price : _____

Cartier
La Panthere Legere
1.6 oz EDP Sp $ 102.00
Your Price : _____
2.5 oz EDP Sp $ 130.00
Your Price : _____

Cartier
La Panthere Soire
1.6 oz EDP Sp $ 112.00
Your Price : _____
2.5 oz EDP Sp $ 142.00
Your Price : _____

Cartier
Le Baiser Du Dragon
3.3 oz EDP Sp $ 150.00
Your Price : _____

Cartier
So Pretty
1.6 oz EDT Sp $ 95.00
Your Price : _____
3.3 oz EDT Sp $ 150.00
Your Price : _____

Cartier
Gold Must
3.3 oz EDP Sp $ 150.00
Your Price : _____

Cartier
Baiser Fou
1.6 Oz EDP Sp $ 95.00
Your Price : _____
2.5 oz EDP Sp $ 120.00
Your Price : _____

Cartier
Baiser Vole Lys Rose
1.6 Oz EDT Sp $ 90.00
Your Price : _____
3.3 Oz EDT Sp $ 130.00
Your Price : _____

Celine Dion
Celine Dion
1.7 oz EDT Sp $ 50.00
Your Price : _____
3.4 oz EDT Sp $ 75.00
Your Price : _____

Celine Dion
Always Belong
1.7 oz EDT Sp $ 47.00
Your Price : _____
3.4 oz EDT Sp $ 59.00
Your Price : _____

Celine Dion
Belong
1.7 oz EDT Sp $ 47.00
Your Price : _____
3.4 oz EDT Sp $ 59.00
Your Price : _____

Celine Dion
Chic
1.7 oz EDT Sp $ 47.00
Your Price : _____
3.4 oz EDT Sp $ 59.00
Your Price : _____

Celine Dion
Enchanting
1.7 oz EDT Sp $ 47.00
Your Price : _____
3.4 oz EDT Sp $ 59.00
Your Price : _____

Celine Dion
Femme
1.7 oz EDT Sp $ 50.00
Your Price : _____
3.4 oz EDT Sp $ 75.00
Your Price : _____

Celine Dion
Magic Celine
1.7 oz EDT Sp $ 47.00
Your Price : _____
3.4 oz EDT Sp $ 59.00
Your Price : _____

Celina Dion
Notes
1.7 oz EDT Sp $ 47.00
Your Price : _____
3.4 oz EDT Sp $ 59.00
Your Price : _____

Celine Dion
Oriental Summer
1.7 oz EDT Sp $ 47.00
Your Price : _____
3.4 oz EDT Sp $ 59.00
Your Price : _____

Chanel
Gabrielle
1.7 oz EDP Sp $ 105.00
Your Price : _____
3.4 oz EDP Sp $ 135.00
Your Price : _____

Chanel
Coco Mademoiselle Intense
1.7 oz EDP Sp $ 110.00
Your Price : _____
3.4 oz EDP Sp $ 140.00
Your Price : _____

Chanel
Allure (EDT)
1.7 oz EDT Sp $ 80.00
Your Price : _____
3.4 oz EDT Sp $ 102.00
Your Price : _____

Chanel
Chance Eau Vive
1.7 oz EDT Sp $ 80.00
Your Price : _____
3.4 oz EDT Sp $ 102.00
Your Price : _____
5.0 oz EDT Sp $ 130.00
Your Price : _____

Chanel
Coco Chanel (EDT)
1.7 oz EDT Sp $ 80.00
Your Price : _____
3.4 oz EDT Sp $ 102.00
Your Price : _____

Chanel
Coco Mademoiselle (EDT)
1.7 oz EDT Sp $ 80.00
Your Price : _____
3.4 oz EDT Sp $ 102.00
Your Price : _____

Chanel
No. 22
1.7 oz EDT Sp $ 85.00
Your Price : _____
3.3 oz EDT Sp $ 115.00
Your Price : _____

Chanel
Allure
1.7 oz EDP Sp $ 100.00
Your Price : _____
3.4 oz EDP Sp $ 130.00
Your Price : _____

Chanel
Allure Sensuelle
1.7 oz EDP Sp $ 100.00
Your Price : _____
3.4 oz EDP Sp $ 130.00
Your Price : _____

Chanel
Bois Des Iles
1.7 oz EDP Sp $ 195.00
Your Price : _____
3.4 oz EDP Sp $ 220.00
Your Price : _____

Chanel
Chance Eau Tendre
1.7 oz EDT Sp $ 80.00
Your Price : _____
3.4 oz EDT Sp $ 102.00
Your Price : _____
5.0 oz EDT Sp $ 130.00
Your Price : _____

Chanel
Chance
1.7 oz EDP Sp $ 100.00
Your Price : _____
3.4 oz EDP Sp $ 130.00
Your Price : _____

Chanel
Chance
1.7 oz EDT Sp $ 80.00
Your Price : _____
3.4 oz EDT Sp $ 102.00
Your Price : _____
5.0 oz EDT Sp $ 130.00
Your Price : _____

Chanel
Chance Eau Fraiche
1.7 oz EDT Sp $ 80.00
Your Price : _____
3.4 oz EDT Sp $ 102.00
Your Price : _____
5.0 oz EDT Sp $ 130.00
Your Price : _____

Chanel
Coco Chanel
1.2 oz EDP Sp $ 75.00
Your Price : _____
1.7 oz EDP Sp $ 100.00
Your Price : _____
3.4 oz EDP Sp $ 130.00
Your Price : _____

Chanel
Coco Noir
1.7 oz EDP Sp $ 100.00
Your Price : _____
3.4 oz EDP Sp $ 130.00
Your Price : _____

Chanel
Coco Mademoiselle
1.7 oz EDP Sp $ 100.00
Your Price : _____
3.4 oz EDP Sp $ 130.00
Your Price : _____
6.8 oz EDP Sp $ 210.00
Your Price : _____

Chanel
Cristalle Eau Verte
1.7 oz EDT Sp $ 80.00
Your Price : _____
3.4 oz EDT Sp $ 105.00
Your Price : _____

Chanel
No. 5
1.7 oz EDP Sp $ 105.00
Your Price : _____
3.4 oz EDP Sp $ 135.00
Your Price : _____
6.8 oz EDP Sp $ 215.00
Your Price : _____

Chanel
No. 5 L'Eau
1.7 oz EDT Sp $ 105.00
Your Price : _____
3.4 oz EDT Sp $ 135.00
Your Price : _____
6.8 oz EDT Sp $ 215.00
Your Price : _____

Chanel
No. 19
1.7 oz EDP Sp $ 94.00
Your Price : _____
3.3 oz EDP Sp $ 130.00
Your Price : _____

Chanel No. 5 (EDT)
Chanel
1.7 oz EDT Sp $ 85.00
Your Price : _____
3.4 oz EDT Sp $ 107.00
Your Price : _____

Chloe
Classic
3.0 oz EDT Sp $ 75.00
Your Price : _____

Chloe
Chloe'
1.0 oz EDP Sp $ 75.00
Your Price : _____
1.7 oz EDP Sp $ 105.00
Your Price : _____
2.5 oz EDP Sp $ 132.00
Your Price : _____

Chloe
Intense
1.7 oz EDP Sp $ 98.00
Your Price : _____
2.5 oz EDP Sp $ 120.00
Your Price : _____

Chloe
Love Chloe
1.7 oz EDT Sp $ 85.00
Your Price : _____
2.5 oz EDT Sp $ 110.00
Your Price : _____

Chloe
Love Story
1.7 oz EDP Sp $ 105.00
Your Price : _____
2.5 oz EDP Sp $ 132.00
Your Price : _____

Chloe
Love Story Eau Sensuelle
1.7 oz EDP Sp $ 105.00
Your Price : _____
2.5 oz EDP Sp $ 132.00
Your Price : _____

Chloe
Narcisse
1.7 oz EDT Sp $ 52.00
Your Price : _____
3.4 oz EDT Sp $ 75.00
Your Price : _____

Chloe
Roses
1.7 oz EDT Sp $ 95.00
Your Price : _____
2.5 oz EDT Sp $ 122.00
Your Price : _____

Chopard
Casmir
1.7 oz EDP Sp $ 75.00
Your Price : _____
3.4 oz EDP Sp $ 100.00
Your Price : _____

Chopard
Pure Wish
1.7 oz EDP Sp $ 68.00
Your Price : _____
2.5 oz EDP Sp $ 85.00
Your Price : _____

Chopard
Wish
1.7 oz EDP Sp $ 80.00
Your Price : _____
3.4 oz EDP Sp $ 100.00
Your Price : _____

Chopard
Wish Pink Diamond
1.7 oz EDP Sp $ 60.00
Your Price : _____
3.4 oz EDP Sp $ 85.00
Your Price : _____

Christian Audigier
Born Wild Ed Hardy
1.7 oz EDP Sp $ 55.00
Your Price : _____
3.4 oz EDP Sp $ 75.00
Your Price : _____

Christian Audigier
Ed Hardy
1.7 oz EDP Sp $ 55.00
Your Price : _____
3.4 oz EDP Sp $ 75.00
Your Price : _____

Christian Audigier
Hearts & Daggers Ed Hardy
1.7 oz EDP Sp $ 55.00
Your Price : _____
3.4 oz EDP Sp $ 75.00
Your Price : _____

Christian Audigier
Love & Luck Ed Hardy
1.7 oz EDP Sp $ 55.00
Your Price : _____
3.4 oz EDP Sp $ 75.00
Your Price : _____

Christian Audigier
Skulls & Roses
1.7 oz EDP Sp $ 48.00
Your Price : _____
3.4 oz EDP Sp $ 65.00
Your Price : _____

Christian Audigier
Skulls & Roses Chalkboard
1.7 oz EDP Sp $ 48.00
Your Price : _____
3.4 oz EDP Sp $ 65.00
Your Price : _____

Christian Audigier
Villain Ed Hardy
2.5 oz EDP Sp $ 65.00
Your Price : _____
4.2 oz EDP Sp $ 75.00
Your Price : _____

Christian Dior
Addict
1.7 oz EDP Sp $ 94.00
Your Price : _____
3.4 oz EDP Sp $ 124.00
Your Price : _____

Christian Dior
Diorling
3.4 oz EDT Sp $ 100.00
Your Price : _____

Christian Dior
Addict 2
1.7 oz EDT Sp $ 70.00
Your Price : _____
3.4 oz EDT Sp $ 99.00
Your Price : _____

Christian Dior
Addict Shine
1.7 oz EDT Sp $ 59.00
Your Price : _____
3.4 oz EDT Sp $ 90.00
Your Price : _____

Christian Dior
Chris 1947
1.7 oz EDT Sp $ 55.00
Your Price : _____
3.4 oz EDT Sp $ 90.00
Your Price : _____

Christian Dior
Dior Me, Dior Me Not
1.7 oz EDT Sp $ 59.00
Your Price : _____
3.4 oz EDT Sp $ 90.00
Your Price : _____

Christian Dior
Diorella
1.7 oz EDT Sp $ 59.00
Your Price : _____
3.4 oz EDT Sp $ 100.00
Your Price : _____

Christian Dior
Dioressence
1.7 oz EDT Sp $ 59.00
Your Price : _____
3.4 oz EDT Sp $ 100.00
Your Price : _____

Christian Dior
Diorissimo
1.7 oz EDT Sp $ 59.00
Your Price : _____
3.4 oz EDT Sp $ 100.00
Your Price : _____

Christian Dior
Dolce Vita
1.7 oz EDT Sp $ 78.00
Your Price : _____
3.4 oz EDT Sp $ 100.00
Your Price : _____

Christian Dior
Dune
1.0 oz EDT Sp $ 60.00
Your Price : _____
1.7 oz EDT Sp $ 78.00
Your Price : _____
3.4 oz EDT Sp $ 100.00
Your Price : _____

Christian Dior
Hypnotic Poison
1.7 oz EDP Sp $ 94.00
Your Price : _____
3.4 oz EDP Sp $ 124.00
Your Price : _____

Christian Dior
Hypnotic Poison Eau Sensuelle
1.7 oz EDT Sp $ 78.00
Your Price : _____
3.4 oz EDT Sp $ 100.00
Your Price : _____

Christian Dior
Hypnotic Poison
1.7 oz EDT Sp $ 78.00
Your Price : _____
3.4 oz EDT Sp $ 100.00
Your Price : _____
5.0 oz EDT Sp $ 125.00
Your Price : _____

Christian Dior
J'adore Eau Lumiere
1.7 oz EDT Sp $ 86.00
Your Price : _____
3.4 oz EDT Sp $ 124.00
Your Price : _____
5.0 oz EDT Sp $ 155.00
Your Price : _____

Christian Dior
J'adore Injoy
1.7 oz EDT Sp $ 94.00
Your Price : _____
3.4 oz EDT Sp $ 124.00
Your Price : _____

Christian Dior
J'adore L'Absolu
2.5 oz EDP Sp $ 124.00
Your Price : _____

Christian Dior
J'adore L'Or
1.35 oz EDP Sp $ 124.00
Your Price : _____

Christian Dior
J'adore
1.0 oz EDP Sp $ 74.00
Your Price : _____
1.7 oz EDP Sp $ 94.00
Your Price : _____
3.4 oz EDP Sp $ 124.00
Your Price : _____
5.0 oz EDP Sp $ 155.00
Your Price : _____

Christian Dior
Miss Dior Absolutely Blooming
1.7 oz EDP Sp $ 94.00
Your Price : _____
3.4 oz EDP Sp $ 124.00
Your Price : _____

Christian Dior
Miss Dior Blooming Bouquet
1.7 oz EDT Sp $ 78.00
Your Price : _____
3.4 oz EDT Sp $ 100.00
Your Price : _____
5.0 oz EDT Sp $ 120.00
Your Price : _____

Christian Dior
Miss Dior Cherie
1.7 oz EDP Sp $ 85.00
Your Price : _____
3.4 oz EDP Sp $ 105.00
Your Price : _____

Christian Dior
Miss Dior
1.7 oz EDP Sp $ 94.00
Your Price : _____
3.4 oz EDP Sp $ 124.00
Your Price : _____

Christian Dior
Miss Dior Cherie
Eau de Printemps
1.7 oz EDP Sp $ 65.00
Your Price : _____
3.4 oz EDP Sp $ 90.00
Your Price : _____

Christian Dior
Miss Dior Cherie L'Eau
1.7 oz EDP Sp $ 60.00
Your Price : _____
3.4 oz EDP Sp $ 80.00
Your Price : _____

Christian Dior
Midnight Poison
1.7 oz EDT Sp $ 78.00
Your Price : _____
3.4 oz EDT Sp $ 100.00
Your Price : _____

Christian Dior
Poison
1.0 oz EDT Sp $ 60.00
Your Price : _____
1.7 oz EDT Sp $ 78.00
Your Price : _____
3.4 oz EDT Sp $ 100.00
Your Price : _____

Christian Dior
Pure Poison
1.0 oz EDP Sp $ 74.00
Your Price : _____
1.7 oz EDP Sp $ 94.00
Your Price : _____
3.4 oz EDP Sp $ 124.00
Your Price : _____

Christian Dior
Pure Poison Elixir
1.7 oz EDT Sp $ 78.00
Your Price : _____
3.4 oz EDT Sp $ 100.00
Your Price : _____

Christian Dior
Star
1.7 oz EDP Sp $ 59.00
Your Price : _____
3.4 oz EDP Sp $ 90.00
Your Price : _____

Christian Dior
Tendre Poison
1.7 oz EDT Sp $ 78.00
Your Price : _____
3.4 oz EDT Sp $ 100.00
Your Price : _____

Clinique
Aromatics Elixir
0.85 oz EDP Sp $ 40.00
Your Price : _____
1.15 oz EDP Sp $ 55.00
Your Price : _____
3.4 oz EDP Sp $ 73.00
Your Price : _____

Clinique
Aromatics In Black
1.7 oz EDT Sp $ 60.00
Your Price : _____
3.4 oz EDP Sp $ 80.00
Your Price : _____

Clinique
Aromatics In White
1.7 oz EDT Sp $ 60.00
Your Price : _____
3.4 oz EDP Sp $ 80.00
Your Price : _____

Clinique
Happy in Bloom
3.4 oz EDP Sp $ 59.00
Your Price : _____

Clinique
Happy Heart
1.7 oz EDP Sp $ 51.00
Your Price : _____
3.4 oz EDP Sp $ 68.00
Your Price : _____

Clinique
Happy
1.0 oz EDP Sp $ 35.00
Your Price : _____
1.7 oz EDP Sp $ 51.00
Your Price : _____
3.4 oz EDP Sp $ 68.00
Your Price : _____

Clinique
Happy To Be
1 oz EDP Sp $ 39.00
Your Price : _____
1.7 oz EDP Sp $ 59.00
Your Price : _____
3.4 oz EDP Sp $ 78.00
Your Price : _____

Coach
Legacy
1.7 oz EDP Sp $ 82.00
Your Price : _____

Coach
Poppy
1.7 oz EDP Sp $ 65.00
Your Price : _____
3.4 oz EDP Sp $ 85.00
Your Price : _____

Coach
Signature
1.7 oz EDP Sp $ 78.00
Your Price : _____
3.4 oz EDP Sp $ 98.00
Your Price : _____

Coach
Love
1.7 oz EDP Sp $ 70.00
Your Price : _____
3.4 oz EDP Sp $ 90.00
Your Price : _____

Coach
Love Eau Blush
1.7 oz EDP Sp $ 70.00
Your Price : _____
3.4 oz EDP Sp $ 90.00
Your Price : _____

Coach
Poppy Flower
1.7 oz EDP Sp $ 65.00
Your Price : _____
3.4 oz EDP Sp $ 85.00
Your Price : _____

Coach
Poppy Blossom
1.7 oz EDP Sp $ 65.00
Your Price : _____
3.4 oz EDP Sp $ 85.00
Your Price : _____

Coach
Poppy Citrine Blossom
1.7 oz EDP Sp $ 65.00
Your Price : _____
3.4 oz EDP Sp $ 85.00
Your Price : _____

Coach
Poppy Freesia Blossom
1.7 oz EDP Sp $ 65.00
Your Price : _____
3.4 oz EDP Sp $ 85.00
Your Price : _____

Coach
Poppy Wildflower
1.7 oz EDP Sp $ 65.00
Your Price : _____
3.4 oz EDP Sp $ 85.00
Your Price : _____

Coach
Signature Rose D'OR
1.7 oz EDP Sp $ 70.00
Your Price : _____
3.4 oz EDP Sp $ 90.00
Your Price : _____

Creed
Fantasia De Fleurs
2.5 oz EDP Sp $ 350.00
Your Price : _____

Creed
Fleurissimo
2.5 oz EDP Sp $ 350.00
Your Price : _____

Creed
Fleurs De Bulgarie
2.5 oz EDP Sp $ 325.00
Your Price : _____

Creed
Love In Black
1.0 oz EDP Sp $ 215.00
Your Price : _____
2.5 oz EDP Sp $ 350.00
Your Price : _____

Creed
Love In White
1.0 oz EDP Sp $ 215.00
Your Price : _____
2.5 oz EDP Sp $ 350.00
Your Price :

Creed
Himalaya
1.0 oz EDP Sp $ 165.00
Your Price : _____
2.5 oz EDP Sp $ 290.00
Your Price : _____
4.2 oz EDP Sp $ 395.00
Your Price : _____

Creed
Spring Flower for Women
1.0 oz EDP Sp $ 215.00
Your Price : _____
2.5 oz EDP Sp $ 350.00
Your Price :

Creed
Vanisia
2.5 oz EDP Sp $ 325.00
Your Price : _____

Dana
Chantilly
2.0 oz EDT Sp $ 39.00
Your Price : _____
3.4 oz EDT Sp $ 69.00
Your Price : _____

Dana
Tabu
1.5 oz EDC Sp $ 39.00
Your Price : _____
3.0 oz EDC Sp $ 69.00
Your Price : _____

Dana
White Chantilly
1.7 oz EDT Sp $ 39.00
Your Price : _____
3.4 oz EDT Sp $ 69.00
Your Price : _____

Davidoff
Cool Water Sea Rose
3.4 oz EDT Sp $ 58.00
Your Price : _____

Davidoff
Cool Water Sea Rose Coral Reef
3.4 oz EDT Sp $ 58.00
Your Price : _____

Davidoff
Cool Water Ice Fresh
1.7 oz EDT Sp $ 50.00
Your Price : _____
3.4 oz EDT Sp $ 75.00
Your Price : _____

Davidoff
Cool Water Summer Fizz
1.7 oz EDT Sp $ 59.00
Your Price : _____
3.4 oz EDT Sp $ 72.00
Your Price : _____

Davidoff
Cool Water Wave
1.7 oz EDT Sp $ 49.00
Your Price : _____
3.4 oz EDT Sp $ 70.00
Your Price : _____

Davidoff
Good Life
1.7 oz EDP Sp $ 45.00
Your Price : _____
3.4 oz EDP Sp $ 65.00
Your Price : _____

Davidoff
Cool Water Game
1.7 oz EDT Sp $ 59.00
Your Price : _____
3.4 oz EDT Sp $ 72.00
Your Price : _____

Davidoff
Cool Water
1.7 oz EDT Sp $ 59.00
Your Price : _____
3.4 oz EDT Sp $ 72.00
Your Price : _____

Davidoff
Echo
1.7 oz EDT Sp $ 59.00
Your Price : _____
3.4 oz EDT Sp $ 72.00
Your Price : _____

Dennis Basso
Dennis Basso
2.5 oz EDP Sp $ 72.00
Your Price : _____

Designer Parfums
Ocean Dream
1 oz EDT Sp $ 49.00
Your Price : _____
3.4 oz EDP Sp $ 79.00
Your Price : _____

Diesel
Fuel for Life
2.5 oz EDP Sp $ 68.00
Your Price : _____

Diesel
Fuel for Life Unlimited
1.7 oz EDP Sp $ 65.00
Your Price : _____
2.5 oz EDP Sp $ 85.00
Your Price : _____

Diesel
Green
3.4 oz EDP Sp $ 45.00
Your Price : _____

Diesel
Lover Dose
1.7 oz EDP Sp $ 60.00
Your Price : _____
2.5 oz EDP Sp $ 75.00
Your Price : _____

Diesel
Plus Plus
2.5 oz EDP Sp $ 45.00
Your Price : _____

Diesel
Zero Plus
2.5 oz EDT Sp $ 45.00
Your Price : _____

Dolce & Gabbana
1 Le Batcleur
1.7 oz EDT Sp $ 50.00
Your Price : _____
3.3 oz EDT Sp $ 65.00
Your Price : _____

Dolce & Gabbana
3 L' Imperatrice
1.7 oz EDT Sp $ 50.00
Your Price : _____
3.3 oz EDT Sp $ 65.00
Your Price : _____

Dolce & Gabbana
6 L' Amoureaux
1.7 oz EDT Sp $ 50.00
Your Price : _____
3.3 oz EDT Sp $ 65.00
Your Price : _____

Dolce & Gabbana
10 La Roue De La Fortune
1.7 oz EDT Sp $ 50.00
Your Price : _____
3.3 oz EDT Sp $ 65.00
Your Price : _____

Dolce & Gabbana
18 La Lune
1.7 oz EDT Sp $ 50.00
Your Price : _____
3.3 oz EDT Sp $ 65.00
Your Price : _____

Dolce & Gabbana
Dolce
1.6 oz EDP Sp $ 94.00
Your Price : _____
2.5 oz EDP Sp $ 117.00
Your Price : _____
5.0 oz EDP Sp $ 160.00
Your Price : _____

Dolce & Gabbana
Dolce Floral Drops
1.6 oz EDT Sp $ 85.00
Your Price : _____
2.5 oz EDT Sp $ 103.00
Your Price : _____
5.0 oz EDT Sp $ 152.00
Your Price : _____

Dolce & Gabbana
Dolce & Gabbana
1.7 oz EDT Sp $ 70.00
Your Price : _____
3.4 oz EDT Sp $ 95.00
Your Price : _____

Dolce & Gabbana
Feminine
1.0 oz EDP Sp $ 55.00
Your Price : _____
1.7 oz EDP Sp $ 75.00
Your Price : _____
3.4 oz EDP Sp $ 105.00
Your Price : _____

Dolce & Gabbana
L' Eau The One
1.0 oz EDT Sp $ 55.00
Your Price : _____
1.6 oz EDT Sp $ 70.00
Your Price : _____
2.5 oz EDT Sp $ 90.00
Your Price : _____

Dolce & Gabbana
Light Blue
0.85 oz EDT Sp $ 60.00
Your Price : _____
1.6 oz EDT Sp $ 76.00
Your Price : _____
3.3 oz EDT Sp $ 98.00
Your Price : _____
6.7 oz EDT Sp $ 134.00
Your Price : _____

Dolce & Gabbana
Light Blue
Dreaming in Portofino
0.84 oz EDT Sp $ 49.00
Your Price : _____
1.6 oz EDT Sp $ 64.00
Your Price : _____
3.3 oz EDT Sp $ 85.00
Your Price : _____

Dolce & Gabbana
Light Blue Escape To Panarea
1.6 oz EDT Sp $ 64.00
Your Price : _____
3.3 oz EDT Sp $ 85.00
Your Price : _____

Dolce & Gabbana
Light Blue Eau Intense
1.6 oz EDP Sp $ 84.00
Your Price : _____
3.3 oz EDP Sp $ 108.00
Your Price : _____

Dolce & Gabbana
Pour Femme
1.6 oz EDP Sp $ 94.00
Your Price : _____
3.3 oz EDP Sp $ 102.00
Your Price : _____

Dolce & Gabbana
Pour Femme Intense
0.8 oz EDP Sp $ 85.00
Your Price : _____
1.7 oz EDP Sp $ 99.00
Your Price : _____
3.4 oz EDP Sp $ 123.00
Your Price : _____

Dolce & Gabbana
Rose The One
1.0 oz EDP Sp $ 60.00
Your Price : _____
1.6 oz EDP Sp $ 82.00
Your Price : _____
2.5 oz EDP Sp $ 103.00
Your Price : _____

Dolce and Gabbana
Sicily
1.0 oz EDP Sp $ 55.00
Your Price : _____
1.7 oz EDP Sp $ 75.00
Your Price : _____
3.4 oz EDP Sp $ 105.00
Your Price : _____

Dolce & Gabbana
The One
1.0 oz EDP Sp $ 76.00
Your Price : _____
1.6 oz EDP Sp $ 94.00
Your Price : _____
2.5 oz EDP Sp $ 117.00
Your Price : _____

Dolce & Gabbana
The One Desire
1.0 oz EDP Sp $ 85.00
Your Price : _____
1.6 oz EDP Sp $ 101.00
Your Price : _____
2.5 oz EDP Sp $ 125.00
Your Price : _____

Dolce & Gabbana
The One Essence
2.5 oz EDP Sp $ 115.00
Your Price : _____

Donna Karan
Black Cashmere
1.7 oz EDT Sp $ 60.00
Your Price : _____
3.4 oz EDT Sp $ 89.00
Your Price : _____

Donna Karan
Cashmere Mist
1.0 oz EDP Sp $ 70.00
Your Price : _____
1.7 oz EDP Sp $ 92.00
Your Price : _____
3.4 oz EDP Sp $ 112.00
Your Price : _____
6.7 oz EDP Sp $ 148.00
Your Price : _____

Donna Karan
Cashmere Blush
3.4 Oz EDP Sp $ 85.00
Your Price : _____

Donna Karan
Cashmere Mist
1.0 oz EDT Sp $ 58.00
Your Price : _____
1.7 oz EDT Sp $ 78.00
Your Price : _____
3.4 oz EDT Sp $ 96.00
Your Price : _____

Donna Karan
Cashmere White
3.4 oz EDP Sp $ 85.00
Your Price : _____

Donna Karan
Be Delicious fresh Blossom
1.7 oz EDP Sp $ 60.00
Your Price : _____
3.4 oz EDP Sp $ 80.00
Your Price : _____

Donna Karan
Be Delicious Fresh Blossom Juiced
1.0 oz EDP Sp $ 50.00
Your Price : _____
1.7 oz EDP Sp $ 68.00
Your Price : _____
3.4 oz EDP Sp $ 85.00
Your Price : _____

Donna Karan
Be Delicious intense
1.0 oz EDP Sp $ 50.00
Your Price : _____
1.7 oz EDP Sp $ 70.00
Your Price : _____
3.4 oz EDP Sp $ 90.00
Your Price : _____

Donna Karan
Be Delicious Juiced
1.0 oz EDP Sp $ 50.00
Your Price : _____
1.7 oz EDP Sp $ 68.00
Your Price : _____
3.4 oz EDP Sp $ 85.00
Your Price : _____

Donna Karan
Cashmere Mist Gold Essence
1.7 oz EDP Sp $ 75.00
Your Price : _____
3.4 oz EDP Sp $ 95.00
Your Price : _____

Donna Karan
Cashmere Black
3.4 Oz EDP Sp $ 85.00
Your Price : _____

Donna Karan
Cashmere Mist Pearl Essence
1.7 oz EDP Sp $ 75.00
Your Price : _____
3.4 oz EDP Sp $ 95.00
Your Price : _____

Donna Karan
DKNY
1.7 oz EDP Sp $ 70.00
Your Price : _____
3.4 oz EDP Sp $ 90.00
Your Price : _____

Donna Karan
Cashmere Veil
1.7 oz EDP Sp $ 95.00
Your Price : _____
3.4 oz EDP Sp $ 115.00
Your Price : _____

Donna Karan
Be Delicious
1.0 oz EDP Sp $ 50.00
Your Price : _____
1.7 oz EDP Sp $ 70.00
Your Price : _____
3.4 oz EDP Sp $ 90.00
Your Price : _____

Donna Karan
DKNY Gold
1.7 oz EDP Sp $ 75.00
Your Price : _____
3.4 oz EDP Sp $ 89.00
Your Price : _____

Donna Karan
Golden Delicious
1.0 oz EDP Sp $ 60.00
Your Price : _____
1.7 oz EDP Sp $ 75.00
Your Price : _____
3.4 oz EDP Sp $ 89.00
Your Price : _____

Donna Karan
DKNY Love from New York
1.7 oz EDT Sp $ 79.00
Your Price : _____

Donna Karan
DKNY New York Summer
1.7 oz EDT Sp $ 60.00
Your Price : _____
3.4 oz EDT Sp $ 89.00
Your Price : _____

Donna Karan
DKNY Be Desired
1.7 oz EDP Sp $ 70.00
Your Price : _____
3.4 oz EDP Sp $ 90.00
Your Price : _____

Donna Karan
Pure DKNY A Drop of Verbena
1.0 oz EDP Sp $ 45.00
Your Price : _____
1.7 oz EDP Sp $ 65.00
Your Price : _____
3.4 oz EDP Sp $ 85.00
Your Price : _____

Donna Karan
Pure DKNY A Drop of Vanilla
1.0 oz EDP Sp $ 45.00
Your Price : _____
1.7 oz EDP Sp $ 65.00
Your Price : _____
3.4 oz EDP Sp $ 85.00
Your Price : _____

Donna Karan
Red Delicious
1.0 oz EDP Sp $ 50.00
Your Price : _____
1.7 oz EDP Sp $ 68.00
Your Price : _____
3.4 oz EDP Sp $ 85.00
Your Price : _____

Donna Karan
Sparkling Gold
1.7 oz EDP Sp $ 75.00
Your Price : _____
3.4 oz EDP Sp $ 89.00
Your Price : _____

Donna Karan
Woman
1.7 oz EDP Sp $ 85.00
Your Price : _____
3.4 oz EDP Sp $ 115.00
Your Price : _____

Elizabeth Arden
5th Avenue
2.5 oz EDP Sp $ 48.00
Your Price : _____
4.2 oz EDP Sp $ 58.00
Your Price : _____

Elizabeth Arden
5th Avenue After Five
2.5 oz EDP Sp $ 59.00
Your Price : _____
4.2 oz EDP Sp $ 79.00
Your Price : _____

Elizabeth Arden
5th Avenue Nights
2.5 oz EDP Sp $ 59.00
Your Price : _____

Elizabeth Arden
5th Avenue Style
2.5 oz EDP Sp $ 59.00
Your Price : _____
4.2 oz EDP Sp $ 79.00
Your Price : _____

Elizabeth Arden
Always Red
1.7 Oz EDT Sp $ 50.00
Your Price : _____
3.3 Oz EDT Sp $ 69.00
Your Price : _____

Elizabeth Arden
Always Red Femme
1.7 Oz EDT Sp $ 50.00
Your Price : _____
3.3 Oz EDT Sp $ 69.00
Your Price : _____

Elizabeth Arden
Blue Grass
1.7 oz EDP Sp $ 27.00
Your Price : _____
3.3 oz EDP Sp $ 37.00
Your Price : _____

Elizabeth Arden
Eau Fraiche
1.7 oz EDP Sp $ 40.00
Your Price : _____
3.3 oz EDP Sp $ 60.00
Your Price : _____

Elizabeth Arden
Iced Green Tea
1.7 oz EDP Sp $ 40.00
Your Price : _____
3.4 oz EDP Sp $ 60.00
Your Price : _____

Elizabeth Arden
Green Tea
1.7 oz EDT Sp $ 29.50
Your Price : _____
3.3 oz EDT Sp $ 39.50
Your Price : _____

Elizabeth Arden
Green Tea Intense
2.5 oz EDP Sp $ 39.50
Your Price :
4.2 oz EDP Sp $ 49.50
Your Price :

Elizabeth Arden
Green Tea Revitalize
1.7 oz EDP Sp $ 50.00
Your Price :
3.4 oz EDP Sp $ 70.00
Your Price :

Elizabeth Arden
Mediterranean
1.7 oz EDP Sp $ 47.50
Your Price :
3.3 oz EDP Sp $ 57.50
Your Price :

Elizabeth Arden
Mediterranean Breeze
1.7 oz EDP Sp $ 47.50
Your Price :
3.3 oz EDP Sp $ 57.50
Your Price :

Elizabeth Arden
Pretty
1.7 oz EDP Sp $ 52.00
Your Price :
3.4 oz EDP Sp $ 65.00
Your Price :

Elizabeth Arden
Pretty Hot
1.7 oz EDP Sp $ 52.00
Your Price :
3.4 oz EDP Sp $ 65.00
Your Price :

Elizabeth Arden
Provocative
1.0 oz EDP Sp $ 32.50
Your Price :
1.7 oz EDP Sp $ 42.50
Your Price :
3.3 oz EDP Sp $ 52.50
Your Price :

Elizabeth Arden
Provocative Interlude
1.7 oz EDP Sp $ 59.00
Your Price :
3.4 oz EDP Sp $ 79.00
Your Price :

Elizabeth Arden
Red Door
1.7 oz EDT Sp $ 50.00
Your Price :
3.4 oz EDT Sp $ 69.00
Your Price :

Elizabeth Arden
Red Door Aura
1.7 oz EDT Sp $ 49.00
Your Price :
3.4 oz EDT Sp $ 68.00
Your Price :

Elizabeth Arden
Red Door Revealed
1.7 oz EDP Sp $ 59.00
Your Price :
3.4 oz EDP Sp $ 79.00
Your Price :

Elizabeth Arden
Red Door Velvet
1.7 oz EDP Sp $ 50.00
Your Price :
3.3 oz EDP Sp $ 70.00
Your Price :

Elizabeth Arden
Spiced Green Tea
1.7 oz EDT Sp $ 59.00
Your Price :
3.3 oz EDT Sp $ 79.00
Your Price :

Elizabeth Arden
Splendor
1.7 oz EDT Sp $ 59.00
Your Price :
3.3 oz EDT Sp $ 79.00
Your Price :

Elizabeth Arden
Sunflowers
1.7 oz EDP Sp $ 29.50
Your Price :
3.3 oz EDP Sp $ 39.50
Your Price :

Elizabeth Arden
True Love
1.7 oz EDP Sp $ 59.00
Your Price :
3.3 oz EDP Sp $ 79.00
Your Price :

Elizabeth Arden
Untold
1.7 oz EDP Sp $ 62.00
Your Price :
3.4 oz EDP Sp $ 75.00
Your Price :

Elizabeth Arden
Arden Beauty
1 oz EDP Sp $ 38.00
Your Price :
1.7 oz EDP Sp $ 46.00
Your Price :
3.4 oz EDP Sp $ 60.00
Your Price :

Elizabeth Taylor
Black Pearls
1.7 oz EDP Sp $ 55.00
Your Price :
3.3 oz EDP Sp $ 75.00
Your Price :

Elizabeth Taylor
Brilliant White
Diamonds
1.7 oz EDP Sp $ 55.00
Your Price :

Elizabeth Taylor
Diamonds & Rubies
1.7 oz EDT Sp $ 55.00
Your Price : _____
3.4 oz EDT Sp $ 75.00
Your Price : _____

Elizabeth Taylor
Diamonds & Sapphires
1.7 oz EDT Sp $ 55.00
Your Price : _____
3.4 oz EDT Sp $ 75.00
Your Price : _____

Elizabeth Taylor
Diamonds & Emeralds
1.7 oz EDT Sp $ 55.00
Your Price : _____
3.4 oz EDT Sp $ 75.00
Your Price : _____

Elizabeth Taylor
Forever Elizabeth
1.7 oz EDT Sp $ 55.00
Your Price : _____
3.4 oz EDT Sp $ 75.00
Your Price : _____

Elizabeth Taylor
Gardenia
1 oz EDP Sp $ 45.00
Your Price : _____
1.7 oz EDP Sp $ 55.00
Your Price : _____
3.3 oz EDP Sp $ 75.00
Your Price : _____

Elizabeth Taylor
Passion
1.5 oz EDT Sp $ 48.00
Your Price : _____
2.5 oz EDT Sp $ 69.00
Your Price : _____

Elizabeth Taylor
Sparkling White Diamonds
1.7 oz EDT Sp $ 55.00
Your Price : _____
3.4 oz EDT Sp $ 75.00
Your Price : _____

Elizabeth Taylor
Violet Eyes
1.7 oz EDP Sp $ 52.00
Your Price : _____
3.3 oz EDP Sp $ 72.00
Your Price : _____

Elizabeth Taylor
White Diamonds
1.7 oz EDT Sp $ 53.00
Your Price : _____
3.3 oz EDT Sp $ 69.00
Your Price : _____

Ellen Tracy
ELLEN
1.7 oz EDP Sp $ 55.00
Your Price : _____
3.4 oz EDP Sp $ 75.00
Your Price : _____

Ellen Tracy
Linda Allard
1.7 oz EDT Sp $ 50.00
Your Price : _____
3.4 oz EDT Sp $ 72.00
Your Price : _____

Ellen Tracy
1.7 oz EDP Sp $ 55.00
Your Price : _____
3.4 oz EDP Sp $ 75.00
Your Price : _____

Ellen Tracy
Inspire
1.7 oz EDP Sp $ 59.00
Your Price : _____
2.5 oz EDP Sp $ 69.00
Your Price : _____

Ellen Tracy
Tracy
1.7 oz EDP Sp $ 59.00
Your Price : _____
2.5 oz EDP Sp $ 69.00
Your Price : _____

Ellen Tracy
Pretty Petals
1.7 oz EDP Sp $ 63.00
Your Price : _____
2.5 oz EDP Sp $ 75.00
Your Price : _____

Ellen Tracy
Love Notes
1.7 oz EDP Sp $ 63.00
Your Price : _____
3.4 oz EDP Sp $ 75.00
Your Price : _____

Erox
Inner Realm
1.7 oz EDT Sp $ 65.00
Your Price : _____
2.5 oz EDT Sp $ 80.00
Your Price : _____

Erox
Realm
1.7 oz EDP Sp $ 65.00
Your Price : _____
3.4 oz EDP Sp $ 80.00
Your Price : _____

Escada
Especially Escada Delicate Notes
1.0 oz EDT Sp $ 48.00
Your Price : _____
1.7 oz EDT Sp $ 65.00
Your Price : _____

Escada
Desire Me
1.7 oz EDP Sp $ 65.00
Your Price : _____
3.4 oz EDP Sp $ 80.00
Your Price : _____

Escada
En fleur
1.7 oz EDP Sp $ 55.00
Your Price :
3.4 oz EDP Sp $ 75.00
Your Price :

Escada
Ibiza Hippie
1.7 oz EDP Sp $ 55.00
Your Price :
3.4 oz EDP Sp $ 75.00
Your Price :

Escada
Into the Blue
1 oz EDP Sp $ 50.00
Your Price :
1.6 oz EDP Sp $ 65.00
Your Price :
2.5 oz EDP Sp $ 85.00
Your Price :

Escada
Magnetism
1.7 oz EDP Sp $ 69.00
Your Price :
2.5 oz EDP Sp $ 84.00
Your Price :

Escada
Magnetic Beat
1.7 oz EDT Sp $ 52.00
Your Price :

Escada
Ocean Lounge
1 oz EDT Sp $ 35.00
Your Price :
1.7 oz EDT Sp $ 50.00
Your Price :
3.4 oz EDT Sp $ 70.00
Your Price :

Escada
Que Viva
1.7 oz EDT Sp $ 55.00
Your Price :
3.4 oz EDT Sp $ 75.00
Your Price :

Escada
Signature
1 oz EDP Sp $ 40.00
Your Price :
1.7 oz EDP Sp $ 55.00
Your Price :
2.5 oz EDP Sp $ 75.00
Your Price :

Escada
Cherry In The Air
1.0 oz EDT Sp $ 45.00
Your Price :
1.7 oz EDT Sp $ 60.00
Your Price :
3.4 oz EDT Sp $ 80.00
Your Price :

Estee Lauder
Aliage Sport
2.0 oz EDP Sp $ 68.00
Your Price :
3.0 oz EDP Sp $ 85.00
Your Price :

Estee Lauder
Azuree
1.0 oz EDP Sp $ 48.00
Your Price :
1.7 oz EDP Sp $ 53.00
Your Price :
2.0 oz EDP Sp $ 68.00
Your Price :

Estee Lauder
Azuree Soleil
1.7 oz EDP Sp $ 62.00
Your Price :
2.5 oz EDP Sp $ 78.00
Your Price :
3.4 oz EDP Sp $ 85.00
Your Price :

Estee Lauder
Bali Dream
1.7 oz EDP Sp $ 62.00
Your Price :
2.5 oz EDP Sp $ 70.00
Your Price :
3.4 oz EDP Sp $ 85.00
Your Price :

Estee Lauder
Beautiful
1.0 oz EDP Sp $ 58.00
Your Price :
2.5 oz EDP Sp $ 80.00
Your Price :
3.4 oz EDP Sp $ 92.00
Your Price :

Estee Lauder
Beautiful Love
1.7 oz EDP Sp $ 55.00
Your Price :
2.5 oz EDP Sp $ 80.00
Your Price :

Estee Lauder
Beautiful Sheer
1.7 oz EDP Sp $ 55.00
Your Price :
2.5 oz EDP Sp $ 80.00
Your Price :
3.4 oz EDP Sp $ 92.00
Your Price :

Estee Lauder
Beautiful Summer Bouquet
Bouquet3
1.7 oz EDP Sp $ 55.00
Your Price :
2.5 oz EDP Sp $ 70.00
Your Price :
3.4 oz EDP Sp $ 85.00
Your Price :

Estee Lauder
Beyond Paradise
1.7 oz EDP Sp $ 60.00
Your Price :
3.4 oz EDP Sp $ 80.00
Your Price :

Estee Lauder
Bronze Goddess
Eau Fraiche Skinscent
1.7 oz EDP Sp $ 60.00
Your Price :
3.4 oz EDP Sp $ 85.00
Your Price :

Estee Lauder
Bronze Goddess
Soleil Skinscent
1.7 oz EDP Sp $ 60.00
Your Price :
3.4 oz EDP Sp $ 85.00
Your Price :

Estee Lauder
Cinnabar
1.7 oz EDP Sp $ 55.00
Your Price : _____
2.5 oz EDP Sp $ 70.00
Your Price : _____

Estee Lauder
Dazzling Gold
1.0 oz EDP Sp $ 45.00
Your Price : _____
2.5 oz EDP Sp $ 70.00
Your Price : _____

Estee Lauder
Dazzling Silver
1.7 oz EDT Sp $ 55.00
Your Price : _____
2.5 oz EDT Sp $ 70.00
Your Price : _____

Estee Lauder
Emerald Dream
1.7 oz EDP Sp $ 55.00
Your Price : _____
2.5 oz EDP Sp $ 70.00
Your Price : _____
3.4 oz EDP Sp $ 85.00
Your Price : _____

Estee Lauder
Estee
1.7 oz EDP Sp $ 53.00
Your Price : _____
2.0 oz EDP Sp $ 68.00
Your Price : _____

Estee Lauder
Intuition
1.7 oz EDP Sp $ 62.00
Your Price : _____
3.4 oz EDP Sp $ 85.00
Your Price : _____

Estee Lauder
Knowing
1.0 oz EDP Sp $ 60.00
Your Price : _____
2.5 oz EDP Sp $ 85.00
Your Price : _____

Estee Lauder
Modern Muse
1.0 oz EDP Sp $ 68.00
Your Price : _____
1.7 oz EDP Sp $ 88.00
Your Price : _____
3.4 oz EDP Sp $ 120.00
Your Price : _____

Estee Lauder
Modern Muse Chic
1.0 oz EDP Sp $ 68.00
Your Price : _____
1.7 oz EDP Sp $ 88.00
Your Price : _____
3.4 oz EDP Sp $ 120.00
Your Price : _____

Estee Lauder
Modern Muse Le Rouge
1.0 oz EDP Sp $ 68.00
Your Price : _____
1.7 oz EDP Sp $ 88.00
Your Price : _____
3.4 oz EDP Sp $ 120.00
Your Price : _____

Estee Lauder
Modern Muse Le Rouge Gloss
1.0 oz EDP Sp $ 68.00
Your Price : _____
1.7 oz EDP Sp $ 88.00
Your Price : _____
3.4 oz EDP Sp $ 120.00
Your Price : _____

Estee Lauder
Pleasures
1.7 oz EDP Sp $ 68.00
Your Price : _____
3.4 oz EDP Sp $ 92.00
Your Price : _____

Estee Lauder
Pleasures Bloom
1.7 oz EDP Sp $ 55.00
Your Price : _____
3.4 oz EDP Sp $ 75.00
Your Price : _____

Estee Lauder
Pleasures Delight
1.7 oz EDP Sp $ 62.00
Your Price : _____
2.5 oz EDP Sp $ 70.00
Your Price : _____
3.4 oz EDP Sp $ 85.00
Your Price : _____

Estee Lauder
Pleasures Exotic
1.0 oz EDP Sp $ 45.00
Your Price : _____
1.7 oz EDP Sp $ 70.00
Your Price : _____
3.4 oz EDP Sp $ 85.00
Your Price : _____

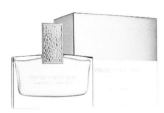

Estee Lauder
Private Collection
Tuberose Gardenia
1.0 oz EDP Sp $ 95.00
Your Price : _____
2.5 oz EDP Sp $ 160.00
Your Price : _____

Estee Lauder
Pure White Linen
1.7 oz EDP Sp $ 62.00
Your Price : _____
3.3 oz EDP Sp $ 85.00
Your Price : _____

Estee Lauder
Pure White
Linen Breeze
2.0 oz EDT Sp $ 67.00
Your Price : _____
3.4 oz EDT Sp $ 85.00
Your Price : _____

Estee Lauder
Sensuous Noir
1.7 oz EDP Sp $ 69.00
Your Price : _____
3.4 oz EDP Sp $ 85.00
Your Price : _____

Estee Lauder
Sensuous Nude
1.0 oz EDP Sp $ 60.00
Your Price : _____
1.7 oz EDP Sp $ 69.00
Your Price : _____
3.4 oz EDP Sp $ 92.00
Your Price : _____

Estee Lauder
Pleasures Intense
1.0 oz EDP Sp $ 45.00
Your Price : _____
1.7 oz EDP Sp $ 68.00
Your Price : _____
3.4 oz EDP Sp $ 92.00
Your Price : _____

Estee Lauder
Private Collection
1.7 oz EDP Sp $ 62.00
Your Price : _____
3.4 oz EDP Sp $ 85.00
Your Price : _____

Estee Lauder
Private Collection
Amber Ylang Lang
1.7 oz EDP Sp $ 95.00
Your Price : _____
2.5 oz EDP Sp $ 135.00
Your Price : _____

Estee Lauder
Sensuous
1.7 oz EDP Sp $ 69.00
Your Price : _____
3.4 oz EDP Sp $ 92.00
Your Price : _____

Estee Lauder
Spell Bound
1.7 oz EDP Sp $ 68.00
Your Price : _____
3.4 oz EDP Sp $ 85.00
Your Price : _____

Estee Lauder
Tuscany Per Donna
1.7 oz EDP Sp $ 53.00
Your Price : _____

Estee Lauder
Very Estee
1.7 oz EDP Sp $ 65.00
Your Price : _____
3.4 oz EDP Sp $ 85.00
Your Price : _____

Estee Lauder
Wild Elixir
1.7 oz EDP Sp $ 55.00
Your Price : _____
3.4 oz EDP Sp $ 75.00
Your Price : _____

Estee Lauder
Youth Dew
2.0 oz EDT Sp $ 69.00
Your Price : _____
3.4 oz EDT Sp $ 85.00
Your Price : _____

Estee Lauder
Youth Dew Amber Nude
1.7 oz EDP Sp $ 62.00
Your Price : _____
2.5 oz EDP Sp $ 70.00
Your Price : _____
3.4 oz EDP Sp $ 85.00
Your Price : _____

Estee Lauder
Pleasures Summer Bouquet
1.7 oz EDP Sp $ 62.00
Your Price : _____
2.5 oz EDP Sp $ 70.00
Your Price : _____
3.4 oz EDP Sp $ 85.00
Your Price : _____

Estelle Ewen
In Black Pour Femme
3.4 oz EDP Sp $ 70.00
Your Price : _____

Estelle Ewen
In Pink Pour Femme
3.4 oz EDP Sp $ 70.00
Your Price : _____

Estelle Ewen
In Red Pour Femme
3.4 oz EDP Sp $ 70.00
Your Price : _____

Estelle Ewen
Star In Black Pour Femme
3.4 oz EDP Sp $ 70.00
Your Price : _____

Estelle Vendome
Apple Heart
3.4 Oz EDP Sp $ 70.00
Your Price : _____

Estelle Vendome
Elixir Pleasure
3.4 oz EDP Sp $ 70.00
Your Price : _____

Eva Longoria
Eva
3.3 oz EDP Sp $ 60.00
Your Price : _____

Fendi
L'Acquarossa
1.7 oz EDP Sp $ 80.00
Your Price : _____
2.5 oz EDP Sp $ 95.00
Your Price : _____

Fendi
Fendi Fan Di
1.7 oz EDP Sp $ 76.00
Your Price : _____
2.5 oz EDP Sp $ 92.00
Your Price : _____

Ferrari
Donna
1.7 oz EDT Sp $ 60.00
Your Price : _____
3.4 oz EDT Sp $ 75.00
Your Price : _____

Five Star
Galore
4.0 oz EDT Sp $ 54.00
Your Price : _____

Five Star
Royal Secret
1.7 oz EDC Sp $ 35.00
Your Price : _____
3.3 oz EDC Sp $ 55.00
Your Price : _____

Five Star
Xoxo
1.7 oz EDP Sp $ 55.00
Your Price : _____
3.3 oz EDP Sp $ 72.50
Your Price : _____

Frances Denney
Interlude
4.0 oz COL Sp $ 60.00
Your Price : _____

Franck Olivier
Passion
1.7 oz EDT Sp $ 45.00
Your Price : _____
2.5 oz EDT Sp $ 65.00
Your Price : _____

Franck Olivier
1.7 oz EDT Sp $ 45.00
Your Price : _____

Franck Olivier
Private
1.7 oz EDT Sp $ 45.00
Your Price : _____
2.5 oz EDT Sp $ 65.00
Your Price : _____

Fred Hayman
273
1.7 oz EDP Sp $ 50.00
Your Price : _____
2.5 oz EDP Sp $ 65.00
Your Price : _____

Fred Hayman
273 Red
1.7 oz EDP Sp $ 50.00
Your Price : _____
2.5 oz EDP Sp $ 65.00
Your Price : _____

Fred Hayman
Hollywood
1.7 oz EDP Sp $ 50.00
Your Price : _____
2.5 oz EDP Sp $ 65.00
Your Price : _____

Fred Hayman
Hollywood Star
1.7 oz EDP Sp $ 55.00
Your Price : _____
2.5 oz EDP Sp $ 75.00
Your Price : _____

Fred Hayman
273 Indigo
1.7 oz EDP Sp $ 50.00
Your Price : _____
2.5 oz EDP Sp $ 65.00
Your Price : _____

Fred Hayman
Touch
1.7 oz EDP Sp $ 50.00
Your Price : _____
3.3 oz EDP Sp $ 75.00
Your Price : _____

Fred Hayman
Touch with Love
1.7 oz EDP Sp $ 50.00
Your Price : _____
3.4 oz EDP Sp $ 75.00
Your Price : _____

French Connection
Fcuk
1.7 oz EDT Sp $ 58.00
Your Price : _____
3.4 oz EDT Sp $ 79.00
Your Price : _____

Gale Hayman
Delicious
1.7 oz EDT Sp $ 50.00
Your Price : _____
3.4 oz EDT Sp $ 70.00
Your Price : _____

Gale Hayman
Delicious Amber
1.7 oz EDT Sp $ 50.00
Your Price : _____
3.3 oz EDT Sp $ 70.00
Your Price : _____

Gale Hayman
Delicious Chocolate
1.7 oz EDT Sp $ 50.00
Your Price : _____
3.3 oz EDT Sp $ 70.00
Your Price : _____

Gale Hayman
Delicious Cotton
Candy
1.7 oz EDT Sp $ 50.00
Your Price : _____
3.4 oz EDT Sp $ 70.00
Your Price : _____

Gale Hayman
Delicious Feelings
1.7 oz EDT Sp $ 50.00
Your Price : _____
3.4 oz EDT Sp $ 70.00
Your Price : _____

Gale Hayman
Golden Delicious
1.7 oz EDT Sp $ 50.00
Your Price : _____
3.4 oz EDT Sp $ 70.00
Your Price : _____

Gale Hayman
So Delicious
1.7 oz EDT Sp $ 59.00
Your Price : _____
3.3 oz EDT Sp $ 79.00
Your Price : _____

Gemina B
You are Beautiful
3.0 oz EDP Sp $ 95.00
Your Price : _____

Gemina B
You Are Beautiful Like Diamond
3.0 oz EDP Sp $ 95.00
Your Price : _____

Geparlys Women
Blue
3.4 oz EDP Sp $ 80.00
Your Price : _____

Giorgio Armani
Acqua Di Gio
1.7 oz EDT Sp $ 68.00
Your Price : _____
3.4 oz EDT Sp $ 83.00
Your Price : _____

Giorgio Armani
Acqua Di Gioia Eau Fraiche
1.7 oz EDT Sp $ 60.00
Your Price : _____
3.4 oz EDT Sp $ 77.00
Your Price : _____

Giorgio Armani
Acqua Di Gioia Jasmine
1.0 oz EDP Sp $ 45.00
Your Price : _____
3.4 oz EDP Sp $ 89.00
Your Price : _____

Giorgio Armani
Acqua Di Gioia Essenza
1.7 oz EDP Sp $ 90.00
Your Price : _____
3.4 oz EDP Sp $ 110.00
Your Price : _____

Giorgio Armani
Acqua Di Gioia
1.0 oz EDP Sp $ 50.00
Your Price : _____
1.7 oz EDP Sp $ 72.00
Your Price : _____
3.4 oz EDP Sp $ 92.00
Your Price : _____

Giorgio Armani
Armani Code
1.7 oz EDP Sp $ 70.00
Your Price : _____
2.5 oz EDP Sp $ 90.00
Your Price : _____

Giorgio Armani
Armani Code Luna
1.7 oz EDP Sp $ 58.00
Your Price : _____
2.5 oz EDT Sp $ 75.00
Your Price : _____

Giorgio Armani
Armani Code Sheer
1.7 oz EDT Sp $ 70.00
Your Price : _____
2.5 oz EDT Sp $ 90.00
Your Price : _____

Giorgio Armani
Armani Mania
1.7 oz EDT Sp $ 70.00
Your Price : _____
2.5 oz EDT Sp $ 90.00
Your Price : _____

Giorgio Armani
Gity Glam
1.7 oz EDP Sp $ 60.00
Your Price : _____
3.4 oz EDP Sp $ 79.00
Your Price : _____

Giorgio Armani
Emporio Armani
1.7 oz EDP Sp $ 69.00
Your Price : _____
3.4 oz EDP Sp $ 85.00
Your Price : _____

Giorgio Armani
Emporio Armani
Diamonds
1.7 oz EDP Sp $ 75.00
Your Price : _____
3.4 oz EDP Sp $ 105.00
Your Price : _____

Giorgio Armani
Emporio Armani
Diamonds Intense
1.7 oz EDP Sp $ 75.00
Your Price : _____
3.4 oz EDP Sp $ 105.00
Your Price : _____

Giorgio Armani
Idole D'Armani
1.7 oz EDP Sp $ 75.00
Your Price : _____
2.5 oz EDP Sp $ 89.00
Your Price : _____

Giorgio Armani
Emporio Armani
Night
1.7 oz EDP Sp $ 69.00
Your Price :_____
3.3 oz EDP Sp $ 85.00
Your Price :_____

Giorgio Armani
Emporio Armani
Remix
1.7 oz EDP Sp $ 69.00
Your Price :_____
3.3 oz EDP Sp $ 85.00
Your Price :_____

Giorgio Armani
Emporio Armani White
1.7 oz EDP Sp $ 69.00
Your Price :_____
3.3 oz EDP Sp $ 85.00
Your Price :_____

Giorgio Armani
Onde Extase
1.7 oz EDP Sp $ 85.00
Your Price :_____
3.4 oz EDP Sp $ 135.00
Your Price :_____

Giorgio Armani
Onde Mystere
1.7 oz EDP Sp $ 85.00
Your Price :_____
3.4 oz EDP Sp $ 135.00
Your Price :_____

Giorgio Armani
Onde Vertige
1.7 oz EDP Sp $ 85.00
Your Price :_____
3.4 oz EDP Sp $ 135.00
Your Price :_____

Giorgio Armani
SI
1.7 oz EDP Sp $ 92.00
Your Price :_____
3.4 oz EDP Sp $ 120.00
Your Price :_____
5.0 oz EDP Sp $ 140.00
Your Price :_____

Giorgio Armani
SI Intense
3.4 oz EDP Sp $ 125.00
Your Price :_____

Giorgio Armani
Sun Di Gioia
1.7 oz EDP Sp $ 50.00
Your Price :_____
3.4 oz EDP Sp $ 72.00
Your Price :_____
5.0 oz EDP Sp $ 92.00
Your Price :_____

Giorgio Beverly Hills
Aire
1.7 oz EDT Sp $ 60.00
Your Price :_____
3.0 oz EDT Sp $ 75.00
Your Price :_____

Giorgio Beverly Hills
G
1.7 oz EDP Sp $ 60.00
Your Price :_____
3.0 oz EDP Sp $ 75.00
Your Price :_____

Giorgio Beverly Hills
Giorgio
1.7 oz EDP Sp $ 50.00
Your Price :_____
3.0 oz EDP Sp $ 65.00
Your Price :_____

Giorgio Beverly Hills
Holiday
1.0 oz EDT Sp $ 45.00
Your Price :_____
1.7 oz EDT Sp $ 60.00
Your Price :_____

Giorgio Beverly Hills
Red
1.7 oz EDT Sp $ 60.00
Your Price :_____
3.0 oz EDT Sp $ 75.00
Your Price :_____

Giorgio Beverly Hills
Red 2
1.7 oz EDP Sp $ 60.00
Your Price :_____
3.0 oz EDP Sp $ 75.00
Your Price :_____

Giorgio Beverly Hills
So You
1.0 oz EDP Sp $ 45.00
Your Price :_____
1.7 oz EDP Sp $ 60.00
Your Price :_____

Giorgio
Wings
1.7 oz EDT Sp $ 60.00
Your Price :_____
3.0 oz EDT Sp $ 75.00
Your Price :_____

Giorgio Valenti
One & Only
1.7 oz EDP Sp $ 45.00
Your Price :_____
3.3 oz EDP Sp $ 59.00
Your Price :_____

Giorgio Valenti
GV Moment
1.7 oz EDP Sp $ 45.00
Your Price :_____
3.3 oz EDP Sp $ 59.00
Your Price :_____

Giorgio Valenti
G Pure
1.7 oz EDP Sp $ 45.00
Your Price :_____
3.3 oz EDP Sp $ 59.00
Your Price :_____

Giorgio Valenti
Magic Kiss
1.7 oz EDP Sp $ 45.00
Your Price : _____
3.3 oz EDP Sp $ 59.00
Your Price : _____

Giorgio Valenti
One O One
1.7 oz EDP Sp $ 45.00
Your Price : _____
3.3 oz EDP Sp $ 59.00
Your Price : _____

Giorgio Valenti
So Valenti
1.7 oz EDP Sp $ 45.00
Your Price : _____
3.3 oz EDP Sp $ 59.00
Your Price : _____

Giorgio Valenti
Pink Heart Perfume
1.7 oz EDP Sp $ 45.00
Your Price : _____
3.3 oz EDP Sp $ 79.00
Your Price : _____

Giorgio Valenti
Rose Noire
1.7 oz EDP Sp $ 45.00
Your Price : _____
3.3 oz EDP Sp $ 59.00
Your Price : _____

Givenchy
Ange Ou Demon Le Secret Elixir
1.7 oz EDP Sp $ 75.00
Your Price : _____
3.3 oz EDP Sp $ 95.00
Your Price : _____

Givenchy
Absolutely Irresistible
1.0 oz EDP Sp $55.00
Your Price : _____
1.7 oz EDP Sp $ 75.00
Your Price : _____
2.5 oz EDP Sp $ 90.00
Your Price : _____

Givenchy
Amarige
1.0 oz EDT Sp $ 50.00
Your Price : _____
1.6 oz EDT Sp $ 76.00
Your Price : _____
3.3 oz EDT Sp $ 102.00
Your Price : _____

Givenchy
Amarige D'amour
1 oz EDT Sp $ 45.00
Your Price : _____
1.7 oz EDT Sp $ 60.00
Your Price : _____
3 oz EDT Sp $ 75.00
Your Price : _____

Givenchy
Amarige Mariage
1 oz EDP Sp $ 49.00
Your Price : _____
1.7 oz EDP Sp $ 60.00
Your Price : _____
2.5 oz EDP Sp $ 75.00
Your Price : _____

Givenchy
Ange Ou Demon
1.7 oz EDP Sp $ 75.00
Your Price : _____
3.3 oz EDP Sp $ 95.00
Your Price : _____

Givenchy
Ange Ou Demon
Le Secret
1.7 oz EDP Sp $ 75.00
Your Price : _____
3.3 oz EDP Sp $ 116.00
Your Price : _____

Givenchy
Ange Ou Demon
Tendre
1.7 oz EDT Sp $ 68.00
Your Price : _____
3.3 oz EDT Sp $ 85.00
Your Price : _____

Givenchy
Dahlia Divine Le Nectar
1.7 oz EDP Sp $ 94.00
Your Price : _____
2.5 oz EDP Sp $ 114.00
Your Price : _____

Givenchy
Dahlia Noir L'Eau
1.7 oz EDT Sp $ 70.00
Your Price : _____
2.5 oz EDT Sp $ 90.00
Your Price : _____

Givenchy
Dahlia Divine
1.7 oz EDP Sp $ 90.00
Your Price : _____
2.5 oz EDP Sp $ 110.00
Your Price : _____

Givenchy
Dahlia Divine
2.5 oz EDT Sp $ 91.00
Your Price : _____

Givenchy
Eau De Givenchy
3.4 oz EDT Sp $ 80.00
Your Price : _____

Givenchy
Extravagance D' Amarige
1.7 oz EDT Sp $ 58.00
Your Price : _____
3.3 oz EDT Sp $ 75.00
Your Price : _____

Givenchy
Hot Couture
1.7 oz EDT Sp $ 70.00
Your Price : _____
3.3 oz EDT Sp $ 102.00
Your Price : _____

Givenchy
Live Irresistible
1.3 oz EDT Sp $ 58.00
Your Price : _____
2.5 oz EDT Sp $ 91.00
Your Price : _____

Givenchy
Live Irresistible
1.3 oz EDP Sp $ 70.00
Your Price : _____
2.5 oz EDT Sp $ 105.00
Your Price : _____

Givenchy
Lovely Prizm
1.7 oz EDT Sp $ 60.00
Your Price : _____
3.4 oz EDT Sp $ 75.00
Your Price : _____

Givenchy
L'interdit
1.7 oz EDT Sp $ 60.00
Your Price : _____
3.4 oz EDT Sp $ 80.00
Your Price : _____

Givenchy
My Couture
1.7 oz EDP Sp $ 67.00
Your Price : _____
3.3 oz EDP Sp $ 88.00
Your Price : _____

Givenchy
Organza
1.7 oz EDP Sp $ 60.00
Your Price : _____
3.4 oz EDP Sp $ 116.00
Your Price : _____

Givenchy
Organza Indecence
1.7 oz EDP Sp $ 60.00
Your Price : _____
3.4 oz EDP Sp $ 80.00
Your Price : _____

Givenchy
Play
1.7 oz EDP Sp $ 70.00
Your Price : _____
2.5 oz EDP Sp $ 85.00
Your Price : _____

Givenchy
Play Intense
1.7 oz EDP Sp $ 70.00
Your Price : _____
2.5 oz EDP Sp $ 85.00
Your Price : _____

Givenchy
So Givenchy
1.7 oz EDT Sp $ 60.00
Your Price : _____
3.4 oz EDT Sp $ 80.00
Your Price : _____

Givenchy
Very Irresistible
1.0 oz EDT Sp $ 50.00
Your Price : _____
1.7 oz EDT Sp $ 69.00
Your Price : _____
2.5 oz EDT Sp $ 91.00
Your Price : _____

Givenchy
Very Irresistible Sensual
1.0 oz EDP Sp $ 64.00
Your Price : _____
1.7 oz EDP Sp $ 89.00
Your Price : _____
2.5 oz EDP Sp $ 105.00
Your Price : _____

Givenchy
Very Irresistible
Summer
1.7 oz EDP Sp $ 60.00
Your Price : _____
2.5 oz EDP Sp $ 75.00
Your Price : _____

Givenchy
Very Irresistible L'eau En Rose
1.7 oz EDT Sp $ 76.00
Your Price : _____
2.5 oz EDT Sp $ 91.00
Your Price : _____

Givenchy
Very Irresistible
Summer Sorbet
1.7 oz EDP Sp $ 60.00
Your Price : _____
2.5 oz EDP Sp $ 75.00
Your Price : _____

Givenchy
Very Irresistible
L'intense
1.7 oz EDP Sp $ 80.00
Your Price : _____
2.5 oz EDP Sp $ 95.00
Your Price : _____

Givenchy
Ysatis Iris
1.7 oz EDP Sp $ 60.00
Your Price : _____
3.4 oz EDP Sp $ 85.00
Your Price : _____

Givenchy
Ysatis
1.7 oz EDT Sp $ 76.00
Your Price : _____
3.3 oz EDT Sp $ 90.00
Your Price : _____

Givenchy
Dahlia Noir
1.7 oz EDT Sp $75.00
Your Price : _____
2.5 oz EDT Sp $ 90.00
Your Price : _____

Givenchy
Dahlia Noir
1.7 oz EDP Sp $85.00
Your Price : _____
2.5 oz EDP Sp $ 105.00
Your Price : _____

Glenn Perri
Black is Beautiful
3.4 oz EDP Sp $ 90.00
Your Price : _____

Glenn Perri
Beautiful Lady
3.4 oz EDP Sp $ 90.00
Your Price : _____

Glenn Perri
Elegancia
3.0 oz EDP Sp $ 80.00
Your Price : _____

Glenn Perri
Hexane
3.4 oz EDP Sp $ 76.00
Your Price : _____

Glenn Perri
Iwan
3.4 oz EDP Sp $ 76.00
Your Price : _____

Glenn Perri
Pink
3.4 oz EDP Sp $ 85.00
Your Price : _____

Glenn Perri
Romantic Touch
3.0 oz EDP Sp $ 78.00
Your Price : _____

Glenn Perri
Unbelievable Lady
3.4 oz EDP Sp $ 85.00
Your Price : _____

Glenn Perri
Unpredictable Girl
3.4 oz EDP Sp $ 90.00
Your Price : _____

Glenn Perri
Unpredictable Lady
3.4 oz EDP Sp $ 90.00
Your Price : _____

Gloria Vanderbilt
Vanderbilt
3.3 oz EDT Sp $ 60.00
Your Price : _____

Gucci
Envy
1.7 oz EDT Sp $ 70.00
Your Price : _____
3.4 oz EDT Sp $ 90.00
Your Price : _____

Gucci
Envy Me
1.0 oz EDT Sp $ 65.00
Your Price : _____
1.7 oz EDT Sp $ 80.00
Your Price : _____
3.4 oz EDT Sp $ 99.00
Your Price : _____

Gucci
Envy Me 2
1.7 oz EDT Sp $ 79.00
Your Price : _____
3.3 oz EDT Sp $ 95.00
Your Price : _____

Gucci
Flora
1.0 oz EDT Sp $ 65.00
Your Price : _____
1.7 oz EDT Sp $ 77.00
Your Price : _____
2.5 oz EDT Sp $ 95.00
Your Price : _____

Gucci
Flora
1.0 oz EDP Sp $ 72.00
Your Price : _____
1.7 oz EDP Sp $ 85.00
Your Price : _____
2.5 oz EDP Sp $ 117.00
Your Price : _____

Gucci
Bamboo
1.0 Oz EDP Sp $ 72.00
Your Price : _____
1.6 Oz EDP Sp $ 94.00
Your Price : _____
2.5 Oz EDP Sp $ 117.00
Your Price : _____

Gucci
Flora Eau Fraiche
1.7 oz EDT Sp $ 77.00
Your Price : _____
2.5 oz EDT Sp $ 90.00
Your Price : _____

Gucci
Flora Glorious Mandarine
1.7 oz EDT Sp $ 78.00
Your Price : _____
3.3 oz EDT Sp $ 100.00
Your Price : _____

Gucci
Flora Gorgeous Gardenia
1.7 oz EDT Sp $ 78.00
Your Price : _____
3.3 oz EDT Sp $ 100.00
Your Price : _____

Gucci
Flora Glamorous Magnolia
1.7 oz EDT Sp $ 78.00
Your Price : _____
3.3 oz EDT Sp $ 100.00
Your Price : _____

Gucci
Flora Gracious Tuberose
1.7 oz EDT Sp $ 78.00
Your Price : _____
3.3 oz EDT Sp $ 100.00
Your Price : _____

Gucci
Guilty
1.0 oz EDT Sp $ 65.00
Your Price : _____
1.6 oz EDT Sp $ 78.00
Your Price : _____
2.5 oz EDT Sp $ 99.00
Your Price : _____

Gucci
Guilty Eau
1.0 oz EDT Sp $ 65.00
Your Price : _____
1.6 oz EDT Sp $ 78.00
Your Price : _____
2.5 oz EDT Sp $ 99.00
Your Price : _____

Gucci
Guilty Black
1.0 oz EDT Sp $ 65.00
Your Price : _____
1.6 oz EDT Sp $ 78.00
Your Price : _____
2.5 oz EDT Sp $ 99.00
Your Price : _____

Gucci
Gucci II
1.7 oz EDP Sp $ 94.00
Your Price : _____
2.5 oz EDP Sp $ 118.00
Your Price : _____

Gucci
Gucci
1.7 oz EDP Sp $ 85.00
Your Price : _____
2.5 oz EDP Sp $ 117.00
Your Price : _____

Gucci
Gucci
1.7 oz EDT Sp $ 75.00
Your Price : _____
2.5 oz EDT Sp $ 90.00
Your Price : _____

Gucci
Guilty Intense
1.0 oz EDP Sp $ 75.00
Your Price : _____
1.6 oz EDP Sp $ 92.00
Your Price : _____
2.5 oz EDP Sp $ 117.00
Your Price : _____

Gucci
Premiere
1.6 oz EDP Sp $ 90.00
Your Price : _____
2.5 oz EDP Sp $ 115.00
Your Price : _____

  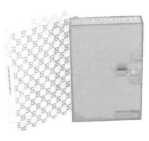 

Gucci
Premiere
1.0 oz EDT Sp $ 67.00
Your Price : _____
1.6 oz EDP Sp $ 84.00
Your Price : _____
2.5 oz EDP Sp $ 102.00
Your Price : _____

Gucci
Rush
1.0 oz EDT Sp $ 50.00
Your Price : _____
1.7 oz EDT Sp $ 78.00
Your Price : _____
2.5 oz EDT Sp $ 90.00
Your Price : _____

Gucci
Rush 2
1.7 oz EDT Sp $ 65.00
Your Price : _____
2.5 oz EDT Sp $ 75.00
Your Price : _____

Gucci
Rush Summer
1.7 oz EDT Sp $ 65.00
Your Price : _____
3.3 oz EDT Sp $ 75.00
Your Price : _____

Guess
By Marciano
1.7 oz EDP Sp $ 50.00
Your Price : _____
3.4 oz EDP Sp $ 65.00
Your Price : _____

Guess
Dare
1.7 Oz EDT Sp $ 49.00
Your Price : _____
3.4 Oz EDT Sp $ 65.00
Your Price : _____

Guess
Double Dare
1.7 Oz EDT Sp $ 49.00
Your Price : _____
3.4 Oz EDT Sp $ 65.00
Your Price : _____

Guess
Girl
1.7 oz EDT Sp $ 50.00
Your Price : _____
3.4 oz EDT Sp $ 65.00
Your Price : _____

Guess
Girl Belle
1.7 oz EDT Sp $ 50.00
Your Price : _____
3.4 oz EDT Sp $ 65.00
Your Price : _____

Guess
Guess
1.7 oz EDP Sp $ 60.00
Your Price : _____
2.5 oz EDP Sp $ 75.00
Your Price : _____

Guess
Gold
1.7 oz EDP Sp $ 60.00
Your Price :
2.5 oz EDP Sp $ 75.00
Your Price :

Guess
Guess Seductive I'm Yours
1.7 oz EDT Sp $ 50.00
Your Price :
3.4 oz EDT Sp $ 65.00
Your Price :

Guess
Seductive Guess
1.7 oz EDT Sp $ 50.00
Your Price :
3.4 oz EDT Sp $ 65.00
Your Price :

Guerlain
Aqua Allegoria Tiare' Mimosa
1.7 oz EDT Sp $ 55.00
Your Price :
4.2 oz EDT Sp $ 85.00
Your Price :

Guerlain
Champ Elysees
1.7 oz EDT Sp $ 82.00
Your Price :
3.4 oz EDT Sp $ 112.00
Your Price :

Guerlain
Champ Elysees
1.7 oz EDP Sp $ 107.00
Your Price :
3.4 oz EDP Sp $ 126.00
Your Price :

Guerlain
Champ Elysees Too Much
1.7 oz EDT Sp $ 55.00
Your Price :
2.5 oz EDT Sp $ 70.00
Your Price :

Guerlain
Chant D'Aromes
1.7 oz EDT Sp $ 75.00
Your Price :
3.4 oz EDT Sp $ 125.00
Your Price :

Guerlain
Insolence
1.7 oz EDT Sp $ 70.00
Your Price :
3.4 oz EDT Sp $ 90.00
Your Price :

Guerlain
L' Instant De Guerlain
1.0 oz EDP Sp $ 80.00
Your Price :
2.7 oz EDP Sp $ 126.00
Your Price :

Guerlain
Love is All
1.7 oz EDT Sp $ 70.00
Your Price :
3.4 oz EDT Sp $ 85.00
Your Price :

Guerlain
Mitsouko
1.7 oz EDP Sp $ 80.00
Your Price :
2.5 oz EDP Sp $ 118.00
Your Price :

Guerlain
My Insolence
1.0 oz EDT Sp $ 52.00
Your Price :
1.7 oz EDT Sp $ 65.00
Your Price :
3.4 oz EDT Sp $ 90.00
Your Price :

Guerlain
Samsara
1.7 oz EDP Sp $ 107.00
Your Price :
3.4 oz EDP Sp $ 126.00
Your Price :

Guerlain
Samsara
3.4 oz EDT Sp $ 118.00
Your Price :

Guerlain
Samsara Shine
1.7 oz EDT Sp $ 65.00
Your Price :

Guerlain
Shalimar
1.0 oz EDT Sp $ 66.00
Your Price :
1.7 oz EDT Sp $ 82.00
Your Price :
3.0 oz EDT Sp $ 112.00
Your Price :

Guerlain
Shalimar
1.0 oz EDP Sp $ 80.00
Your Price :
1.7 oz EDP Sp $ 107.00
Your Price :
3.0 oz EDP Sp $ 155.00
Your Price :

Guy Laroche
Jai Ose
1.7 oz EDT Sp $ 69.00
Your Price :
3.4 oz EDT Sp $ 85.00
Your Price :

Guy Laroche
FIDJI
1.7 oz EDT Sp $ 70.00
Your Price :
3.4 oz EDT Sp $ 95.00
Your Price :

Gwen Stefani
L Lamb
1.7 oz EDP Sp $ 75.00
Your Price :
3.4 oz EDP Sp $ 90.00
Your Price :

Halle Berry
Halle
1.7 oz EDP Sp $ 36.00
Your Price :
3.4 oz EDP Sp $ 55.00
Your Price :

Halston
1.0 oz EDP Sp $ 39.00
Your Price :
3.3 oz EDP Sp $ 69.00
Your Price :

Halston
Catalyst
1.7 oz EDT Sp $ 49.00
Your Price :
3.3 oz EDT Sp $ 69.00
Your Price :

Halston
Couture
1.7 oz EDP Sp $ 49.00
Your Price :
3.3 oz EDP Sp $ 69.00
Your Price :

Halston
Unbound
1.7 oz EDT Sp $ 49.00
Your Price :
3.4 oz EDT Sp $ 69.00
Your Price :

Hanae Mori
Hanae
3.4 Oz EDP Sp $ 78.00
Your Price :

Hanae Mori
Hanae Mori
1.7 oz EDP Sp $ 70.00
Your Price :
3.4 oz EDP Sp $ 90.00
Your Price :

Hanae Mori
Hanae Mori
1.7 oz EDT Sp $ 60.00
Your Price :
3.4 oz EDT Sp $ 80.00
Your Price :

Hanae Mori
Magical Moon
1.7 oz EDT Sp $ 65.00
Your Price :
3.4 oz EDT Sp $ 85.00
Your Price :

Hermes
24 Faubourg
1.6 oz EDP Sp $ 140.00
Your Price :
3.3 oz EDP Sp $ 185.00
Your Price :

Hermes
Amazone
1 oz EDT Sp $ 70.00
Your Price :
1.5 oz EDT Sp $ 120.00
Your Price :
3.3 oz EDT Sp $ 155.00
Your Price :

Hermes
Caleche
1.6 oz EDT Sp $ 112.00
Your Price :
3.3 oz EDT Sp $ 155.00
Your Price :

Hermes
Caleche
1.7 oz EDP Sp $ 140.00
Your Price :
3.4 oz EDP Sp $ 185.00
Your Price :

Hermes
Caleche Eau Delicate
1.7 oz EDT Sp $ 75.00
Your Price :
3.4 oz EDT Sp $ 120.00
Your Price :

Hermes
Eau De Merveilles
1.7 oz EDT Sp $ 108.00
Your Price :
3.4 oz EDT Sp $ 146.00
Your Price :

Hermes
Eau Des Merveilles
Pegasus
1.7 oz EDT Sp $ 75.00
Your Price :
3.4 oz EDT Sp $ 120.00
Your Price :

Hermes
Elixir Des Merveilles
1.6 oz EDP Sp $ 120.00
Your Price :
3.3 oz EDP Sp $ 160.00
Your Price :

Hermes
Hiris
1.7 oz EDT Sp $ 112.00
Your Price :
3.4 oz EDT Sp $ 155.00
Your Price :

Hermes
Kelly Caleche
1.0 oz EDT Sp $ 60.00
Your Price :
1.7 oz EDT Sp $ 108.00
Your Price :
3.4 oz EDT Sp $ 146.00
Your Price :

Hermes
Kelly Caleche
1.6 oz EDP Sp $ 120.00
Your Price : _____
3.3 oz EDP Sp $ 160.00
Your Price : _____

Hermes
L'Ambre De Merveilles
1.6 oz EDP Sp $ 120.00
Your Price : _____
3.3 oz EDP Sp $ 160.00
Your Price : _____

Hermes
Rouge
1.7 oz EDT Sp $ 112.00
Your Price : _____
3.4 oz EDT Sp $ 155.00
Your Price : _____

Hermes
Un Jardin
Apres La Mousson
1.7 oz EDT Sp $ 99.00
Your Price : _____
3.4 oz EDT Sp $ 137.00
Your Price : _____

Hermes
Un Jardin En Mediterrane
1.6 oz EDT Sp $ 99.00
Your Price : _____
3.3 oz EDT Sp $ 137.00
Your Price : _____

Hillary Duff
With Love
1.oz EDP Sp $ 50.00
Your Price : _____
1.7 oz EDP Sp $ 65.00
Your Price : _____
3.4 oz EDP Sp $ 75.00
Your Price : _____

Hugo Boss
Boss Ma Vie
1.6 oz EDP Sp $ 68.00
Your Price : _____
2.5 oz EDP Sp $ 82.00
Your Price : _____

Hugo Boss
Hugo
2.5 oz EDP Sp $ 73.00
Your Price : _____

Hugo Boss
NUIT Pour Femme
1.6 oz EDP Sp $ 68.00
Your Price : _____
2.5 oz EDP Sp $ 82.00
Your Price : _____

Hugo Boss
Boss Femme
1.7 oz EDP Sp $ 65.00
Your Price : _____
2.5 oz EDP Sp $ 80.00
Your Price : _____

Hugo Boss
Boss Orange
1.5 oz EDT Sp $ 48.00
Your Price : _____
2.5 oz EDT Sp $ 60.00
Your Price : _____

Hugo Boss
Boss Woman
1.6 oz EDP Sp $ 50.00
Your Price : _____
3.0 oz EDP Sp $ 72.00
Your Price : _____

Hugo Boss
Deep Red
1.6 oz EDP Sp $ 55.00
Your Price : _____
3 oz EDP Sp $ 72.00
Your Price : _____

Hugo Boss
Essence De Femme
1.6 oz EDP Sp $ 59.00
Your Price : _____
3.3 oz EDP Sp $ 78.00
Your Price : _____

Hugo Boss
Hugo XX
1.3 oz EDT Sp $ 45.00
Your Price : _____
2.0 oz EDT Sp $ 52.00
Your Price : _____
3.3 oz EDT Sp $ 65.00
Your Price : _____

Hugo Boss
Hugo
2.5 oz EDT Sp $ 59.00
Your Price : _____
4.2 oz EDT Sp $ 75.00
Your Price : _____

Hugo Boss
Intense
1.6 oz EDP Sp $ 59.00
Your Price : _____
3.3 oz EDP Sp $ 78.00
Your Price : _____

Hugo Boss
JOUR Pour Femme
1.6 oz EDP Sp $ 68.00
Your Price : _____
2.5 oz EDP Sp $ 82.00
Your Price : _____

Hugo Boss
Pure Purple
1.6 oz EDP Sp $ 59.00
Your Price : _____
3.3 oz EDP Sp $ 80.00
Your Price : _____

Hugo Boss
The Scent
1.6 oz EDP Sp $ 80.00
Your Price : _____
3.4 oz EDP Sp $ 100.00
Your Price : _____

Ilano Jivago
7 Notes
1.7 oz EDP Sp $ 77.00
Your Price :
3.4 oz EDP Sp $ 95.00
Your Price :

Ilano Jivago
24 K
1.7 oz EDP Sp $ 60.00
Your Price :
2.5 oz EDP Sp $ 85.00
Your Price :

Ilano Jivago
Jivago Connect
1.7 oz EDP Sp $ 77.00
Your Price :
3.4 oz EDP Sp $ 95.00
Your Price :

Ilana Jivago
Millennium Hope
4.0 oz EDP Sp $ 95.00
Your Price :

Il Bacio
1.0 oz EDP Sp $ 35.00
Your Price :
1.7 oz EDP Sp $ 46.00
Your Price :
3.4 oz EDP Sp $ 65.00
Your Price :

Issey Miyake
L'eau D'issey
1.6 oz EDT Sp $ 78.00
Your Price :
3.3 oz EDT Sp $ 104.00
Your Price :

Issey Miyake
L'eau D'issey
A Drop of Cloud
1.6 oz EDT Sp $ 70.00
Your Price :
3.3 oz EDT Sp $ 90.00
Your Price :

Issey Miyake
'L'Eau d'Issey Florale'
1.6 oz EDT Sp $ 66.00
Your Price :
3.3 oz EDT Sp $ 89.00
Your Price :

Jaclyn Smith
California
1.7 oz EDT Sp $ 45.00
Your Price :
3.4 oz EDT Sp $ 65.00
Your Price :

Jacoma
Paradox
1.7 oz EDT Sp $ 50.00
Your Price :
3.4 oz EDT Sp $ 79.00
Your Price :

Jacoma
Paradox Green
1.7 oz EDT Sp $ 50.00
Your Price :
3.4 oz EDT Sp $ 79.00
Your Price :

Jacoma
Silences
1.7 oz EDP Sp $ 50.00
Your Price :
3.4 oz EDP Sp $ 79.00
Your Price :

Jean Desprez
Bal A Versailles
1.7 oz EDT Sp $ 75.00
Your Price :
3.4 oz EDT Sp $ 95.00
Your Price :

Jean Louis Vermeil
Vermeil
3.3 oz EDP Sp $ 60.00
Your Price :

Jean Patou
Amour Amour
1.7oz EDT Sp $ 80.00
Your Price :
2.5 oz EDT Sp $ 95.00
Your Price :

Jean Patou
Chaldee
1.7 oz EDT Sp $ 80.00
Your Price :
2.5 oz EDT Sp $ 95.00
Your Price :

Jean Patou
Colony
1.6 oz EDT Sp $ 90.00
Your Price :
2.5 oz EDT Sp $ 105.00
Your Price :

Jean Patou
Hip
1.7 oz EDP Sp $ 300.00
Your Price :

Jean Patou
L'Heure Attendue
1.6 oz EDT Sp $ 80.00
Your Price :
2.5 oz EDT Sp $ 95.00
Your Price :

Jean Patou
Nacre
1.7 oz EDP Sp $ 250.00
Your Price :

Jean Patou
Pan Ame
1.0 oz EDT Sp $ 65.00
Your Price : _____
1.7 oz EDT Sp $ 85.00
Your Price : _____

Jean Patou
Patou Forever
1.7 oz EDP Sp $ 95.00
Your Price : _____
3.4 oz EDP Sp $ 128.00
Your Price : _____

Jean Patou
Sira Des Indes
1.7 oz EDP Sp $ 80.00
Your Price : _____
2.5 oz EDP Sp $ 95.00
Your Price : _____

Jean Patou
1000
1.6 oz EDP Sp $ 155.00
Your Price : _____
2.5 oz EDP Sp $ 190.00
Your Price : _____

Jean Patou
1000
1.7 oz EDT Sp $ 95.00
Your Price : _____
2.5 oz EDT Sp $ 130.00
Your Price : _____

Jean Patou
Enjoy
1.6 oz EDP Sp $ 85.00
Your Price : _____
2.5 oz EDP Sp $ 115.00
Your Price : _____

Jean Patou
Enjoy
1.6 oz EDT Sp $ 70.00
Your Price : _____
2.5 oz EDT Sp $ 90.00
Your Price : _____

Jean Patou
Joy
1.6 oz EDP Sp $ 150.00
Your Price : _____
2.5 oz EDP Sp $ 190.00
Your Price : _____

Jean Patou
Joy
1.6 oz EDT Sp $ 95.00
Your Price : _____
2.5 oz EDT Sp $ 130.00
Your Price : _____

Jean Patou
Sublime
1.6 oz EDP Sp $ 85.00
Your Price : _____
2.5 oz EDP Sp $ 115.00
Your Price : _____

Jean Patou
Sublime
1.6 oz EDT Sp $ 70.00
Your Price : _____
2.5 oz EDT Sp $ 95.00
Your Price : _____

Jean Paul Gaultier
Classique
1.6 oz EDT Sp $ 76.00
Your Price : _____
3.3 oz EDT Sp $ 100.00
Your Price : _____

Jean Paul Gaultier
Classique
1.6 oz EDP Sp $ 86.00
Your Price : _____
3.3 oz EDP Sp $ 112.00
Your Price : _____

Jean Paul Gaultier
Fragile
1.7 oz EDP Sp $ 80.00
Your Price : _____
3.3 oz EDP Sp $ 100.00
Your Price : _____

Jean Paul Gaultier
Gaultier 2
1.7 oz EDP Sp $ 80.00
Your Price : _____
3.3 oz EDP Sp $ 100.00
Your Price : _____

Jean Paul Gaultier
Ma Dame
1.7 oz EDT Sp $ 80.00
Your Price : _____
3.4 oz EDT Sp $ 100.00
Your Price : _____

Jenni Rivera
Forever
3.4 oz EDP Sp $ 65.00
Your Price : _____

Jenni Rivera
Jenni
3.4 oz EDP Sp $ 65.00
Your Price : _____

Jenni Rivera
JR by Jenni Rivera
3.4 oz EDP Sp $ 65.00
Your Price : _____

Jennifer Lopez
Blue Glow
1.7 oz EDT Sp $ 65.00
Your Price : _____
3.4 oz EDT Sp $ 95.00
Your Price : _____

Jennifer Lopez
Love and Glamour
1.7 oz EDP Sp $ 50.00
Your Price : _____
2.5 oz EDP Sp $ 65.00
Your Price : _____

Jennifer Lopez
Love & Light
1.7 oz EDT Sp $ 50.00
Your Price : _____
2.5 oz EDT Sp $ 65.00
Your Price : _____

Jennifer Lopez
JLove
1.0 oz EDP Sp $ 39.00
Your Price : _____
1.7 oz EDP Sp $ 49.00
Your Price : _____

Jennifer Lopez
Deseo
1.7 oz EDT Sp $ 65.00
Your Price : _____
3.4 oz EDT Sp $ 90.00
Your Price : _____

Jennifer Lopez
Forever Glowing
1.0 oz EDP Sp $ 40.00
Your Price : _____
1.7 oz EDP Sp $ 55.00
Your Price : _____

Jennifer Lopez
Glow
1.7 oz EDT Sp $ 65.00
Your Price : _____
3.3 oz EDT Sp $ 90.00
Your Price : _____

Jennifer Lopez
Glow After Dark
1.7 oz EDT Sp $ 65.00
Your Price : _____
3.4 oz EDT Sp $ 90.00
Your Price : _____

Jennifer Lopez
LA Glow
1.7 oz EDT Sp $ 69.00
Your Price : _____
3.4 oz EDT Sp $ 95.00
Your Price : _____

Jennifer Lopez
Live
1.7 oz EDT Sp $ 65.00
Your Price : _____
3.4 oz EDT Sp $ 90.00
Your Price : _____

Jennifer Lopez
Live Luxe
1.7 oz EDT Sp $ 65.00
Your Price : _____
3.4 oz EDT Sp $ 90.00
Your Price : _____

Jennifer Lopez
Live Platinum
1.7 oz EDP Sp $ 65.00
Your Price : _____
3.4 oz EDP Sp $ 90.00
Your Price : _____

Jennifer Lopez
Love At First Glow
1.7 oz EDT Sp $ 65.00
Your Price : _____
3.3 oz EDT Sp $ 90.00
Your Price : _____

Jennifer Lopez
Miami Glow
1.7 oz EDT Sp $ 65.00
Your Price : _____
3.4 oz EDT Sp $ 90.00
Your Price : _____

Jennifer Lopez
My Glow
1.7 oz EDT Sp $ 69.00
Your Price : _____
3.4 oz EDT Sp $ 95.00
Your Price : _____

Jennifer Lopez
Rio Glow
1.7 oz EDP Sp $ 49.00
Your Price : _____
3.4 oz EDP Sp $ 60.00
Your Price : _____

Jennifer Lopez
Still
1.7 oz EDP Sp $ 65.00
Your Price : _____
3.3 oz EDP Sp $ 90.00
Your Price : _____

Jennifer Lopez
Sunkissed Glow
1.7 oz EDT Sp $ 65.00
Your Price : _____
3.4 oz EDT Sp $ 90.00
Your Price : _____

Jessica Simpson
Fancy
1.7 oz EDP Sp $ 45.00
Your Price : _____
3.4 oz EDP Sp $ 61.00
Your Price : _____

Jessica Simpson
Fancy Girl
1.7 oz EDP Sp $ 45.00
Your Price : _____
3.4 oz EDP Sp $ 61.00
Your Price : _____

Jessica Simpson
Fancy Love
1.7 oz EDP Sp $ 45.00
Your Price : _____
3.4 oz EDP Sp $ 61.00
Your Price : _____

Jessica Simpson
Fancy Nights
1.7 oz EDP Sp $ 45.00
Your Price : _____
3.4 oz EDP Sp $ 61.00
Your Price : _____

Jessica Simpson
I Fancy You
1.7 oz EDP Sp $ 45.00
Your Price : _____
3.4 oz EDP Sp $ 61.00
Your Price : _____

Jessica McClintock
1.7 oz EDP Sp $ 55.00
Your Price : _____
3.4 oz EDP Sp $ 75.00
Your Price : _____

Jessica McClintock
Silk Ribbons
1.7 oz EDT Sp $ 50.00
Your Price : _____
3.4 oz EDT Sp $ 70.00
Your Price : _____

Jesus Del Pozo
Duende
3.4 oz EDT Sp $ 45.00
Your Price : _____

Jesus Del Pozo
Esencia de Duende
3.4 oz EDT Sp $ 55.00
Your Price : _____

Jesus Del Pozo
Halloween
3.4 oz EDT Sp $ 48.00
Your Price : _____

Jesus Del Pozo
Halloween Fever
3.4 oz EDP Sp $ 48.00
Your Price : _____

Jesus Del Pozo
Halloween Fluer
3.4 oz EDT Sp $ 45.00
Your Price : _____

Jesus Del Pozo
Halloween Fressia
3.4 oz EDT Sp $ 45.00
Your Price : _____

Jesus Del Pozo
Halloween Kiss
3.4 oz EDT Sp $ 48.00
Your Price : _____

Jesus Del Pozo
Halloween Kiss Sexy
3.4 oz EDT Sp $ 48.00
Your Price : _____

Jesus Del Pozo
Halloween Sun
3.4 oz EDT Sp $ 45.00
Your Price : _____

Jesus Del Pozo
Halloween Water Lily
3.4 oz EDT Sp $ 45.00
Your Price : _____

Jimmy Choo
Blossom
3.3 oz EDP Sp $ 90.00
Your Price : _____

Jimmy Choo
Exotic
1.7 oz EDT Sp $ 60.00
Your Price : _____
3.3 oz EDT Sp $ 80.00
Your Price : _____

Jimmy Choo
Flash
1.0 oz EDP Sp $ 50.00
Your Price : _____
2.0 oz EDP Sp $ 70.00
Your Price : _____
3.3 oz EDP Sp $ 90.00
Your Price : _____

Jimmy Choo
Flash London Club
1.0 oz EDP Sp $ 50.00
Your Price : _____
2.0 oz EDP Sp $ 70.00
Your Price : _____
3.0 oz EDP Sp $ 90.00
Your Price : _____

Jimmy Choo
Illicit
2.0 Oz EDP Sp $ 85.00
Your Price : _____
3.3 Oz EDP Sp $ 112.00
Your Price : _____

Jimmy Choo
Illicit Flower
2.0 Oz EDT Sp $ 78.00
Your Price : _____
3.3 Oz EDT Sp $ 98.00
Your Price : _____

Jimmy Choo
Jimmy Choo
1.0 oz EDP Sp $ 50.00
Your Price : _____
2.0 oz EDP Sp $ 82.00
Your Price : _____
3.3 oz EDP Sp $ 108.00
Your Price : _____

Jimmy Choo
L'eau
2.0 oz EDT Sp $ 78.00
Your Price : _____
3.0 oz EDT Sp $ 98.00
Your Price : _____

Jimmy Choo
Stars
3.3 Oz EDP Sp $ 90.00
Your Price : _____

Jo Malone
Amber & Patchouli Intense
1.7 oz COL Sp $ 120.00
Your Price : _____
3.3 oz COL Sp $ 180.00
Your Price : _____

Jo Malone
French Lime Blossom
1.7 oz EDC Sp $ 65.00
Your Price : _____
3.3 oz EDT Sp $ 130.00
Your Price : _____

Jo Malone
Orange Blossom
1.7 oz COL Sp $ 65.00
Your Price : _____
3.3 oz COL Sp $ 130.00
Your Price : _____

Jo Malone
Tuberose Angelica
1.7 oz EDC Sp $ 120.00
Your Price : _____
3.3 oz EDC Sp $ 180.00
Your Price : _____

Johan B.
Addiction
3.4 oz EDP Sp $ 50.00
Your Price : _____

Johan B.
Beaute
3.4 oz EDP Sp $ 50.00
Your Price : _____

Johan B.
Beaute d'Orient
3.4 oz EDP Sp $ 50.00
Your Price : _____

Johan B.
Beautiful Rich
2.8 oz EDP Sp $ 50.00
Your Price : _____

Johan B.
Elixir Sensual
2.8 oz EDP Sp $ 50.00
Your Price : _____

Johan B.
Innocence
2.8 oz EDP Sp $ 50.00
Your Price : _____

Johan B
Merveille
3.4 oz EDP Sp $ 48.00
Your Price : _____

Johan B.
Merveille In Blue
3.4 oz EDP Sp $ 50.00
Your Price : _____

Johan B
Moment
3.4 oz EDP Sp $ 48.00
Your Price : _____

Johan B
Pink
3.4 oz EDP Sp $ 48.00
Your Price : _____

Johan B.
Rich
2.8 oz EDP Sp $ 50.00
Your Price : _____

Johan B.
Venisia
3.0 oz EDP Sp $ 85.00
Your Price : _____

Johan B.
Rich Delice
2.8 oz EDP Sp $ 50.00
Your Price : _____

Johan B.
Rich Rose Again
2.8 oz EDP Sp $ 50.00
Your Price : _____

Johan B.
Sensual
2.8 oz EDP Sp $ 50.00
Your Price : _____

Johan B.
Sensual Obsession
3.4 oz EDP Sp $ 50.00
Your Price : _____

Johan B.
Silver Spirit
3.4 oz EDP Sp $ 80.00
Your Price : _____

Johan B.
So Love
3.0 oz EDP Sp $ 50.00
Your Price : _____

John Varvatos
John Varvatos
1.7 oz EDP Sp $ 45.00
Your Price : _____
3.4 oz EDP Sp $ 60.00
Your Price : _____

Joop
By Night Jette
2.5 oz EDP Sp $ 80.00
Your Price : _____

Joop
Go Hot Contact
3.4 oz EDT Sp $ 70.00
Your Price : _____

Joop
Jette
2.5 oz EDT Sp $ 70.00
Your Price : _____

Joop
Joop
1.7 oz EDT Sp $ 65.00
Your Price : _____
3.4 oz EDT Sp $ 80.00
Your Price : _____

Jovan
Musk
3.25 oz EDC Sp $ 60.00
Your Price : _____

Jovan
White Musk
3.25 oz EDC Sp $ 60.00
Your Price : _____

Juicy Couture
Couture LA LA
1.7 oz EDP Sp $ 65.00
Your Price : _____
3.4 oz EDP Sp $ 85.00
Your Price : _____

Juicy Couture
Couture Couture
1.7 oz EDP Sp $ 60.00
Your Price : _____
3.4 oz EDP Sp $ 80.00
Your Price : _____

Juicy Couture
Hollywood Royal
2.5 oz EDP Sp $ 72.00
Your Price : _____
5.0 oz EDP Sp $ 92.00
Your Price : _____

Juicy Couture
I Am Juicy Couture
1.0 oz EDP Sp $ 56.00
Your Price : _____
1.7 oz EDP Sp $ 76.00
Your Price : _____
3.4 oz EDP Sp $ 96.00
Your Price : _____

Juicy Couture
I Love Juicy Couture
1.0 oz EDP Sp $ 56.00
Your Price : _____
1.7 oz EDP Sp $ 76.00
Your Price : _____
3.4 oz EDP Sp $ 96.00
Your Price : _____

Juicy Couture
Juicy Couture
1.7 oz EDP Sp $ 76.00
Your Price : _____
3.4 oz EDP Sp $ 96.00
Your Price : _____

Juicy Couture
Peace, Love & Juicy Couture
1.7 oz EDP Sp $ 60.00
Your Price : _____
3.4 oz EDP Sp $ 80.00
Your Price : _____

Juicy Couture
Viva La Juicy Gold Couture
1.0 oz EDP Sp $ 56.00
Your Price : _____
1.7 oz EDP Sp $ 76.00
Your Price : _____
3.4 oz EDP Sp $ 96.00
Your Price : _____

Juicy Couture
Viva La juicy La Fleur
2.5 oz EDP Sp $ 70.00
Your Price :
5.0 oz EDP Sp $ 92.00
Your Price :

Juicy Couture
Viva La juicy Noir
1.0 oz EDP Sp $ 56.00
Your Price :
1.7 oz EDP Sp $ 76.00
Your Price :
3.4 oz EDP Sp $ 96.00
Your Price :

Juicy Couture
Viva La Juicy Rose
1.0 oz EDP Sp $ 56.00
Your Price :
1.7 oz EDP Sp $ 76.00
Your Price :
3.4 oz EDP Sp $ 96.00
Your Price :
6.7 oz EDP Sp $ 140.00
Your Price :

Juicy Couture
Viva La juicy
1.0 oz EDP Sp $ 56.00
Your Price :
1.7 oz EDP Sp $ 76.00
Your Price :
3.4 oz EDP Sp $ 96.00
Your Price :
6.7 oz EDP Sp $ 140.00
Your Price :

Justin Bieber
Girlfriend
1.7 oz EDP Sp $ 45.00
Your Price :
3.4 oz EDP Sp $ 60.00
Your Price :

Justin Bieber
Someday
1.7 oz EDP Sp $ 45.00
Your Price :
3.4 oz EDP Sp $ 60.00
Your Price :

Justin Bieber
The Key
1.7 oz EDP Sp $ 45.00
Your Price :
3.4 oz EDP Sp $ 60.00
Your Price :

Karen Low
KL Interview
3.0 oz EDP Sp $ 68.00
Your Price :

Karen Low
Code 37
3.4 oz EDP Sp $ 80.00
Your Price :

Karen Low
Indescence Girl's
3.4 oz EDP Sp $ 72.00
Your Price :

Karen Low
Lady Gold
3.4 oz EDP Sp $ 80.00
Your Price :

Karen Low
Obsession
3.4 oz EDP Sp $75.00
Your Price :

Karen Low
Pure Couture
3.4 oz EDP Sp $ 55.00
Your Price :

Karl Lagerfeld
Lagerfield
1.7 oz EDP Sp $ 60.00
Your Price :
3.4 oz EDP Sp $ 75.00
Your Price :

Karl Lagerfeld
Sun Moon Stars
1.7 oz EDP Sp $ 50.00
Your Price :
3.3 oz EDP Sp $ 65.00
Your Price :

Kate Spade
Beauty
1.7 oz EDP Sp $ 55.00
Your Price :
3.4 oz EDP Sp $ 75.00
Your Price :

Kate Spade
Live Colour Fully
1.7 oz EDP Sp $ 75.00
Your Price :
3.4 oz EDP Sp $ 95.00
Your Price :

Kate Spade
Twirl
1.7 oz EDP Sp $ 55.00
Your Price :
3.4 oz EDP Sp $ 75.00
Your Price :

Kate Spade
Walk on Air
1.7 oz EDP Sp $ 75.00
Your Price :
3.4 oz EDP Sp $ 95.00
Your Price :

Kate Spade
Walk on Air Sunset
1.7 oz EDP Sp $ 75.00
Your Price :
3.4 oz EDP Sp $ 95.00
Your Price :

Katy Perry
Killer Queen
1.7 oz EDP Sp $ 45.00
Your Price :_____
3.4 oz EDP Sp $ 60.00
Your Price :_____

Katy Perry
Mad Potion
1.7 oz EDP Sp $ 45.00
Your Price :_____
3.4 oz EDP Sp $ 60.00
Your Price :_____

Katy Perry
Meow
1.7 oz EDP Sp $ 45.00
Your Price :_____
3.4 oz EDP Sp $ 60.00
Your Price :_____

Katy Perry
Purrs
1.7 oz EDP Sp $ 45.00
Your Price :_____
3.4 oz EDP Sp $ 60.00
Your Price :_____

Katy Perry
Royal Revolution
1.7 oz EDP Sp $ 45.00
Your Price :_____
3.4 oz EDP Sp $ 60.00
Your Price :_____

Kenneth Cole
Black
1.7 oz EDP Sp $ 60.00
Your Price :_____
3.4 oz EDP Sp $ 77.00
Your Price :_____

Kenneth Cole
NewYork
1.7 oz EDP Sp $ 60.00
Your Price :_____
3.4 oz EDP Sp $ 77.00
Your Price :_____

Kenneth Cole
Reaction
1.7 oz EDP Sp $ 55.00
Your Price :_____
3.4 oz EDP Sp $ 65.00
Your Price :_____

Kenneth Cole
White
1.7 oz EDT Sp $ 55.00
Your Price :_____
3.4 oz EDT Sp $ 65.00
Your Price :_____

Kenzo
5:40 in Madagasear
1.7 oz EDP Sp $ 60.00
Your Price :_____
3.4 oz EDP Sp $ 75.00
Your Price :_____

Kenzo
Amour
1.0 oz EDP Sp $ 62.00
Your Price :_____
1.7 oz EDP Sp $ 87.00
Your Price :_____
3.4 oz EDP Sp $ 112.00
Your Price :_____

Kenzo
Amour Indian Holi
1.0 oz EDP Sp $ 62.00
Your Price :_____
1.7 oz EDP Sp $ 87.00
Your Price :_____
3.4 oz EDP Sp $ 112.00
Your Price :_____

Kenzo
Ca Sent Beau
1.7 oz EDP Sp $ 60.00
Your Price :_____
3.4 oz EDP Sp $ 75.00
Your Price :_____

Kenzo
Flower
1.0 oz EDP Sp $ 62.00
Your Price :_____
1.7 oz EDP Sp $ 87.00
Your Price :_____
3.4 oz EDP Sp $ 112.00
Your Price :_____

Kenzo
Eau de Fleurs Magnolia
1.7 oz EDP Sp $ 60.00
Your Price :_____
3.4 oz EDP Sp $ 75.00
Your Price :_____

Kenzo
Eau de Fleurs Soie Silk
1.7 oz EDP Sp $ 60.00
Your Price :_____
3.4 oz EDP Sp $ 75.00
Your Price :_____

Kenzo
Eau de Fleurs Tea
1.7 oz EDP Sp $ 60.00
Your Price :_____
3.4 oz EDP Sp $ 75.00
Your Price :_____

Kenzo
Flower in The Air
1.7 oz EDP Sp $ 87.00
Your Price :_____
3.4 oz EDP Sp $ 112.00
Your Price :_____

Kenzo
Flower Red
1.7 oz EDP Sp $ 60.00
Your Price :_____
3.4 oz EDP Sp $ 80.00
Your Price :_____

Kenzo
Jungle Elephant
1.0 oz EDP Sp $ 40.00
Your Price :_____
1.7 oz EDP Sp $ 60.00
Your Price :_____
3.4 oz EDP Sp $ 80.00
Your Price :_____

Kenzo
L'eau Par
1.7 oz EDP Sp $ 60.00
Your Price : _____
3.4 oz EDP Sp $ 80.00
Your Price : _____

Kenzo
Parfum D'Ete
1.7 oz EDP Sp $ 60.00
Your Price : _____
2.5 oz EDP Sp $ 75.00
Your Price : _____

Kenzo
Summer
1.7 oz EDP Sp $ 60.00
Your Price : _____
3.4 oz EDP Sp $ 75.00
Your Price : _____

Kenzo
Summer Flower
1.7 oz EDP Sp $ 60.00
Your Price : _____
3.4 oz EDP Sp $ 75.00
Your Price : _____

Kenzo
World
1.7 oz EDP Sp $ 87.00
Your Price : _____
2.5 oz EDP Sp $ 100.00
Your Price : _____

Khloe and Lamar
Unbreakable Bond
3.4 oz EDT Sp $ 65.00
Your Price : _____

Khloe and Lamar
Unbreakable Joy
3.4 oz EDT Sp $ 65.00
Your Price : _____

Khloe and Lamar
Unbreakable Love
3.4 oz EDT Sp $ 65.00
Your Price : _____

Kim Kardashian
Fleur Fatale
3.4 Oz EDP Sp $ 65.00
Your Price : _____

Kim Kardashian
Glam
1.7 oz EDP Sp $ 50.00
Your Price : _____
3.4 oz EDP Sp $ 65.00
Your Price : _____

Kim Kardashian
Gold
1.7 oz EDP Sp $ 50.00
Your Price : _____
3.4 oz EDP Sp $ 65.00
Your Price : _____

Kim Kardashian
Kim Kardashian
1.7 oz EDP Sp $ 50.00
Your Price : _____
3.4 oz EDP Sp $ 65.00
Your Price : _____

Kim Kardashian
Pure Honey
3.4 oz EDP Sp $ 65.00
Your Price : _____

Kim Kardashian
True Reflection
1.7 oz EDP Sp $ 50.00
Your Price : _____
3.4 oz EDP Sp $ 65.00
Your Price : _____

Kristel Saint Martin
Lovely Parfum D'Or
3.4 oz EDP Sp $ 55.00
Your Price : _____

Kristel Saint Martin
Parfum D'Or
3.4 oz EDP Sp $ 55.00
Your Price : _____

Kristel Saint Martin
Parfum D'Or Elixir
3.4 oz EDP Sp $ 55.00
Your Price : _____

Krizia
K
1.7 oz EDP Sp $ 50.00
Your Price : _____
3.3 oz EDP Sp $ 78.00
Your Price : _____

Krizia
Krazy Krizia
1.7 oz EDT Sp $ 60.00
Your Price : _____
3.4 oz EDT Sp $ 80.00
Your Price : _____

Lacoste
L.12.12 Eau Elegant
1.6 Oz EDT Sp $ 62.00
Your Price : _____
3.0 Oz EDT Sp $ 77.00
Your Price : _____

Lacoste
L.12.12 Eau Magnetic
1.7 oz EDP Sp $ 65.00
Your Price : _____
2.7 oz EDP Sp $ 80.00
Your Price : _____

Lacoste
L.12.12 Eau Naturale
1.6 oz EDT Sp $ 62.00
Your Price : _____
3.0 oz EDT Sp $ 77.00
Your Price : _____

Lacoste
L.12.12 Eau Sparkling
1.6 Oz EDT Sp $ 62.00
Your Price : _____
3.0 Oz EDT Sp $ 77.00
Your Price : _____

Lacoste
Eau De Lacoste Sensuelle
1.6 Oz EDP Sp $ 70.00
Your Price : _____
3.0 Oz EDP Sp $ 90.00
Your Price : _____

Lacoste
Inspiration
1.7 oz EDP Sp $ 52.00
Your Price : _____
2.5 oz EDP Sp $ 65.00
Your Price : _____

Lacoste
Dream of Pink
1.7 oz EDT Sp $ 55.00
Your Price : _____
3.0 oz EDT Sp $ 75.00
Your Price : _____

Lacoste
Love of Pink
1.7 oz EDT Sp $ 45.00
Your Price : _____
3.0 oz EDT Sp $ 68.00
Your Price : _____

Lacoste
Joy of Pink
1.7 oz EDT Sp $ 45.00
Your Price : _____
3.0 oz EDT Sp $ 60.00
Your Price : _____

Lacoste
Pour Femme
1.6 oz EDP Sp $ 50.00
Your Price : _____
3.0 oz EDP Sp $ 70.00
Your Price : _____

Lacoste
Touch of Pink
1.6 oz EDT Sp $ 52.00
Your Price : _____
3.0 oz EDT Sp $ 70.00
Your Price : _____

Lacoste
Touch of Spring
1.7 oz EDT Sp $ 52.00
Your Price : _____
3.0 oz EDT Sp $ 70.00
Your Price : _____

Lacoste
Touch of Sun
1.7 oz EDT Sp $ 52.00
Your Price : _____
3.0 oz EDT Sp $ 65.00
Your Price : _____

Lacoste
Eau De Lacoste
1.6 oz EDP Sp $ 70.00
Your Price : _____
3.0 oz EDP Sp $ 82.00
Your Price : _____

La Perla
J'AIME
3.3 oz EDT Sp $ 85.00
Your Price : _____

La Perla
La Perla Charme
1.7 oz EDP Sp $ 65.00
Your Price : _____
3.3 oz EDP Sp $ 85.00
Your Price : _____

La Perla
1.7 oz EDP Sp $ 45.00
Your Price : _____
3.4 oz EDP Sp $ 70.00
Your Price : _____

Lady Gaga
Fame
1.7 oz EDP Sp $ 55.00
Your Price : _____
3.4 oz EDP Sp $ 70.50
Your Price : _____

Lalique
Lalique
1.7 oz EDP Sp $ 50.00
Your Price : _____
3.3 oz EDP Sp $ 75.00
Your Price : _____
3.3 oz EDT Sp $ 65.00
Your Price : _____

Lalique
Le Baiser
1.7 oz EDT Sp $ 45.00
Your Price : _____
3.4 oz EDT Sp $ 60.00
Your Price : _____

Lancome
Tresor Midnight Rose
1.0 oz EDP Sp $ 58.00
Your Price : _____
1.7 oz EDT Sp $ 68.00
Your Price : _____
2.5 oz EDT Sp $ 83.00
Your Price : _____

Lancome
Clypso
1.7 oz EDT Sp $ 65.00
Your Price : _____
3.4 oz EDT Sp $ 80.00
Your Price : _____

Lancome
Hypnose
1.0 oz EDP Sp $ 57.00
Your Price : _____
1.7 oz EDP Sp $ 71.00
Your Price : _____
2.5 oz EDP Sp $ 88.00
Your Price : _____

Lancome
Hypnose Senses
1.7 oz EDP Sp $ 60.00
Your Price : _____
2.5 oz EDP Sp $ 78.00
Your Price : _____

Lancome
La Vie Est Belle Intense
1.7 oz EDP Sp $110.00
Your Price : _____

Lancome
La Vie Est Belle
1.0 oz EDP Sp $ 69.00
Your Price : _____
1.7 oz EDP Sp $ 90.00
Your Price : _____
2.5 oz EDP Sp $ 116.00
Your Price : _____
2.5 oz EDP Sp $ 122.00
Your Price : _____

Lancome
Magie Noire
1.7 oz EDT Sp $ 45.00
Your Price : _____
3.4 oz EDT Sp $ 60.00
Your Price : _____

Lancome
Magnifique
1.7 oz EDP Sp $ 59.00
Your Price : _____
2.5 oz EDP Sp $ 80.00
Your Price : _____

Lancome
Miracle
1.7 oz EDP Sp $ 74.00
Your Price : _____
3.4 oz EDP Sp $ 99.00
Your Price : _____

Lancome
Miracle Forever
1.0 oz EDP Sp $ 50.00
Your Price : _____
1.7 oz EDP Sp $ 65.00
Your Price : _____
2.5 oz EDP Sp $ 80.00
Your Price : _____

Lancome
Miracle So Magic
1.7 oz EDP Sp $ 60.00
Your Price : _____
3.4 oz EDP Sp $ 80.00
Your Price : _____

Lancome
Miracle Summer
1.7 oz EDP Sp $ 55.00
Your Price : _____
3.4 oz EDP Sp $ 79.00
Your Price : _____

Lancome
O De Lancome
1.7 oz EDT Sp $ 45.00
Your Price : _____
2.5 oz EDT Sp $ 60.00
Your Price : _____

Lancome
Poeme
1.7 oz EDP Sp $ 72.00
Your Price : _____
3.4 oz EDP Sp $ 99.00
Your Price : _____

Lancome
Tresor
1.0 oz EDP Sp $ 59.00
Your Price : _____
1.7 oz EDP Sp $ 84.00
Your Price : _____
3.4 oz EDP Sp $ 106.00
Your Price : _____

Lancome
Tresor in Love
1.0 oz EDP Sp $ 58.00
Your Price : _____
1.7 oz EDP Sp $ 68.00
Your Price : _____
2.5 oz EDP Sp $ 84.00
Your Price : _____

Lancome
Tresor La Nuit
1.0 oz EDP Sp $ 69.00
Your Price : _____
1.7 oz EDP Sp $ 90.00
Your Price : _____
2.5 oz EDP Sp $ 116.00
Your Price : _____
3.4 oz EDP Sp $ 122.00
Your Price : _____

Lanvin
Arpege
1.7 oz EDP Sp $ 65.00
Your Price : _____
3.4 oz EDP Sp $ 90.00
Your Price : _____

Lanvin
Eclat D' arpege
1.7 oz EDP Sp $ 75.00
Your Price : _____
3.4 oz EDP Sp $ 85.00
Your Price : _____

Lanvin
Jeanne Lanvin
1.7 oz EDP Sp $ 70.00
Your Price : _____
3.4 oz EDP Sp $ 90.00
Your Price : _____

Lanvin
Oxygene
1.7 oz EDP Sp $ 65.00
Your Price : _____
3.3 oz EDP Sp $ 85.00
Your Price : _____

Lanvin
Rumeur
1.7 oz EDP Sp $ 65.00
Your Price : _____
3.3 oz EDP Sp $ 85.00
Your Price : _____

Lanvin
Rumeur Intense
1.7 oz EDP Sp $ 65.00
Your Price : _____
3.4 oz EDP Sp $ 85.00
Your Price : _____

Lanvin
Rumeur 2 Rose
1.7 oz EDP Sp $ 75.00
Your Price : _____
3.4 oz EDP Sp $ 85.00
Your Price : _____

Lanvin
ME
1.7 oz EDP Sp $ 75.00
Your Price : _____
2.6 oz EDP Sp $ 95.00
Your Price : _____

Laura Biagiotti
Laura
1.7 oz EDP Sp $ 48.00
Your Price : _____
2.5 oz EDP Sp $ 60.00
Your Price : _____

Laura Biagiotti
Roma
1.7 oz EDP Sp $ 60.00
Your Price : _____
3.3 oz EDP Sp $ 75.00
Your Price : _____

Lily Pulitzer
Squeeze
1.7 oz EDP Sp $ 57.00
Your Price : _____
3.3 oz EDP Sp $ 79.00
Your Price : _____

Lily Pulitzer
Beachy
1.7 oz EDP Sp $ 57.00
Your Price : _____
3.3 oz EDP Sp $ 79.00
Your Price : _____

Lily Pulitzer
Wink
1.7 oz EDP Sp $ 57.00
Your Price : _____
3.4 oz EDP Sp $ 79.00
Your Price : _____

Liz Claiborne
Liz Claiborne
1.7 oz EDT Sp $ 50.00
Your Price : _____
3.4 oz EDT Sp $ 72.00
Your Price : _____

Liz Claiborne
Bora Bora
1.7 oz EDP Sp $ 55.00
Your Price : _____
3.4 oz EDP Sp $ 75.00
Your Price : _____

Liz Claiborne
Bora Bora Exotic
1.7 oz EDP Sp $ 49.00
Your Price : _____
3.4 oz EDP Sp $ 72.00
Your Price : _____

Liz Claiborne
Candies
1.6 oz EDT Sp $ 55.00
Your Price : _____
3.4 oz EDT Sp $ 72.00
Your Price : _____

Liz Claiborne
Curve Appeal
1.7 oz EDT Sp $ 35.00
Your Price : _____
2.5 oz EDT Sp $ 48.00
Your Price : _____

Liz Claiborne
Curve
1.7 oz EDT Sp $ 49.00
Your Price : _____
3.4 oz EDT Sp $ 72.00
Your Price : _____

Liz Claiborne
Curve Chill
1.7 oz EDT Sp $ 49.00
Your Price : _____
3.4 oz EDT Sp $ 70.00
Your Price : _____

Liz Claiborne
Curve Connect
1.7 oz EDT Sp $ 49.00
Your Price : _____
3.4 oz EDT Sp $ 70.00
Your Price : _____

Liz Claiborne
Curve Crush
1.6 oz EDT Sp $ 49.00
Your Price : _____
3.4 oz EDT Sp $ 72.00
Your Price : _____

Liz Claiborne
Curve Kicks
1.7 oz EDT Sp $ 49.00
Your Price : _____
3.4 oz EDT Sp $ 72.00
Your Price : _____

Liz Claiborne
Curve Soul
1.7 oz EDP Sp $ 49.00
Your Price : _____
3.4 oz EDP Sp $ 72.00
Your Price : _____

Liz Claiborne
Curve Wave
1.7 oz EDT Sp $ 49.00
Your Price : _____
3.4 oz EDT Sp $ 72.00
Your Price : _____

Liz Claiborne
Vintage Curve Soul
1.7 oz EDT Sp $ 50.00
Your Price : _____
3.4 oz EDT Sp $ 72.00
Your Price : _____

Liz Claiborne
Liz
1.7 oz EDP Sp $ 49.00
Your Price : _____
3.4 oz EDP Sp $ 72.00
Your Price : _____

Liz Claiborne
Liz Sport
1.7 oz EDT Sp $ 49.00
Your Price : _____
3.4 oz EDT Sp $ 72.00
Your Price : _____

Liz Claiborne
Lucky Number 6
1.7 oz EDP Sp $ 54.00
Your Price : _____
3.4 oz EDP Sp $ 75.00
Your Price : _____

Liz Claiborne
Lucky You
1.0 oz EDP Sp $ 34.00
Your Price : _____
1.7 oz EDP Sp $ 49.00
Your Price : _____
3.4 oz EDP Sp $ 72.00
Your Price : _____

Liz Claiborne
Mambo
1.7 oz EDP Sp $ 49.00
Your Price : _____
3.4 oz EDP Sp $ 72.00
Your Price : _____

Liz Claiborne
Mambo Mix
1.7 oz EDT Sp $ 45.00
Your Price : _____
3.4 oz EDT Sp $ 60.00
Your Price : _____

Liz Claiborne
Realities
1.7 oz EDP Sp $ 50.00
Your Price : _____
3.4 oz EDP Sp $ 72.00
Your Price : _____

Liz Claiborne
Realities New
1.7 oz EDP Sp $ 49.00
Your Price : _____
3.4 oz EDP Sp $ 72.00
Your Price : _____

Liz Claiborne
Realities Sweet Desire
1.7 oz EDP Sp $ 49.00
Your Price : _____
3.4 oz EDP Sp $ 72.00
Your Price : _____

Liz Claiborne
Red Sunset
1.7 oz EDP Sp $ 50.00
Your Price : _____
3.4 oz EDP Sp $ 72.00
Your Price : _____

Liz Claiborne
Sunrise
1.7 oz EDT Sp $ 50.00
Your Price : _____
3.4 oz EDT Sp $ 72.00
Your Price : _____

Liz Claiborne
Vivid
1.7 oz EDT Sp $ 50.00
Your Price : _____
3.4 oz EDT Sp $ 72.00
Your Price : _____

Lolita Lempicka
Elle L'Aime
2.7 oz EDP Sp $ 68.00
Your Price : _____

Lolita Lempicka
L De Lolita
1.0 oz EDP Sp $ 48.00
Your Price : _____
1.7 oz EDP Sp $ 58.00
Your Price : _____
2.7 oz EDP Sp $ 69.00
Your Price : _____

Lolita Lempicka
L De Lolita
Fleur De Corail
1.7 oz EDP Sp $ 59.00
Your Price : _____
2.7 oz EDP Sp $ 75.00
Your Price : _____

Lolita Lempicka
1.7 oz EDP Sp $ 55.00
Your Price : _____
3.4 oz EDP Sp $ 75.00
Your Price : _____
3.4 oz EDT Sp $ 60.00
Your Price : _____

Lolita Lempicka
Forbidden Flower
1.7 oz EDP Sp $ 58.00
Your Price : _____
2.7 oz EDP Sp $ 69.00
Your Price : _____

Lolita Lempicka
Midnight
1.7 oz EDP Sp $ 58.00
Your Price : _____
2.7 oz EDP Sp $ 69.00
Your Price : _____

Lolita Lempicka
Si Lolita
1.7 oz EDP Sp $ 58.00
Your Price :
2.7 oz EDP Sp $ 69.00
Your Price :

Lomani
Amitabh Bachchan
Women Shine
3.3 oz EDP Sp $ 59.00
Your Price :

Lomani
Best Lady
3.3 oz EDP Sp $ 59.00
Your Price :

Lomani
Miss Lomani
3.3 oz EDP Sp $ 59.00
Your Price :

Lomani
Original Love
3.3 oz EDP Sp $ 59.00
Your Price :

Lomani
Si Fleuri
3.3 oz EDP Sp $ 59.00
Your Price :

Lomani
Si Fleuri Passion
3.3 oz EDP Sp $ 59.00
Your Price :

Lomani
Ignition
3.3 oz EDP Sp $ 55.00
Your Price :

Lomani Femme
3.3 oz EDP Sp $ 59.00
Your Price :

Lulu Guinness
Lulu Guinness
1.7 oz EDT Sp $ 48.00
Your Price :
3.4 oz EDT Sp $ 65.00
Your Price :

Madonna
Truth or Dare
2.5 oz EDP Sp $ 75.00
Your Price :

Madonna
Truth or Dare Naked
2.5 oz EDP Sp $ 75.00
Your Price :

Marc Jacobs
1.7 oz EDP Sp $ 90.00
Your Price :
3.4 oz EDP Sp $ 108.00
Your Price :

Marc Jacobs
Honey
1.7 oz EDP Sp $ 70.00
Your Price :
3.4 oz EDP Sp $ 96.00
Your Price :

Marc Jacobs
Blush
1.0 oz EDP Sp $ 48.00
Your Price :
1.7 oz EDP Sp $ 60.00
Your Price :
2.7 oz EDP Sp $ 85.00
Your Price :

Marc Jacobs
Cotton
3.4 oz EDT Sp $ 62.00
Your Price :

Marc Jacobs
Cucumber
3.4 oz EDT Sp $ 62.00
Your Price :

Marc Jacobs
Daisy
1.7 oz EDT Sp $80.00
Your Price :
3.4 oz EDT Sp $100.00
Your Price :

Marc Jacobs
Decadence
1.7 oz EDP Sp $ 97.00
Your Price :
3.4 oz EDP Sp $ 122.00
Your Price :

Marc Jacbs
Divine Decadence
1.7 oz EDP Sp $ 97.00
Your Price :
3.4 oz EDP Sp $ 122.00
Your Price :

Marc Jacobs
Daisy Dream
1.7 oz EDT Sp $ 58.00
Your Price : _____
3.4 oz EDT Sp $ 100.00
Your Price : _____

Marc Jacobs
Daisy Dream Forever
1.7 oz EDP Sp $ 90.00
Your Price : _____

Marc Jacobs
Daisy
1.7 oz EDP Sp $ 95.00
Your Price : _____

Marc Jacobs
Essence
1.7 oz EDP Sp $ 60.00
Your Price : _____
2.7 oz EDP Sp $ 85.00
Your Price : _____

Marc Jacobs
Fig
3.4 oz EDT Sp $ 62.00
Your Price : _____

Marc Jacobs
Gardenia
3.4 oz EDT Sp $ 62.00
Your Price : _____

Marc Jacobs
Grapefruit
3.4 oz EDT Sp $ 62.00
Your Price : _____

Marc Jacobs
Grass
3.4 oz EDT Sp $ 62.00
Your Price : _____

Marc Jacobs
Lola
1.7 oz EDT Sp $ 65.00
Your Price : _____
3.4 oz EDT Sp $ 85.00
Your Price : _____

Marc Jacobs
Orange
3.4 oz EDT Sp $ 62.00
Your Price : _____

Marc Jacobs
Pear
3.4 oz EDT Sp $ 62.00
Your Price : _____

Marc Jacobs
Rain
3.4 oz EDT Sp $ 62.00
Your Price : _____

Marc Jacobs
Violet
1.7 oz EDP Sp $ 75.00
Your Price : _____

Marc Jacobs
Violet
3.4 oz EDT Sp $ 62.00
Your Price : _____

Marc Jacobs
Daisy Sunshine
1.7 oz EDT Sp $ 65.00
Your Price : _____

Marc Jacobs
Daisy Eau So
Fresh Sunshine
2.5 oz EDT Sp $ 75.00
Your Price : _____
4.2 oz EDT Sp $ 90.00
Your Price : _____

Marc Jacobs
Daisy Eau So Fresh
2.5 oz EDT Sp $ 96.00
Your Price : _____
4.2 oz EDT Sp $ 108.00
Your Price : _____

Marc Jacobs
Dot
1.7 oz EDT Sp $ 75.00
Your Price : _____
3.4 oz EDT Sp $ 96.00
Your Price : _____

Marc Jacobs
Oh Lola
1.7 oz EDP Sp $ 65.00
Your Price : _____
3.4 oz EDP Sp $ 85.00
Your Price : _____

Mariah Carey
M
1.7 oz EDP Sp $ 60.00
Your Price : _____
3.4 oz EDP Sp $ 75.00
Your Price : _____

Estelle Ewen
IN BLACK
3.4 oz EDT Sp $72.00

Estelle Ewen
IN PINK
3.4 oz EDT Sp $72.00

Estelle Ewen
IN RED
3.4 oz EDT Sp $72.00

Estelle Ewen
L'ORIENTALE FOR HER
3.4 oz EDT Sp $80.00

Estelle Ewen
LOVE SIXTEEN APPLE
3.4 oz EDT Sp $68.00

Estelle Vendome
APPLE HEART
3.4 oz EDT Sp $85.00

Estelle Vendome
ELIXIR PLEASURE
3.4 oz EDT Sp $78.00

Estelle Vendome
WITH ALL MY LOVE
3.4 oz EDT Sp $80.00

Gemina B.
FLOWER BLOSSOM
2.8 oz EDP Sp $159.00

Gemina B.
LOVE PARIS
2.8 oz EDP Sp $149.00

Gemina B
SUBLISSIME
2.5 oz EDP Sp $110.00

Gemina B
SUBLISSIME NIGHT
2.5 oz EDP Sp $126.00

Geparlys
BLUE
3.4 oz EDP Sp $80.00

Glenn Perri
BEAUTIFUL LADY
3.4 oz EDP Sp $90.00

Glenn Perri
BLACK IS BEAUTIFUL
3.4 oz EDP Sp $90.00

Glenn Perri
ECLAT D' ELEGANCE
3.0 oz EDP Sp $120.00

Gemina B
YOU Are Beautiful
3.0 oz EDP Sp $98.00

Gemina B
You Are Beautiful LIKE DIAMOND
3.0 oz EDP Sp $98.00

Glenn Perri
ELEGANCIA
3.0 oz EDP Sp $80.00

Glenn Perri
FASHION ADDICT
3.4 oz EDP Sp $85.00

Glenn Perri
HEXANE
3.4 oz EDP Sp $76.00

Glenn Perri
IWAN
3.4 oz EDP Sp $76.00

Glenn Perri
MIDNIGHT ELEGANCE
3.4 oz EDT Sp $123.00

Glenn Perri
ROMANTIC TOUCH
3.0 oz EDP Sp $78.00

Glenn Perri
UNBELIEVABLE FAME
3.4 oz EDP Sp $85.00

Glenn Perri
UNBELIEVABLE Lady
3.4 oz EDT Sp $85.00

Glenn Perri
UNPREDICTABLE & BEAUTIFUL
3.2 oz EDT Sp $98.00

Glenn Perri
UNPREDICTABLE & CHIC
3.4 oz EDT Sp $90.00

Glenn Perri
Unpredictable & FAMOUS
3.2 oz EDP Sp $98.00

Glenn Perri
Unpredictable & SEXY
3.2 oz EDT Sp $98.00

Glenn Perri
UNPREDICTABLE LADY
3.4 oz EDT Sp $90.00

Glenn Perri
UNPREDICTABLE BABE
3.4 oz EDT Sp $92.00

Glenn Perri
UNPREDICTABLE GIRL
3.4 oz EDP Sp $90.00

Johan B
FANCY BLOOMING
3.4 oz EDP Sp $152.00

Karen Low
CODE 37
3.4 oz EDT Sp $80.00

Karen Low
INDESCENCE FASHION BLACK
3.4 oz EDT Sp $72.00

Karen Low
KL INTERVIEW
3.4 oz EDT Sp $68.00

Karen Low
KL OBSESSION
3.4 oz EDT Sp $70.00

Karen Low
LADY DIAMOND
3.4 oz EDT Sp $79.00

Karen Low
LADY GOLD
3.4 oz EDT Sp $79.00

Mariah Carey
Luscious Pink
1.7 oz EDP Sp $ 60.00
Your Price :_____
3.4 oz EDP Sp $ 75.00
Your Price :_____

Mariah Carey
Forever Mariah Carey
1.7 oz EDP Sp $ 60.00
Your Price :_____
3.4 oz EDP Sp $ 75.00
Your Price :_____

Mariah Carey
Lollipop Bling Honey
1.0 oz EDP Sp $ 45.00
Your Price :_____
3.4 oz EDP Sp $ 65.00
Your Price :_____

Mariah Carey
Lollipop Bling Mine Again
1.0 oz EDP Sp $ 45.00
Your Price :_____
3.4 oz EDP Sp $ 65.00
Your Price :_____

Mariah Carey
Lollipop Bling Ribbon
1.0 oz EDP Sp $ 45.00
Your Price :_____
3.4 oz EDP Sp $ 65.00
Your Price :_____

Mariah Carey
Dreams
1.7 oz EDP Sp $ 45.00
Your Price :_____

Mariella Burani
Bouquet De Roses
Rafraichissante (Green)
1.7 oz EDT Sp $ 60.00
Your Price :_____
3.4 oz EDT Sp $ 85.00
Your Price :_____

Mariella Burani
1.7 oz EDT Sp $ 62.00
Your Price :_____
3.4 oz EDT Sp $ 85.00
Your Price :_____

Mariella Burani
Bouquet De Roses
Sensuelle (pink)
1.7 oz EDT Sp $ 60.00
Your Price :_____
3.4 oz EDT Sp $ 85.00
Your Price :_____

Mary J. Blige
My Life
1.7 oz EDP Sp $ 60.00
Your Price :_____

Michael Germain
Sexual
2.5 oz EDP Sp $ 60.00
Your Price :_____
4.2 oz EDP Sp $ 80.00
Your Price :_____

Michael Germain
Sexual Femme
2.5 oz EDP Sp $ 55.00
Your Price :_____
4.2 oz EDP Sp $ 75.00
Your Price :_____

Michael Kors
Island
1.7 oz EDP Sp $ 59.00
Your Price :_____
3.4 oz EDP Sp $ 75.00
Your Price :_____

Michael Kors
Island Bermuda
1.7 oz EDP Sp $ 59.00
Your Price :_____
3.4 oz EDP Sp $ 75.00
Your Price :_____

Michael Kors
Island Capri
1.7 oz EDP Sp $ 59.00
Your Price :_____
3.4 oz EDP Sp $ 79.00
Your Price :_____

Michael Kors
Island Hawaii
1.7 oz EDP Sp $ 59.00
Your Price :_____
3.4 oz EDP Sp $ 75.00
Your Price :_____

Michael Kors
Michael Kors
1.7 oz EDP Sp $ 70.00
Your Price :_____
3.4 oz EDP Sp $ 112.00
Your Price :_____

Michael Kors
Very Hollywood
1.7 oz EDP Sp $ 70.00
Your Price :_____
3.4 oz EDP Sp $ 92.00
Your Price :_____

Michael Kors
Island Palm Beach
1.7 oz EDP Sp $ 60.00
Your Price :_____
3.4 oz EDP Sp $ 75.00
Your Price :_____

Michael Kors
Suede
1.7 oz EDP Sp $ 65.00
Your Price :_____
3.4 oz EDP Sp $ 98.00
Your Price :_____

Michael Kors
Glam Jasmine
1.7 oz EDP Sp $ 82.00
Your Price : _____
3.4 oz EDP Sp $ 102.00
Your Price : _____

Michael Kors
Sport Citrus
1.7 oz EDP Sp $ 82.00
Your Price : _____
3.4 oz EDP Sp $ 102.00
Your Price : _____

Michael Kors
Sexy Amber
1.7 oz EDP Sp $ 82.00
Your Price : _____
3.4 oz EDP Sp $ 102.00
Your Price : _____
6.3 oz EDP Sp $ 138.00
Your Price : _____

Michael Kors
Gold Rose Edition
1.7 oz EDP Sp $ 75.00
Your Price : _____
3.4 oz EDP Sp $ 95.00
Your Price : _____

Michael Kors
Sexy Blossom
1.7 oz EDP Sp $ 82.00
Your Price : _____
3.4 oz EDP Sp $ 102.00
Your Price : _____

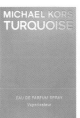

Michael Kors
Turquoise
1.0 oz EDP Sp $ 66.00
Your Price : _____
1.7 oz EDP Sp $ 92.00
Your Price : _____
3.4 oz EDP Sp $ 112.00
Your Price : _____

Michael Kors
Rose Radiant Gold
1.7 oz EDP Sp $ 82.00
Your Price : _____
3.4 oz EDP Sp $ 102.00
Your Price : _____

Michael Kors
Coral
1.7 oz EDP Sp $ 90.00
Your Price : _____
3.4 oz EDP Sp $ 112.00
Your Price : _____

Michael Kors
White Luminous Gold
1.7 oz EDP Sp $ 82.00
Your Price : _____
3.4 oz EDP Sp $ 102.00
Your Price : _____

Michael Kors
Wonderlust
1.7 oz EDP Sp $ 88.00
Your Price : _____
3.4 oz EDP Sp $ 108.00
Your Price : _____

Michael Kors
Gold Luxe Edition
1.7 oz EDP Sp $ 82.00
Your Price : _____
3.4 oz EDP Sp $ 102.00
Your Price : _____

Michael Kors
24 K Brilliant Gold
1.7 oz EDP Sp $ 82.00
Your Price : _____
3.4 oz EDP Sp $ 102.00
Your Price : _____

Midnight Shimmer
Michael Kors
1.7 oz EDP Sp $ 82.00
Your Price : _____
3.4 oz EDP Sp $ 102.00
Your Price : _____

Molinard
Habanita De Molinard
1.7 oz EDT Sp $ 40.00
Your Price : _____
3.4 oz EDT Sp $ 60.00
Your Price : _____

Molinard
Les Feminis Nirmala
1.7 oz EDT Sp $ 45.00
Your Price : _____
3.4 oz EDT Sp $ 65.00
Your Price : _____

Molinard
Molinard De Molinard
1.7 oz EDT Sp $ 45.00
Your Price : _____
3.4 oz EDT Sp $ 60.00
Your Price : _____

Mont Blanc
Femme Individuelle
1.7 oz EDT Sp $ 55.00
Your Price : _____
2.5 oz EDT Sp $ 74.00
Your Price : _____

Mont Blanc
Femme de Mont Blanc
1.7 oz EDT Sp $ 55.00
Your Price : _____
2.5 oz EDT Sp $ 75.00
Your Price : _____

Mont Blanc
Legend Pour Femme
1.7 oz EDP Sp $ 65.00
Your Price : _____
2.5 oz EDP Sp $ 85.00
Your Price : _____

Mont Blanc
Presence d'n Une Femme
1.7 oz EDT Sp $ 55.00
Your Price : _____
2.5 oz EDT Sp $ 75.00
Your Price : _____

Mont Blanc
Individuelle Soul
& Senses
1.7 oz EDT Sp $ 50.00
Your Price : _____
2.5 oz EDT Sp $ 75.00
Your Price : _____

Montana
Turquoise
3.3 oz EDP Sp $ 75.00
Your Price : _____

Montana
Parfum De Peau
3.4 oz EDT Sp $ 78.00
Your Price : _____

Montana
Blu
3.4 oz EDT Sp $ 78.00
Your Price : _____

Montana
Eau Cuivree
3.4 oz EDT Sp $ 78.00
Your Price : _____

Montana
Green
3.4 oz EDT Sp $ 78.00
Your Price : _____

Montana
Just Me
3.4 oz EDT Sp $ 78.00
Your Price : _____

Montana
Parfum D'elle
2.5 oz EDT Sp $ 78.00
Your Price : _____

Montana
Parfum De Femme
3.4 oz EDT Sp $ 78.00
Your Price : _____

Montana
Mood Sensual
3.3 oz EDT Sp $ 78.00
Your Price : _____

Montana
Mood Sexy
3.3 oz EDT Sp $ 78.00
Your Price : _____

Moschino
Cheap and Chic
1.7 oz EDT Sp $ 48.00
Your Price : _____
3.4 oz EDT Sp $ 70.00
Your Price : _____

Moschino
Fresh Couture
1.0 Oz EDT Sp $ 45.00
Your Price : _____
1.7 Oz EDT Sp $ 62.00
Your Price : _____
3.4 Oz EDT Sp $ 82.00
Your Price : _____

Moschino
Funny
3.4 Oz EDT Sp $ 64.00
Your Price : _____

Moschino
Hippy Fizz
1.7 oz EDT Sp $ 48.00
Your Price : _____
3.4 oz EDT Sp $ 70.00
Your Price : _____

Moschino
I Love Love
1.7 oz EDT Sp $ 48.00
Your Price : _____
3.4 oz EDT Sp $ 70.00
Your Price : _____

Narciso Rodriguez
Narciso
1.6 oz EDP Sp $ 97.00
Your Price : _____
3.0 oz EDP Sp $ 115.00
Your Price : _____

Narciso Rodriguez
Narciso
1.6 oz EDT Sp $ 80.00
Your Price : _____
3.0 oz EDT Sp $ 100.00
Your Price : _____

Narciso Rodriguez
Fleur De Musk
1.6 Oz EDP Sp $ 97.00
Your Price : _____
3.3 Oz EDP Sp $ 124.00
Your Price : _____

Narciso Rodriguez
Poudree
1.6 Oz EDP Sp $ 97.00
Your Price : _____
3.0 Oz EDP Sp $ 115.00
Your Price : _____

Narciso Rodriguez
Narciso Rodriguez
1.0 oz EDT Sp $ 56.00
Your Price : _____
1.6 oz EDT Sp $ 80.00
Your Price : _____
3.3 oz EDT Sp $ 107.00
Your Price : _____

Narciso Rodriguez
Narciso Rodriguez
1.6 oz EDP Sp $ 97.00
Your Price : _____
3.3 oz EDP Sp $ 124.00
Your Price : _____

Narciso Rodriguez
Essence
1.6 oz EDP Sp $ 90.00
Your Price : _____
3.3 oz EDP Sp $ 120.00
Your Price : _____

Nautica
Nautica
1.7 oz EDP Sp $ 40.00
Your Price : _____
3.4 oz EDP Sp $ 60.00
Your Price : _____

Nautica
My Voyage
1.7 oz EDP Sp $ 40.00
Your Price : _____
3.4 oz EDP Sp $ 60.00
Your Price : _____

Nicki Minaj
Pink Friday
1.7 oz EDP Sp $ 45.00
Your Price : _____
3.4 oz EDP Sp $ 60.00
Your Price : _____

Nicki Minaj
Minajesty
1.7 oz EDP Sp $ 45.00
Your Price : _____
3.4 oz EDP Sp $ 60.00
Your Price : _____

Nicki Minaj
Onika
1.7 oz EDP Sp $ 45.00
Your Price : _____
3.4 oz EDP Sp $ 60.00
Your Price : _____

Nicole Miller
Nicole Miller
3.3 oz EDP Sp $ 55.00
Your Price : _____

Nicole Polizzi
Snooki
3.3 oz EDP Sp $ 52.00
Your Price : _____

Nicole Richie
Nicole
1.7 oz EDP Sp $ 50.00
Your Price : _____
3.4 oz EDP Sp $ 65.00
Your Price : _____

Niki Taylor
Begin
3.4 oz EDT Sp $ 70.00
Your Price : _____

Nina Ricci
Deci Dela
1.7 oz EDT Sp $ 55.00
Your Price : _____
3.3 oz EDT Sp $ 75.00
Your Price : _____

Nina Ricci
Fleur De Fleurs
1.7 oz EDT Sp $ 55.00
Your Price : _____
3.3 oz EDT Sp $ 75.00
Your Price : _____

Nina Ricci
Les Belles Amour
D'amandier
1.7 oz EDT Sp $ 55.00
Your Price : _____

Nina Ricci
L'air Du Temps
Coloured Doves
1.7 oz EDT Sp $ 55.00
Your Price : _____
3.4 oz EDT Sp $ 75.00
Your Price : _____

Nina Ricci
L'air Du Temps
Love Fills
3.3 oz EDT Sp $ 50.00
Your Price : _____

Nina Ricci
L'air Du Temps
1.7 oz EDT Sp $ 60.00
Your Price : _____
3.3 oz EDT Sp $ 85.00
Your Price : _____

Nina Ricci
L' Elixir
1.7 oz EDP Sp $ 65.00
Your Price : _____
2.7 oz EDP Sp $ 80.00
Your Price : _____

Nina Ricci
Nina
1.7 oz EDT Sp $ 60.00
Your Price : _____
2.7 oz EDT Sp $ 75.00
Your Price : _____

Nina Ricci
Premier Jour
1.6 oz EDT Sp $ 55.00
Your Price : _____
3.3 oz EDT Sp $ 75.00
Your Price : _____

Nina Ricci
Pretty Nina
1.6 oz EDT Sp $ 55.00
Your Price : _____
3.3 oz EDT Sp $ 75.00
Your Price : _____

Nina Ricci
Ricci Ricci
1.7 oz EDP Sp $ 65.00
Your Price : _____
2.7 oz EDP Sp $ 80.00
Your Price : _____

Nina Ricci
Le Paradise De Nina
1.7 oz EDT Sp $ 50.00
Your Price : _____

Nina Ricci
Love in Paris
1.0 oz EDP Sp $ 65.00
Your Price : _____
1.7 oz EDP Sp $ 75.00
Your Price : _____

Nina Ricci
Nina Fantasy
Limited Edition
1.6 oz EDT Sp $ 55.00
Your Price : _____
3.3 oz EDT Sp $ 70.00
Your Price : _____

Nina Ricci
Mademoiselle Ricci
1.7 oz EDP Sp $ 65.00
Your Price : _____
2.7 oz EDP Sp $ 80.00
Your Price : _____

Norell
Norell
2.3 oz EDC Sp $ 55.00
Your Price : _____
3.3 oz EDT Sp $ 65.00
Your Price : _____

Ocean Pacific
OP Juice
1.7 oz EDP Sp $ 45.00
Your Price : _____
2.5 oz EDP Sp $ 60.00
Your Price : _____

Ocean Pacific
OP Juice Blend
1.7 oz EDP Sp $ 49.00
Your Price : _____
2.5 oz EDP Sp $ 60.00
Your Price : _____

Oleg Cassini
Cassini
1.7 oz EDP Sp $ 49.00
Your Price : _____
3.4 oz EDP Sp $ 65.00
Your Price : _____

One Direction
Between Us
1.7 oz EDP Sp $ 39.00
Your Price : _____
3.4 oz EDP Sp $ 49.00
Your Price : _____

One Direction
That Moment
1.7 oz EDP Sp $ 39.00
Your Price : _____
3.4 oz EDP Sp $ 49.00
Your Price : _____

One Direction
You & I
1.7 oz EDP Sp $ 39.00
Your Price : _____
3.4 oz EDP Sp $ 49.00
Your Price : _____

One Direction
Our Moment
1.7 oz EDP Sp $ 39.00
Your Price : _____
3.4 oz EDP Sp $ 49.00
Your Price : _____

Oscar De La Renta
Intrusion
1.0 oz EDT Sp $ 39.00
Your Price : _____
1.7 oz EDT Sp $ 64.00
Your Price : _____

Oscar De La Renta
Citrus
1.7 oz EDP Sp $ 55.00
Your Price : _____
3.4 oz EDP Sp $ 75.00
Your Price : _____

Oscar De La Renta
Oscar
1.7 oz EDT Sp $ 67.00
Your Price : _____
3.4 oz EDT Sp $ 87.00
Your Price : _____

Oscar De La Renta
Oscar Summer Dew
1.7 oz EDT Sp $ 52.00
Your Price : _____
3.4 oz EDT Sp $ 72.00
Your Price : _____

Oscar De La Renta
Oscar Tropical
1.7 oz EDT Sp $ 52.00
Your Price : _____
3.4 oz EDT Sp $ 72.00
Your Price : _____

Oscar De La Renta
Something Blue
1.7 oz EDP Sp $ 85.00
Your Price :
3.4 oz EDP Sp $ 115.00
Your Price :

Oscar De La Renta
Rosamor
1.6 oz EDT Sp $ 52.00
Your Price :
3.4 oz EDT Sp $ 72.00
Your Price :

Oscar De La Renta
So De La Renta
1.7 oz EDT Sp $ 52.00
Your Price :
3.4 oz EDT Sp $ 72.00
Your Price :

Oscar De La Renta
Volupte
1.7 oz EDT Sp $ 52.00
Your Price :
3.4 oz EDT Sp $ 72.00
Your Price :

Oscar De La Renta
Espirit d' Oscar
1.6 oz EDT Sp $ 78.00
Your Price :
3.3 oz EDT Sp $ 98.00
Your Price :

Oscar De La Renta
Oscar Violet
2.0 oz EDT Sp $ 65.00
Your Price :

Paco Rabanne
Black XS
1.7 oz EDT Sp $ 55.00
Your Price :
2.7 oz EDT Sp $ 79.00
Your Price :

Paco Rabanne
Black XS L' Exces
1.7 oz EDP Sp $ 50.00
Your Price :
2.7 oz EDP Sp $ 75.00
Your Price :

Paco Rabanne
Energy
3.4 oz EDT Sp $ 79.00
Your Price :

Paco Rabanne
Lady Million Eau My Gold
1.7 oz EDT Sp $ 68.00
Your Price :
2.7 oz EDT Sp $ 88.00
Your Price :

Paco Rabanne
Lady Million
1.0 oz EDP Sp $ 50.00
Your Price :
1.7 oz EDP Sp $ 77.00
Your Price :
2.7 oz EDP Sp $ 98.00
Your Price :

Paco Rabanne
Metal
3.4 oz EDT Sp $ 79.00
Your Price :

Paco Rabanne
Olympea
1.7 oz EDP Sp $ 75.00
Your Price :
2.7 oz EDP Sp $ 96.00
Your Price :

Paco Rabanne
Olympea Aqua
1.7 oz EDT Sp $ 75.00
Your Price :
2.7 oz EDT Sp $ 96.00
Your Price :

Paco Rabanne
Olympea Intense
1.7 oz EDP Sp $ 83.00
Your Price :
2.7 oz EDP Sp $ 106.00
Your Price :

Paco Rabanne
Pour Elle Paco Rabanne
1.7 oz EDT Sp $ 60.00
Your Price :
2.7 oz EDT Sp $ 95.00
Your Price :

Paco Rabanne
Ultraviolet Aurora
Borealis
3.4 oz EDT Sp $ 55.00
Your Price :

Paco Rabanne
Unisex
1.7 oz EDT Sp $ 55.00
Your Price :
3.4 oz EDT Sp $ 79.00
Your Price :

Paco Rabanne
Ultrared
1.7 oz EDT Sp $ 60.00
Your Price :
2.7 oz EDT Sp $ 75.00
Your Price :

Paco Rabanne
Ultraviolet
1.7 oz EDP Sp $ 60.00
Your Price :
2.7 oz EDP Sp $ 75.00
Your Price :

Paco Rabanne
Ultravoilet
Liquid Metal
1.7 oz EDT Sp $ 55.00
Your Price : _____
2.7 oz EDT Sp $ 75.00
Your Price : _____

Paco Rabanne
Ultravoilet
Colours of Summer
1.7 oz EDT Sp $ 55.00
Your Price : _____
2.7 oz EDT Sp $ 75.00
Your Price : _____

Paco Rabanne
XS Pour Elle
1.7 oz EDT Sp $ 60.00
Your Price : _____
3.4 oz EDT Sp $ 75.00
Your Price : _____

Paloma Picasso
Chapeau Bleu
1.7 oz EDP Sp $ 50.00
Your Price : _____
2.5 oz EDP Sp $ 69.00
Your Price : _____

Paloma Picasso
1.0 oz EDP Sp $ 50.00
Your Price : _____
1.7 oz EDP Sp $ 65.00
Your Price : _____
3.4 oz EDP Sp $ 90.00
Your Price : _____

Paris Hilton
Paris Hilton
1.7 oz EDP Sp $ 54.00
Your Price : _____
3.4 oz EDP Sp $ 79.00
Your Price : _____

Paris Hilton
Can Can
1.7 oz EDP Sp $ 54.00
Your Price : _____
3.4 oz EDP Sp $ 79.00
Your Price : _____

Paris Hilton
Can Can Burlesque
1.7 oz EDP Sp $ 54.00
Your Price : _____
3.4 oz EDP Sp $ 79.00
Your Price : _____

Paris Hilton
Dazzle
4.2 oz EDP Sp $ 62.00
Your Price : _____

Paris Hilton
Fairy Dust
1.7 oz EDP Sp $ 54.00
Your Price : _____
3.4 oz EDP Sp $ 79.00
Your Price : _____

Paris Hilton
Heiress
1.7 oz EDP Sp $ 54.00
Your Price : _____
3.4 oz EDP Sp $ 79.00
Your Price : _____

Paris Hilton
Just Me
1.7 oz EDP Sp $ 54.00
Your Price : _____
3.4 oz EDP Sp $ 79.00
Your Price : _____

Paris Hilton
Passport in South Beach
1.7 oz EDT Sp $ 59.00
Your Price : _____
3.4 oz EDT Sp $ 62.50
Your Price : _____

Paris Hilton
Passport in Tokyo
1.7 oz EDT Sp $ 59.00
Your Price : _____
3.4 oz EDT Sp $ 62.50
Your Price : _____

Paris Hilton
Passport in St. Moritz
1.7 oz EDT Sp $ 59.00
Your Price : _____
3.4 oz EDT Sp $ 62.50
Your Price : _____

Paris Hilton
Sheer
1.7 oz EDP Sp $ 54.00
Your Price : _____
3.4 oz EDP Sp $ 79.00
Your Price : _____

Paris Hilton
Siren
1.7 oz EDP Sp $ 59.00
Your Price : _____
3.4 oz EDP Sp $ 85.00
Your Price : _____

Paris Hilton
Tease
1.7 oz EDP Sp $ 59.00
Your Price : _____
3.4 oz EDP Sp $ 79.00
Your Price : _____

Parlux
Bellagio
3.3 oz EDP Sp $ 69.00
Your Price : _____

Parlux
Phantom of Opera
1.7 oz EDP Sp $ 45.00
Your Price : _____
3.4 oz EDP Sp $ 69.00
Your Price : _____

Perry Ellis
18
1.7 oz EDT Sp $ 50.00
Your Price : _____
3.4 oz EDT Sp $ 65.00
Your Price : _____

Perry Ellis
18 Sensual
1.7 oz EDP Sp $ 50.00
Your Price : _____
3.4 oz EDP Sp $ 65.00
Your Price : _____

Perry Ellis
360
1.7 oz EDT Sp $ 50.00
Your Price : _____
3.4 oz EDT Sp $ 65.00
Your Price : _____

Perry Ellis
360 Black
1.7 oz EDP Sp $ 50.00
Your Price : _____
3.4 oz EDP Sp $ 65.00
Your Price : _____

Perry Ellis
360 Blue
1.7 oz EDP Sp $ 50.00
Your Price : _____
3.4 oz EDP Sp $ 65.00
Your Price : _____

Perry Ellis
360 Coral
1.7 oz EDP Sp $ 50.00
Your Price : _____
3.4 oz EDP Sp $ 65.00
Your Price : _____

Perry Ellis
360 Purple
1.7 oz EDP Sp $ 50.00
Your Price : _____
3.4 oz EDP Sp $ 65.00
Your Price : _____

Perry Ellis
360 PINK
1.7 oz EDP Sp $ 50.00
Your Price : _____
3.4 oz EDP Sp $ 65.00
Your Price : _____

Perry Ellis
360 Red
1.7 oz EDP Sp $ 50.00
Your Price : _____
3.4 oz EDP Sp $ 65.00
Your Price : _____

Perry Ellis
360 White
1.7 oz EDP Sp $ 50.00
Your Price : _____
3.4 oz EDP Sp $ 65.00
Your Price : _____

Perry Ellis
America
1.7 oz EDT Sp $ 50.00
Your Price : _____
3.4 oz EDT Sp $ 65.00
Your Price : _____

Perry Ellis
F
1.7 oz EDP Sp $ 50.00
Your Price : _____
3.3 oz EDP Sp $ 65.00
Your Price : _____

Perry Ellis
Love
1.7 oz EDP Sp $ 50.00
Your Price : _____
3.4 oz EDP Sp $ 65.00
Your Price : _____

Perry Ellis
Portfolio
1.7 oz EDP Sp $ 50.00
Your Price : _____
3.4 oz EDP Sp $ 65.00
Your Price : _____

Perry Ellis
Portfolio Elite
1.7 oz EDP Sp $ 50.00
Your Price : _____
3.4 oz EDP Sp $ 65.00
Your Price : _____

Perry Ellis
Portfolio Green
1.7 oz EDP Sp $ 50.00
Your Price : _____
3.4 oz EDP Sp $ 65.00
Your Price : _____

Perry Ellis
Perry Ellis
1.7 oz EDP Sp $ 50.00
Your Price : _____
3.4 oz EDP Sp $ 65.00
Your Price : _____

Perry Ellis
Perry For Her
1.7 oz EDP Sp $ 50.00
Your Price : _____
3.4 oz EDP Sp $ 65.00
Your Price : _____

Perry Ellis
Perry Woman
1.7 oz EDP Sp $ 50.00
Your Price : _____
3.4 oz EDP Sp $ 65.00
Your Price : _____

Perry Ellis
Reserve
1.7 oz EDP Sp $ 50.00
Your Price : _____
3.4 oz EDP Sp $ 65.00
Your Price : _____

Playboy
Play It Lovely
1.7 oz EDT Sp $ 35.00
Your Price :_____

Playboy
Play It Rock
1.7 oz EDT Sp $ 35.00
Your Price :_____

Playboy
Play It Spicy
1.7 oz EDT Sp $ 35.00
Your Price :_____

Playboy
Play It Sexy
1.7 oz EDT Sp $ 35.00
Your Price :_____

Playboy
V.I.P.
1.7 oz EDT Sp $ 35.00
Your Price :_____

Paul Sebastian
Casual
2.0 oz EDP Sp $ 49.00
Your Price :_____
4.0 oz EDP Sp $ 83.00
Your Price :_____

Paul Sebastian
Design
1.7 oz EDP Sp $ 50.00
Your Price :_____
3.4 oz EDP Sp $ 70.00
Your Price :_____

Paul Sebastian
Funky Sexy Cool
3.4 oz EDP Sp $ 70.00
Your Price :_____

Paul Smith
London
3.3 oz EDP Sp $ 90.00
Your Price :_____

Paul Smith
Rose
3.3 oz EDP Sp $ 90.00
Your Price :_____

Perfumers Workshop
Samba
3.3 oz EDT Sp $ 58.00
Your Price :_____

Perfumers Workshop
Samba Heat
1.7 oz EDT Sp $ 40.00
Your Price :_____
3.4 oz EDT Sp $ 55.00
Your Price :_____

Perfumers Workshop
French Kiss
1.7 oz EDT Sp $ 40.00
Your Price :_____
3.4 oz EDT Sp $ 58.00
Your Price :_____

Perfumers Workshop
Samba Ice
1.7 oz EDT Sp $ 40.00
Your Price :_____
3.4 oz EDT Sp $ 58.00
Your Price :_____

Perfumers Workshop
Samba Kiss
3.4 oz EDT Sp $ 40.00
Your Price :_____

Perfumers Workshop
Samba Nova
1.7 oz EDT Sp $ 40.00
Your Price :_____
3.4 oz EDT Sp $ 58.00
Your Price :_____

Perfumers Workshop
Samba Red
3.4 oz EDT Sp $ 55.00
Your Price :_____

Perfumers Workshop
Samba Rock & Roll
1.7 oz EDT Sp $ 40.00
Your Price :_____
3.4 oz EDT Sp $ 58.00
Your Price :_____

Perfumers Workshop
Samba Sexy
1.7 oz EDT Sp $ 40.00
Your Price :_____
3.4 oz EDT Sp $ 58.00
Your Price :_____

Perfumers Workshop
Tea Rose
1.7 oz EDT Sp $ 40.00
Your Price :_____
4.0 oz EDT Sp $ 55.00
Your Price :_____

Prada
1.7 oz EDP Sp $ 80.00
Your Price : _____
2.7 oz EDP Sp $ 110.00
Your Price : _____

Prada
Amber
1.0 oz EDP Sp $ 70.00
Your Price : _____
1.7 oz EDP Sp $ 90.00
Your Price : _____
2.7 oz EDP Sp $ 120.00
Your Price : _____

Prada
Candy
1.7 oz EDP Sp $ 90.00
Your Price : _____
2.7 oz EDP Sp $ 120.00
Your Price : _____

Prada
Candy Florale
1.7 oz EDT Sp $ 76.00
Your Price : _____
2.7 oz EDT Sp $ 96.00
Your Price : _____

Prada
Candy Kiss
1.7 oz EDP Sp $ 90.00
Your Price : _____
2.7 oz EDP Sp $ 120.00
Your Price : _____

Prada
Candy L'Eau
1.7 oz EDT Sp $ 76.00
Your Price : _____
2.7 oz EDT Sp $ 96.00
Your Price : _____

Prada
Intense
1.7 oz EDP Sp $ 80.00
Your Price : _____
2.7 oz EDP Sp $ 110.00
Your Price : _____

Prada
Infusion D'Iris
1.7 oz EDP Sp $ 95.00
Your Price : _____
3.4 oz EDP Sp $ 160.00
Your Price : _____
6.75 oz EDP Sp $ 230.00
Your Price : _____

Prada
Infusion de Fleur d'Oranger
1.7 oz EDP Sp $ 95.00
Your Price : _____
3.4 oz EDP Sp $ 160.00
Your Price : _____
6.75 oz EDP Sp $ 230.00
Your Price : _____

Prada
Infusion de Tubereuse
1.7 oz EDP Sp $ 95.00
Your Price : _____
3.4 oz EDP Sp $ 160.00
Your Price : _____
6.75 oz EDP Sp $ 230.00
Your Price : _____

Prada
L'Eau Ambree'
1.7 oz EDP Sp $ 80.00
Your Price : _____
2.7 oz EDP Sp $ 110.00
Your Price : _____

Prada
Tendre
1.7 oz EDP Sp $ 75.00
Your Price : _____
2.7 oz EDP Sp $ 110.00
Your Price : _____

Ralph Lauren
Big Pony Collection #1
1.0 oz EDT Sp $ 40.00
Your Price : _____
1.7 oz EDT Sp $ 56.00
Your Price : _____
3.4 oz EDT Sp $ 70.00
Your Price : _____

Ralph Lauren
Big Pony Collection #2
1.0 oz EDT Sp $ 40.00
Your Price : _____
1.7 oz EDT Sp $56.00
Your Price : _____
3.4 oz EDT Sp $70.00
Your Price : _____

Ralph Lauren
Big Pony Collection #3
1.0 oz EDT Sp $ 40.00
Your Price : _____
1.7 oz EDT Sp $56.00
Your Price : _____
3.4 oz EDT Sp $70.00
Your Price : _____

Ralph Lauren
Big Pony Collection #4
1.0 oz EDT Sp $ 40.00
Your Price : _____
1.7 oz EDT Sp $56.00
Your Price : _____
3.4 oz EDT Sp $70.00
Your Price : _____

Ralph Lauren
Blue
1.3 oz EDP Sp $ 46.00
Your Price : _____
2.5 oz EDP Sp $ 66.00
Your Price : _____
4.2 oz EDP Sp $ 82.00
Your Price : _____

Ralph Lauren
Lauren
2.0 oz EDT Sp $ 60.00
Your Price : _____
4.0 oz EDT Sp $ 80.00
Your Price : _____

Ralph Lauren
Lauren Style
2.5 oz EDP Sp $ 70.00
Your Price : _____
4.2 oz EDP Sp $ 95.00
Your Price : _____

Ralph Lauren
Love
1.7 oz EDP Sp $ 95.00
Your Price : _____

Ralph Lauren
Midnight Romance
1.7 oz EDP Sp $ 76.00
Your Price : _____
3.4 oz EDP Sp $ 96.00
Your Price : _____
5.0 oz EDP Sp $ 108.00
Your Price : _____

Ralph Lauren
Notorious
1 oz EDT Sp $ 55.00
Your Price : _____
1.7 oz EDT Sp $ 60.00
Your Price : _____
3.4 oz EDT Sp $ 89.00
Your Price : _____

Ralph Lauren
Polo Sport
1.7 oz EDT Sp $ 60.00
Your Price : _____
3.4 oz EDT Sp $ 89.00
Your Price : _____

Ralph Lauren
Ralph
1.0 oz EDT Sp $ 44.00
Your Price : _____
1.7 oz EDT Sp $ 60.00
Your Price : _____
3.4 oz EDT Sp $ 78.00
Your Price : _____

Ralph Lauren
Ralph Cool
1 oz EDT Sp $ 45.00
Your Price : _____
1.7 oz EDT Sp $ 59.00
Your Price : _____
3.4 oz EDT Sp $ 89.00
Your Price : _____

Ralph Lauren
Ralph Hot
1.7 oz EDT Sp $ 59.00
Your Price : _____
3.4 oz EDT Sp $ 89.00
Your Price : _____

Ralph Lauren
Ralph Rocks
1.7 oz EDT Sp $ 59.00
Your Price : _____
3.4 oz EDT Sp $ 89.00
Your Price : _____

Ralph Lauren
Romance
1.0 oz EDP Sp $ 50.00
Your Price : _____
1.7 oz EDP Sp $ 74.00
Your Price : _____
3.4 oz EDP Sp $ 94.00
Your Price : _____
5.0 oz EDP Sp $ 106.00
Your Price : _____

Ralph Lauren
Romance Always Yours
1.7 oz EDT Sp $ 60.00
Your Price : _____
2.5 oz EDT Sp $ 75.00
Your Price : _____

Ralph Lauren
Safari
2.5 oz EDP Sp $ 85.00
Your Price : _____

Ralph Lauren
Tender Romance
1.7 oz EDP Sp $ 76.00
Your Price : _____
3.4 oz EDP Sp $ 96.00
Your Price : _____

Ralph Lauren
Turquoise
1.0 oz EDP Sp $ 45.00
Your Price : _____
2.5 oz EDP Sp $ 60.00
Your Price : _____
4.2 oz EDP Sp $ 80.00
Your Price : _____

Ralph Lauren
Ralph Wild
1.7 oz EDT Sp $ 59.00
Your Price : _____
3.4 oz EDT Sp $ 89.00
Your Price : _____

Red Pearl
Red Pearl
3.3 oz EDP Sp $ 45.00
Your Price : _____

Remy Latour
Exotica
3.3 oz EDP Sp $ 59.00
Your Price : _____

Remy Latour
Lune D'ete
3.3 oz EDP Sp $ 59.00
Your Price : _____

Remy Latour
Si Fleuri
3.3 oz EDP Sp $ 45.00
Your Price : _____

Remy Latour
Si Fleuri Passion
3.3 oz EDP Sp $ 45.00
Your Price : _____

Reem Acra
Reem Acra
1.6 oz EDP Sp $ 85.00
Your Price : _____
3.0 oz EDP Sp $ 120.00
Your Price : _____

Revlon
Charlie White
3.4 oz EDT Sp $ 35.00
Your Price : _____

Revlon
Charlie Blue
3.4 oz EDP Sp $ 35.00
Your Price : _____

Revlon
Charlie Gold
3.4 oz EDP Sp $ 35.00
Your Price : _____

Revlon
Charlie Red
3.3 oz EDT Sp $ 35.00
Your Price : _____

Revlon
Charlie Silver
3.4 oz EDT Sp $ 35.00
Your Price : _____

Revlon
Charlie Sunshine
3.4 oz EDT Sp $ 35.00
Your Price : _____

Revlon
Ciara
Strength 80/100/20
2.3 oz EDC Sp $ 35.00
Your Price : _____

Revlon
Downtown Girl
3.4 oz EDP Sp $ 35.00
Your Price : _____

Revlon
Fire & Ice
1.0 oz EDC Sp $ 20.00
Your Price : _____
1.7 oz EDC Sp $ 35.00
Your Price : _____

Reyane Tradition
Insurrection
3.3 oz EDT Sp $ 60.00
Your Price : _____

Rihanna
Rogue
2.5 oz EDP Sp $ 45.00
Your Price : _____
4.2 oz EDP Sp $ 65.00
Your Price : _____

Rihanna
Nude
1.0 oz EDP Sp $ 35.00
Your Price : _____
1.7 oz EDP Sp $ 45.00
Your Price : _____
3.4 oz EDP Sp $ 59.00
Your Price : _____

Rihanna
Rebelle
1.0 oz EDP Sp $ 35.00
Your Price : _____
1.7 oz EDP Sp $ 45.00
Your Price : _____
3.4 oz EDP Sp $ 59.00
Your Price : _____

Rihana
Reb'l Fleur
1.0 oz EDP Sp $ 35.00
Your Price : _____
1.7 oz EDP Sp $ 45.00
Your Price : _____
3.4 oz EDP Sp $ 59.00
Your Price : _____

Rihanna
Riri
3.4 oz EDP Sp $ 60.00
Your Price : _____

Rihanna
Riri Crush
3.4 oz EDP Sp $ 60.00
Your Price : _____

Rihanna
Riri Kiss
3.4 oz EDP Sp $ 60.00
Your Price : _____

Roberto Cavalli
Acqua
1.0 oz EDP Sp $ 48.00
Your Price : _____
1.7 oz EDP Sp $ 65.00
Your Price : _____
3.4 oz EDP Sp $ 85.00
Your Price : _____

Roberto Cavalli
Just Cavalli
1.7 oz EDT Sp $ 60.00
Your Price : _____
2.5 oz EDT Sp $ 75.00
Your Price : _____

Roberto Cavalli
Just Cavalli Her
2.0 oz EDP Sp $ 48.00
Your Price : _____

Roberto Cavalli
Oro
2.5 oz EDP Sp $ 95.00
Your Price : _____

Roberto Cavalli
Roberto Cavalli
2.5 oz EDP Sp $ 85.00
Your Price : _____

Roberto Cavalli
Serpentine
1.7 oz EDP Sp $ 45.00
Your Price : _____
3.4 oz EDP Sp $ 60.00
Your Price : _____

Roberto Cavalli
Signature
1.0 oz EDP Sp $ 48.00
Your Price : _____
1.7 oz EDP Sp $ 65.00
Your Price : _____
2.5 oz EDP Sp $ 85.00
Your Price : _____

Rochas
Byzance
1.7 oz EDT Sp $ 65.00
Your Price : _____
3.4 oz EDT Sp $ 90.00
Your Price : _____

Rochas
Madame
1.7 oz EDP Sp $ 65.00
Your Price : _____
3.4 oz EDP Sp $ 90.00
Your Price : _____

Rochas
Rochas Absolu
1.7 oz EDP Sp $ 45.00
Your Price : _____
2.5 oz EDP Sp $ 60.00
Your Price : _____

Rochas
Rochas Femme
1.7 oz EDP Sp $ 65.00
Your Price : _____
3.3 oz EDP Sp $ 85.00
Your Price : _____

Rochas
Tocade
1.7 oz EDP Sp $ 65.00
Your Price : _____
3.3 oz EDP Sp $ 85.00
Your Price : _____

Romeo Britto
Britto
2.5 oz EDP Sp $ 70.00
Your Price : _____
4.2 oz EDP Sp $ 95.00
Your Price : _____

Romeo Gigli
Di Romeo Gigli
1.0 oz EDP Sp $ 32.00
Your Price : _____
1.7 oz EDP Sp $ 45.00
Your Price : _____
3.4 oz EDP Sp $ 60.00
Your Price : _____

Romeo Gigli
G De Gigli
1.7 oz EDP Sp $ 45.00
Your Price : _____
3.4 oz EDP Sp $ 60.00
Your Price : _____

Royal
Royal Secret
3.3 oz Col Sp
Concentrate $ 47.00
Your Price : _____

Salvador Dali
Dalimix
1.7 oz EDT Sp $ 32.00
Your Price : _____
3.3 oz EDT Sp $ 54.00
Your Price : _____

Salvador Dali
Dalimix Gold
1.7 oz EDT Sp $ 32.00
Your Price : _____
3.3 oz EDT Sp $ 54.00
Your Price : _____

Salvador Dali
Daliflor
1.7 oz EDT Sp $ 32.00
Your Price : _____
3.4 oz EDT Sp $ 85.00
Your Price : _____

Salvador Dali
Dalistyle
1.7 oz EDT Sp $ 32.00
Your Price : _____
3.4 oz EDT Sp $ 85.00
Your Price : _____

Salvador Dali
Le Roy Soleil
1.7 oz EDT Sp $ 32.00
Your Price : _____
3.4 oz EDT Sp $ 62.00
Your Price : _____

Salvador Dali
Purple Lips
3.4 oz EDT Sp $ 65.00
Your Price : _____

Salvador Dali
Ruby Lips
3.4 oz EDT Sp $ 69.00
Your Price : _____

Salvatore Ferragamo
Emozione
1.7 oz EDP Sp $ 95.00
Your Price : _____
3.4 oz EDP Sp $ 119.00
Your Price : _____

Salvatore Ferragamo
Emozione Dolce Fiore
1.7 oz EDT Sp $ 79.00
Your Price : _____
3.4 oz EDT Sp $ 99.00
Your Price : _____

Salvatore Ferragamo
F
1.7 oz EDP Sp $ 55.00
Your Price : _____
3.4 oz EDP Sp $ 75.00
Your Price : _____

Salvatore Ferragamo
Incanto
1.7 oz EDP Sp $ 55.00
Your Price : _____
3.4 oz EDP Sp $ 75.00
Your Price : _____

Salvatore Ferragamo
Incanto Amity
1.7 Oz EDT Sp $ 55.00
Your Price : _____
3.4 Oz EDT Sp $ 75.00
Your Price : _____

Salvatore Ferragamo
Incanto Bliss
1.7 oz EDP Sp $ 55.00
Your Price : _____
3.4 oz EDP Sp $ 75.00
Your Price : _____

Salvatore Ferragamo
Incanto Bloom
1.7 Oz EDT Sp $ 55.00
Your Price : _____
3.4 Oz EDT Sp $ 75.00
Your Price : _____

Salvatore Ferragamo
Incanto Charms
1.7 oz EDP Sp $ 55.00
Your Price : _____
3.4 oz EDP Sp $ 75.00
Your Price : _____

Salvatore Ferragamo
Incanto Dream
1.7 oz EDT Sp $ 55.00
Your Price : _____
3.4 oz EDT Sp $ 75.00
Your Price : _____

Salvatore Ferragamo
Incanto Heaven
1.7 oz EDT Sp $ 55.00
Your Price : _____
3.4 oz EDT Sp $ 75.00
Your Price : _____

Salvatore Ferragamo
Incanto Shine
1.7 oz EDT Sp $ 55.00
Your Price : _____
3.4 oz EDT Sp $ 75.00
Your Price : _____

Salvatore Ferragamo
Signorina
3.4 oz EDP Sp $ 99.00
Your Price : _____

Salvatore Ferragamo
Signorina Eleganza
1.7 oz EDT Sp $ 87.00
Your Price : _____
3.4 oz EDT Sp $ 109.00
Your Price : _____

Salvatore Ferragamo
Signorina Misteriosa
1.7 oz EDP Sp $ 87.00
Your Price : _____
3.4 oz EDP Sp $ 109.00
Your Price : _____

Salvatore Ferragamo
Subtil
1.7 oz EDT Sp $ 55.00
Your Price : _____
3.4 oz EDT Sp $ 75.00
Your Price : _____

Sarah Jessica Parker
Covet
1.7 oz EDP Sp $ 58.00
Your Price : _____
3.4 oz EDP Sp $ 68.00
Your Price : _____

Sarah Jessica Parker
Covet Pure Bloom
1.7 oz EDP Sp $ 55.00
Your Price : _____
3.4 oz EDP Sp $ 75.00
Your Price : _____

Sarah Jessica Parker
Lovely
1.7 oz EDP Sp $ 55.00
Your Price : _____
3.4 oz EDP Sp $ 75.00
Your Price : _____

Sarah Jessica Parker
NYC Sarah Jessica Parker
1.0 oz EDT Sp $ 35.00
Your Price : _____
2.0 oz EDT Sp $ 49.00
Your Price : _____

Selective Spa
Gold Sugar
1.7 Oz EDT Sp $ 45.00
Your Price : _____
3.4 Oz EDP Sp $ 60.00
Your Price : _____

Selective Spa
Pink Sugar
1.7 oz EDT Sp $ 45.00
Your Price : _____
3.4 oz EDT Sp $ 60.00
Your Price : _____

Selective Spa
Pink Sugar Sensual
1.7 oz EDT Sp $ 45.00
Your Price : _____
3.4 oz EDT Sp $ 60.00
Your Price : _____

Sean John
Empress
1.7 oz EDP Sp $ 50.00
Your Price : _____
3.4 oz EDP Sp $ 70.00
Your Price : _____

Sean John
Unforgivable Woman
1.0 oz EDP Sp $ 40.00
Your Price : _____
1.7 oz EDP Sp $ 55.00
Your Price : _____
2.5 oz EDP Sp $ 70.00
Your Price : _____
4.2 oz EDT Sp $ 90.00
Your Price : _____

Selena Gomez
Selena Gomez
1.7 oz EDP Sp $ 50.00
Your Price : _____
3.4 oz EDP Sp $ 65.00
Your Price : _____

Selena Gomez
Vivamore
1.7 oz EDP Sp $ 50.00
Your Price : _____
3.4 oz EDP Sp $ 65.00
Your Price : _____

Shakira
Aquamarine
1.7 oz EDT Sp $ 45.00
Your Price : _____
2.7 oz EDT Sp $ 58.00
Your Price : _____

Shakira
S by Shakira Eau Florale
1.7 oz EDT Sp $ 45.00
Your Price : _____
2.7 oz EDT Sp $ 58.00
Your Price : _____

Shakira
Elixir
1.7 oz EDT Sp $ 45.00
Your Price : _____
2.7 oz EDT Sp $ 58.00
Your Price : _____

Shakira
S by Shakira
1.7 oz EDT Sp $ 45.00
Your Price : _____
2.7 oz EDT Sp $ 58.00
Your Price : _____

Sisley
Eau De Soir
1.6 oz EDP Sp $ 188.00
Your Price : _____
3.4 oz EDP Sp $ 225.00
Your Price : _____

Snooki Couture
Snooki
3.4 oz EDP Sp $ 52.00
Your Price : _____

Sonia Rykiel
For Woman Not for Men
1.7 oz EDP Sp $ 45.00
Your Price : _____
4.2 oz EDP Sp $ 60.00
Your Price : _____

Sonia Rykiel
Grey
1.7 oz EDT Sp $ 42.00
Your Price : _____
3.4 oz EDT Sp $ 68.00
Your Price : _____

Sonia Rykiel
L'eau D'Sonia Rykiel
1.7 oz EDT Sp $ 48.00
Your Price : _____
3.3 oz EDT Sp $ 68.00
Your Price : _____

Sonia Rykiel
Rykiel Rose
1.7 oz EDT Sp $ 48.00
Your Price : _____
3.4 oz EDT Sp $ 68.00
Your Price : _____

Sonia Rykiel
Sonia Rykiel
1.7 oz EDT Sp $ 48.00
Your Price : _____
3.3 oz EDT Sp $ 68.00
Your Price : _____

St. Dupont
Signature
1.7 oz EDP Sp $ 54.00
Your Price : _____
3.4 oz EDPSp $ 68.00
Your Price : _____

St. Dupont
St. Dupont
1.0 oz EDP Sp $ 45.00
Your Price : _____
1.7 oz EDP Sp $ 54.00
Your Price : _____
3.4 oz EDP Sp $ 68.00
Your Price : _____

Succes De Paris
Fujiyama
3.4 oz EDT Sp $ 59.00
Your Price : _____

Succes De Paris
Fujiyama
3.4 oz EDT Sp $ 59.00
Your Price : _____

Succes De Paris
Fujiyama Purple
3.4 oz EDT Sp $ 59.00
Your Price : _____

Swiss Army
1.7 oz EDT Sp $ 40.00
Your Price : _____
3.4 oz EDT Sp $ 54.00
Your Price : _____

Swiss Army
Mountain Water
1.7 oz EDT Sp $ 40.00
Your Price : _____
3.4 oz EDT Sp $ 59.00
Your Price : _____

Susan G. Komen
Promise Me
3.4 oz EDT Sp $ 59.00
Your Price : _____

Taylor Swift
Enchanted Wonderstruck
1.7 oz EDP Sp $ 50.00
Your Price : _____
3.4 oz EDP Sp $ 65.00
Your Price : _____

Taylor Swift
Taylor
1.7 oz EDP Sp $ 50.00
Your Price : _____
3.4 oz EDP Sp $ 65.00
Your Price : _____

Taylor Swift
Wonderstruck
1.7 oz EDP Sp $ 50.00
Your Price : _____
3.4 oz EDP Sp $ 65.00
Your Price : _____

Ted Lapidus
Creation
3.4 oz EDT Sp $ 70.00
Your Price : _____

Ted Lapidus
Creation The Vert
3.4 oz EDT Sp $ 70.00
Your Price : _____

Ted Lapidus
Fou D' Elle
3.4 oz EDT Sp $ 70.00
Your Price : _____

Ted Lapidus
Lapidus Woman
3.4 oz EDT Sp $ 70.00
Your Price : _____

Ted Lapidus
Lovely Fantasme
3.4 oz EDT Sp $ 70.00
Your Price : _____

Ted Lapidus
Rumba
3.4 oz EDT Sp $ 70.00
Your Price : _____

Ted Lapidus
Silk Way
2.5 oz EDP Sp $ 55.00
Your Price : _____
3.4 oz EDP Sp $ 70.00
Your Price : _____

Ted Lapidus
TL Pour Elle
3.4 oz EDP Sp $ 70.00
Your Price : _____

Ted Lapidus
White Soul
3.4 oz EDP Sp $ 70.00
Your Price : _____

Thierry Mugler
Alien
1.0 oz EDP Sp $ 82.00
Your Price : _____
2.0 oz EDP Sp $ 120.00
Your Price : _____
3.0 oz EDP Sp $ 170.00
Your Price : _____

Thierry Mugler
Alien
1.0 oz EDT Sp $ 55.00
Your Price : _____
2.0 oz EDT Sp $ 79.00
Your Price : _____

Thierry Mugler
Angel
0.8 oz EDP Sp $ 82.00
Your Price : _____
1.7 oz EDP Sp $ 120.00
Your Price : _____
3.4 oz EDP Sp $ 170.00
Your Price : _____

Thierry Mugler
Angel Sunessence
1.7 oz EDP Sp $ 80.00
Your Price : _____
3.4 oz EDP Sp $ 115.00
Your Price : _____

Thierry Mugler
Eau De Star
0.8 oz EDT Sp $ 45.00
Your Price : _____
1.7 oz EDT Sp $ 60.00
Your Price : _____

Thierry Mugler
Innocent
0.8 oz EDP Sp $ 50.00
Your Price : _____
1.7 oz EDP Sp $ 65.00
Your Price : _____
2.6 oz EDP Sp $ 75.00
Your Price : _____

Thierry Mugler
Innocent Illusion
1.7 oz EDP Sp $ 87.00
Your Price : _____
3.4 oz EDP Sp $ 115.00
Your Price : _____

Thierry Mugler
Innocent Rock
1.7 oz EDT Sp $ 55.00
Your Price : _____
2.6 oz EDT Sp $ 70.00
Your Price : _____

Thierry Mugler
Innocent Secret
1.7 oz EDT Sp $ 55.00
Your Price : _____
2.6 oz EDT Sp $ 70.00
Your Price : _____

Thierry Mugler
La Rose Angel
0.8 oz EDP Sp $ 45.00
Your Price : _____
1.7 oz EDP Sp $ 60.00
Your Price : _____

Thierry Mugler
Lily Angel
0.8 oz EDP Sp $ 45.00
Your Price : _____
1.7 oz EDP Sp $ 60.00
Your Price : _____

Thierry Mugler
Pivoine Angel
0.8 oz EDP Sp $ 45.00
Your Price : _____
1.7 oz EDP Sp $ 60.00
Your Price : _____

Thierry Mugler
Violette Angel
0.8 oz EDP Sp $ 45.00
Your Price : _____
1.7 oz EDP Sp $ 60.00
Your Price : _____

Thierry Muglar
Womanity
1.0 oz EDP Sp $ 55.00
Your Price : _____
1.7 oz EDP Sp $ 70.00
Your Price : _____
2.7 oz EDP Sp $ 95.00
Your Price : _____

Todd Oldham
Todd Oldham
1.0 oz EDP Sp $ 45.00
Your Price : _____
2.5 oz EDP Sp $ 70.00
Your Price : _____

Tom Ford
Black Orchid
1.7 oz EDP Sp $ 110.00
Your Price : _____
3.4 oz EDP Sp $ 155.00
Your Price : _____

Tom Ford
Black Orchid
1.7 oz EDT Sp $ 102.00
Your Price : _____
3.4 oz EDT Sp $ 137.00
Your Price : _____

Tom Ford
Noir Pour Femme
1.7 oz EDP Sp $ 120.00
Your Price : _____
3.4 oz EDP Sp $ 168.00
Your Price : _____

Tom Ford
Orchid Soleil
1.7 Oz EDP Sp $ 120.00
Your Price : _____
3.4 Oz EDP Sp $ 168.00
Your Price : _____

Tom Ford
Sahara Noir
1.7 oz EDP Sp $ 130.00
Your Price : _____

Tom Ford
Velvet Orchid
1.7 oz EDP Sp $ 120.00
Your Price : _____
3.4 oz EDP Sp $ 168.00
Your Price : _____

Tom Ford
Velvet Orchid Lumiere
1.7 oz EDP Sp $ 120.00
Your Price : _____
3.4 oz EDP Sp $ 168.00
Your Price : _____

Tom Ford
Violet Blonde
1.7 oz EDP Sp $ 110.00
Your Price : _____
3.4 oz EDP Sp $ 155.00
Your Price : _____

Tom Ford
White Patchouli
1.7 oz EDP Sp $ 120.00
Your Price : _____
3.4 oz EDP Sp $ 168.00
Your Price : _____

Tommy Bahama
Set Sail Martinique
1.7 oz EDP Sp $ 40.00
Your Price : _____
3.4 oz EDP Sp $ 68.00
Your Price : _____

Tommy Bahama
Tommy Bahama
1.7 oz EDP Sp $ 66.00
Your Price : _____
3.4 oz EDP Sp $ 82.00
Your Price : _____

Tommy Bahama
Very Cool
1.7 oz EDP Sp $ 45.00
Your Price : _____
3.4 oz EDP Sp $ 68.00
Your Price : _____

Tommy Bahama
Tommy Bahama for Her
1.7 oz EDP Sp $ 66.00
Your Price : _____
3.4 oz EDP Sp $ 82.00
Your Price : _____

Tommy Hilfiger
Dreaming
1.7 oz EDP Sp $ 55.00
Your Price : _____
3.4 oz EDP Sp $ 72.00
Your Price : _____

Tommy Hilfiger
Hilfiger Women
1.7 oz EDP Sp $ 49.00
Your Price : _____
3.4 oz EDP Sp $ 65.00
Your Price : _____

Tommy Hilfiger
Hilfiger Cheerfully Pink
1.7 oz EDP Sp $ 49.00
Your Price : _____
3.4 oz EDP Sp $ 65.00
Your Price : _____

Tommy Hilfiger
Hilfiger Flower Violet
1.0 oz EDP Sp $ 48.00
Your Price : _____
1.7 oz EDP Sp $ 65.00
Your Price : _____

Tommy Hilfiger
Loud
1.4 oz EDT Sp $ 40.00
Your Price : _____
2.5 oz EDT Sp $ 52.00
Your Price : _____

Tommy Hilfiger
1.0 oz EDP Sp $ 40.00
Your Price : _____
1.7 oz EDP Sp $ 55.00
Your Price : _____
3.4 oz EDP Sp $ 72.00
Your Price : _____

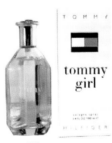

Tommy Hilfiger
The Girl
1.7 oz EDT Sp $ 45.00
Your Price : _____
3.4 oz EDT Sp $ 57.00
Your Price : _____

Tommy Hilfiger
Tommy Eau De Prep
1.7 oz EDP Sp $ 55.00
Your Price : _____
3.4 oz EDP Sp $ 70.00
Your Price : _____

Tommy Hilfiger
Tommy Girl
1.7 oz EDP Sp $ 39.00
Your Price : _____
3.4 oz EDP Sp $ 57.00
Your Price : _____

Tommy Hilfiger
Tommy Girl Jeans
1.0 oz EDP Sp $ 40.00
Your Price : _____
1.7 oz EDP Sp $ 55.00
Your Price : _____
3.4 oz EDP Sp $ 72.00
Your Price : _____

Tommy Hilfiger
True Star
1.0 oz EDP Sp $ 40.00
Your Price : _____
1.7 oz EDP Sp $ 55.00
Your Price : _____
3.4 oz EDP Sp $ 72.00
Your Price : _____

Tommy Hilfiger
True Star Gold
1.0 oz EDP Sp $ 40.00
Your Price : _____
2.5 oz EDP Sp $ 62.00
Your Price : _____

True Religion
Hippie Chic
1.7 oz EDP Sp $ 55.00
Your Price : _____
3.4 oz EDP Sp $ 70.00
Your Price : _____

True Religion
True Religion
1.7 oz EDP Sp $ 55.00
Your Price : _____
3.4 oz EDP Sp $ 70.00
Your Price : _____

Trussardi
Delicate Rose
1.0 oz EDT Sp $ 55.00
Your Price : _____
1.7 oz EDT Sp $ 70.00
Your Price : _____
3.4 oz EDT Sp $ 95.00
Your Price : _____

Trussardi
Donna Trussardi
1.7 oz EDT Sp $ 69.00
Your Price : _____
3.4 oz EDT Sp $ 89.00
Your Price : _____

Trussardi
Jeans
2.5 oz EDT Sp $ 80.00
Your Price : _____

Trussardi
My Name
1.0 oz EDT Sp $ 58.00
Your Price : _____
1.7 oz EDT Sp $ 75.00
Your Price : _____
3.4 oz EDT Sp $ 95.00
Your Price : _____

Trussardi
Trussardi Inside
1.7 oz EDT Sp $ 70.00
Your Price : _____

Ultima II
Head Over Heels
1.9 oz EDT Sp $ 45.00
Your Price : _____
3.9 oz EDT Sp $ 65.00
Your Price : _____

Ungaro
Apparition
1.7 oz EDP Sp $ 68.00
Your Price : _____
3.4 oz EDP Sp $ 113.00
Your Price : _____

Ungaro
Diva
1.7 oz EDP Sp $ 70.00
Your Price : _____
3.4 oz EDP Sp $ 90.00
Your Price : _____

Ungaro
Party
3.0 oz EDP Sp $ 75.00
Your Price : _____

Ungaro
Ungaro
3.0 oz EDT Sp $ 70.00
Your Price : _____

Usher
Usher
1.7 oz EDP Sp $ 45.00
Your Price : _____
3.4 oz EDP Sp $ 65.00
Your Price : _____

Usher
UR
1.7 oz EDP Sp $ 45.00
Your Price : _____
3.4 oz EDP Sp $ 65.00
Your Price : _____

Valentino
Aqua Floreale
1.7 oz EDP Sp $ 90.00
Your Price : _____
2.7 oz EDP Sp $ 120.00
Your Price : _____

Valentino
Donna
1.7 oz EDP Sp $ 95.00
Your Price : _____
3.4 oz EDP Sp $ 130.00
Your Price : _____

Valentino
Rock n' Rose
1.7 oz EDP Sp $ 55.00
Your Price : _____
3.0 oz EDP Sp $ 75.00
Your Price : _____

Valentino
Rock n' Rose Couture
1.6 oz EDP Sp $ 65.00
Your Price : _____
3.0 oz EDP Sp $ 80.00
Your Price : _____

Valentino
V
1 oz EDP Sp $ 60.00
Your Price : _____
3 oz EDP Sp $ 82.00
Your Price : _____

Valentino
Valentina
1.7 oz EDP Sp $ 90.00
Your Price : _____
2.7 oz EDP Sp $ 120.00
Your Price : _____

Valentino
Valentino
2.5 oz EDT Sp $ 55.00
Your Price : _____

Valentino
Valentino Gold
1.7 oz EDP Sp $ 65.00
Your Price : _____

Valentino
V Absolu
1.7 oz EDP Sp $ 62.00
Your Price : _____
3.4 oz EDP Sp $ 82.00
Your Price : _____

Valentino
Valentina Assoluto
1.7 oz EDP Sp $ 80.00
Your Price : _____
2.7 oz EDP Sp $ 105.00
Your Price : _____

Valentino
Very Valentino
1.7 oz EDP Sp $ 62.00
Your Price :_____

Valentino
Valentino (New)
1.7 oz EDP Sp $ 75.00
Your Price :_____

Valentino
Valentina Poudre
1.7 oz EDP Sp $ 89.00
Your Price :_____
2.7 oz EDP Sp $ 120.00
Your Price :_____

Van Cleef & Arpels
Birmane
3 oz EDT Sp $ 85.00
Your Price :_____

Van Cleef & Arpels
First
2.0 oz EDT Sp $ 65.00
Your Price :_____
3.3 oz EDT Sp $ 85.00
Your Price :_____

Van Cleef & Arpels
Les Saisons Par Van
Cleef Automne
3.4 oz EDT Sp $ 79.00
Your Price :_____

Van Cleef & Arpels
Les Saisons Par Van
Cleef Printemps
3.4 oz EDT Sp $ 79.00
Your Price :_____

Van Cleef & Arpels
Miss Arpels
1.7 oz EDT Sp $ 55.00
Your Price :_____
3 oz EDT Sp $ 75.00
Your Price :_____

Van Cleef & Arpels
Murmure
1 oz EDT Sp $ 42.00
Your Price :_____
1.7 oz EDT Sp $ 55.00
Your Price :_____
3 oz EDT Sp $ 75.00
Your Price :_____

Van Cleef & Arpels
Oriens
1.7 oz EDP Sp $ 95.00
Your Price :_____
3.3 oz EDP Sp $ 140.00
Your Price :_____

Van Cleef & Arpels
Van Cleef
1.7 oz EDP Sp $ 60.00
Your Price :_____

Vera Wang
Be Jeweled
1.0 oz EDP Sp $ 40.00
Your Price :_____
2.5 oz EDP Sp $ 65.00
Your Price :_____

Vera Wang
Flower Princess
1.7 oz EDT Sp $ 60.00
Your Price :_____
3.4 oz EDT Sp $ 75.00
Your Price :_____

Vera Wang
Glam Princess
1.7 oz EDT Sp $ 60.00
Your Price :_____
3.4 oz EDT Sp $ 75.00
Your Price :_____

Vera Wang
Look
1.7 oz EDP Sp $ 65.00
Your Price :_____
3.4 oz EDP Sp $ 85.00
Your Price :_____

Vera Wang
Lovestruck
1.7 oz EDP Sp $ 65.00
Your Price :_____
3.4 oz EDP Sp $ 85.00
Your Price :_____

Vera Wang
Lovestruck Floral Rush
1.7 oz EDP Sp $ 65.00
Your Price :_____
3.4 oz EDP Sp $ 85.00
Your Price :_____

Vera Wang
Princess
1.7 oz EDT Sp $ 60.00
Your Price :_____
3.4 oz EDT Sp $ 75.00
Your Price :_____

Vera Wang
Preppy Princess
1.7 oz EDT Sp $ 60.00
Your Price :_____
3.4 oz EDT Sp $ 75.00
Your Price :_____

Vera Wang
Rock Princess
1.7 oz EDT Sp $ 60.00
Your Price :_____
3.4 oz EDT Sp $ 75.00
Your Price :_____

Vera Wang
Sheer Veil
1.7 oz EDT Sp $ 60.00
Your Price : _____
3.4 oz EDT Sp $ 75.00
Your Price : _____

Vera Wang
Truly Pink
1.7 oz EDT Sp $ 60.00
Your Price : _____
3.4 oz EDT Sp $ 75.00
Your Price : _____

Vera Wang
Vera Wang
1.7 oz EDP Sp $ 72.00
Your Price : _____
3.4 oz EDP Sp $ 92.00
Your Price : _____

Versace
Baby Rose
1.7 oz EDT Sp $ 55.00
Your Price : _____

Versace
Bright Crystal
1.0 oz EDT Sp $ 55.00
Your Price : _____
1.7 oz EDT Sp $ 73.00
Your Price : _____
3.0 oz EDT Sp $ 94.00
Your Price : _____
6.7 oz EDT Sp $ 134.00
Your Price : _____

Versace
Bright Crystal Absolute
1.0 oz EDP Sp $ 62.00
Your Price : _____
1.7 oz EDP Sp $ 82.00
Your Price : _____
3.0 oz EDP Sp $ 112.00
Your Price : _____

Versace
Crystal Noir
1.7 oz EDT Sp $ 73.00
Your Price : _____
3.0 oz EDT Sp $ 94.00
Your Price : _____

Versace
Crystal Noir
1.0 oz EDP Sp $ 62.00
Your Price : _____
1.7 oz EDP Sp $ 82.00
Your Price : _____
3.0 oz EDP Sp $ 112.00
Your Price : _____

Versace
Eros
1.7 oz EDP Sp $ 92.00
Your Price : _____
3.4 oz EDP Sp $ 120.00
Your Price : _____

Versace
Eros
1.7 oz EDT Sp $ 78.00
Your Price : _____
3.4 oz EDT Sp $ 96.00
Your Price : _____

Versace
Jeans Couture
2.5 oz EDT Sp $ 85.00
Your Price : _____

Versace
Metal Jeans
2.5 oz EDT Sp $ 62.00
Your Price : _____

Versace
Red Jeans
2.5 oz EDT Sp $ 55.00
Your Price : _____

Versace
Signature
1.7 oz EDP Sp $ 60.00
Your Price : _____
3.4 oz EDP Sp $ 80.00
Your Price : _____

Versace
Vanitas
1.0 oz EDP Sp $ 70.00
Your Price : _____
1.7 oz EDP Sp $ 95.00
Your Price : _____
3 oz EDP Sp $ 125.00
Your Price : _____

Versace
Versense
1.7 oz EDP Sp $ 65.00
Your Price : _____
3 oz EDP Sp $ 89.00
Your Price : _____

Versace
Versus
1.7 oz EDT Sp $ 60.00
Your Price : _____
3 oz EDT Sp $ 80.00
Your Price : _____

Versace
Woman
1.7 oz EDP Sp $ 60.00
Your Price : _____
3.4 oz EDP Sp $ 80.00
Your Price : _____

Versace
Yellow Diamond
1.0 oz EDT Sp $ 55.00
Your Price : _____
1.7 oz EDT Sp $ 73.00
Your Price : _____
3.0 oz EDT Sp $ 94.00
Your Price : _____
6.7 oz EDT Sp $ 134.00
Your Price : _____

Versace
Yellow Diamond Intense
1.0 oz EDP Sp $ 62.00
Your Price : _____
1.7 oz EDP Sp $ 82.00
Your Price : _____
3.0 oz EDP Sp $ 112.00
Your Price : _____

Versace
Yellow Jeans
1.7 oz EDT Sp $ 55.00
Your Price : _____

Vicky Tiel
Couture
3.3 oz EDP Sp $ 70.00
Your Price : _____

Vicky Tiel
Destine
3.3 oz EDP Sp $ 70.00
Your Price : _____

Vicky Tiel
Ethere
1.7 oz EDT Sp $ 59.00
Your Price : _____

Vicky Tiel
Sensuel
3.3 oz EDP Sp $ 80.00
Your Price : _____

Vicky Tiel
Sirene
1.7 oz EDP Sp $ 60.00
Your Price : _____
3.3 oz EDP Sp $ 80.00
Your Price : _____

Vicky Tiel
Venus De L'amour
1.7 oz EDT Sp $ 60.00
Your Price : _____

Victor & Rolf
Bon Bon
1.7 oz EDP Sp $ 115.00
Your Price : _____
3.0 oz EDP Sp $ 165.00
Your Price : _____

Viktor & Rolf
Eau Mega
1.7 oz EDP Sp $ 75.00
Your Price : _____

Viktor & Rolf
Flower Bomb
1.7 oz EDP Sp $ 115.00
Your Price : _____
3.4 oz EDP Sp $ 165.00
Your Price : _____

Viktor & Rolf
Flowerbomb Rose Explosion
1.7 oz EDP Sp $ 105.00
Your Price : _____
3.4 oz EDP Sp $ 160.00
Your Price : _____

Vince Camuto
Amore
3.4 oz EDP Sp $ 85.00
Your Price : _____

Vince Camuto
Bella
3.4 oz EDP Sp $ 85.00
Your Price : _____

Vince Camuto
Capri
3.4 oz EDP Sp $ 85.00
Your Price : _____

Vince Camuto
Ciao
3.4 oz EDT Sp $ 85.00
Your Price : _____

Vince Camuto
Femme
3.4 Oz EDP Sp $ 78.00
Your Price : _____

Vince Camuto
Fiori
3.4 oz EDP Sp $ 85.00
Your Price : _____

Vince Camuto
Vince Camuto
1.7 oz EDP Sp $ 56.00
Your Price : _____
3.4 oz EDP Sp $ 85.00
Your Price : _____

Waterford
Lismore
1.7 oz EDP Sp $ 45.00
Your Price : _____

Yves Saint Laurent
Opium
1.0 oz EDT Sp $ 62.00
Your Price : _____
1.6 oz EDT Sp $ 77.00
Your Price : _____
3.0 oz EDT Sp $ 100.00
Your Price : _____

Yves Saint Laurent
Baby Doll
1.0 oz EDT Sp $ 35.00
Your Price : _____
1.6 oz EDT Sp $ 50.00
Your Price : _____
3.3 oz EDT Sp $ 72.00
Your Price : _____

Yves Saint Laurent
Black Opium
1.0 oz EDP Sp $ 69.00
Your Price : _____
1.6 oz EDP Sp $ 91.00
Your Price : _____
3.0 oz EDP Sp $ 118.00
Your Price : _____

Yves Saint Laurent
Cinema
1.6 oz EDP Sp $ 70.00
Your Price : _____
3.0 oz EDP Sp $ 102.00
Your Price : _____

Yves Saint Laurent
Cinema Festival D' Ete
3.0 oz EDT Sp $ 78.00
Your Price : _____

Yves Saint Laurent
Elle
1.6 oz EDP Sp $ 65.00
Your Price : _____
3.4 oz EDP Sp $ 85.00
Your Price : _____

Yves Saint Laurent
In Love Again
2.7 oz EDT Sp $ 125.00
Your Price : _____

Yves Saint Laurent
Manifesto
1.0 oz EDP Sp $ 60.00
Your Price : _____
1.6 oz EDP Sp $ 75.00
Your Price : _____
3.0 oz EDP Sp $ 102.00
Your Price : _____

Yves Saint Laurent
Manifesto L'eclat
3.0 oz EDT Sp $ 90.00
Your Price : _____

Yves Saint Laurent
Mon Paris
1.7 oz EDP Sp $ 92.00
Your Price : _____
3.0 oz EDP Sp $ 122.00
Your Price : _____

Yves Saint Laurent
NU
2.7 oz EDP Sp $ 125.00
Your Price : _____

Yves Saint Laurent
Opium
1.0 oz EDP Sp $ 60.00
Your Price : _____
1.6 oz EDP Sp $ 92.00
Your Price : _____
3.0 oz EDP Sp $ 122.00
Your Price : _____

Yves Saint Laurent
Opium Eau D'orient
Poesie De Chine
3.4 oz EDT Sp $ 85.00
Your Price : _____

Yves Saint Laurent
Paris
1.6 oz EDT Sp $ 65.00
Your Price : _____
2.5 oz EDT Sp $ 77.00
Your Price : _____
4.2 oz EDT Sp $ 98.00
Your Price : _____

Yves Saint Laurent
Paris
1.6 oz EDP Sp $ 77.00
Your Price : _____
2.5 oz EDP Sp $ 90.00
Your Price : _____

Yves Saint Laurent
Parisienne
1.0 oz EDP Sp $ 39.00
Your Price : _____
1.6 oz EDP Sp $ 65.00
Your Price : _____
3.0 oz EDP Sp $ 80.00
Your Price : _____

Yves Saint Laurent
Rive Gauche
1.7 oz EDT Sp $ 65.00
Your Price : _____
3.3 oz EDT Sp $ 84.00
Your Price : _____

Yves Saint Laurent
Saharienne
4.2 oz EDT Sp $ 110.00
Your Price : _____

Yves Saint Laurent
Young Sexy Lovely YSL
1.6 oz EDT Sp $ 60.00
Your Price : _____
2.5 oz EDT Sp $ 73.00
Your Price : _____

Yves Saint Laurent
Yvresse
2.0 oz EDT Sp $ 60.00
Your Price : _____
4.2 oz EDT Sp $ 85.00
Your Price : _____

Yves Saint Laurent
Y (Old)
1.6 oz EDT Sp $ 65.00
Your Price : _____
2.7 oz EDT Sp $ 125.00
Your Price : _____

Adrienne Vittadini
Adrienne Vittadini
3.3 oz Body Lotion
3.3 oz Shower Gel
3.0 oz EDP Sp $ 78.00
Your Price : _____

Alfred Sung
Sung
3.4 oz EDT Sp
2.5 oz Body Lotion
2.5 oz Shower Gel $ 75.00
Your Price : _____

Animale
Animale
6.7 oz Body Lotion
6.7 oz Shower Gel
3.4 oz EDP Sp $ 85.00
Your Price : _____

Antonio Banderas
Blue Seduction
3.4 oz Body Lotion
3.4 oz EDT Sp $ 60.00
Your Price : _____

Bebe
Bebe Gold
3.4 oz Shower Gel Heart Charm
3.4 oz Body Lotion
3.4 oz EDP Sp $ 60.00
Your Price : _____

Bebe
Bebe Sheer
3.4 oz Shower Gel Heart Charm
3.4 oz Body Lotion
3.4 oz EDP Sp $ 60.00
Your Price : _____

Bebe
Wishes & Dreams
3.4 oz Shower Gel
3.4 oz Body Lotion
3.4 oz EDP Sp $ 60.00
Your Price : _____

Betsey Johnson
Betsey Johnson Parfum
6.7 oz Body Lotion
3.4 oz EDP Sp $ 95.00
Your Price : _____

Gale Hayman
Delicious
3.3 oz Body Lotion
3.3 oz Shower Gel
3.3 oz EDT Sp $ 92.00
Your Price : _____

Beyonce
Midnight Heat
3.4 oz EDP Sp
2.5 oz Body Lotion
2.5 oz Shower Cream
0.5 oz EDP Sp $ 62.00
Your Price : _____

Bijan
Bijan
3.4 oz Bath & Shower Gel
3.4 oz Body Lotion
2.5 oz EDT Sp $ 72.00
Your Price : _____

Boucheron
Boucheron
6.7 oz Body Lotion
3.3 oz EDP Sp $ 140.00
Your Price : _____

Britney Spears
Curious
6.8 oz Body Souffle
6.8 oz Shower Gel
3.3 oz EDP Sp $ 62.00
Your Price : _____

Britney Spears
Fantasy
3.3 oz Body Souffle
3.3 oz Shower Gel
3.3 oz EDP Sp $ 60.00
Your Price : _____

Burberry
Burberry Body
3.3 oz Body Milk
2.8 oz EDP Intense Sp
0.15 oz EDP Sp $ 120.00
Your Price : _____

Burberry
Burberry Body
3.3 oz Body Milk-Special Edition
2.8 oz EDP Sp
0.15 oz EDP Sp $ 115.00
Your Price : _____

Burberry
Burberry Brit
3.3 oz EDP Sp
3.3 oz Body Lotion
3.3 oz Body Wash Gel
0.25 oz EDP Sp $ 110.00
Your Price : _____

Burberry
Burberry Weekend
3.3 oz EDP Sp
3.3 oz Body Lotion
3.3 oz Bath & Shower Gel $ 98.00
Your Price : _____

Bvlgari
Omnia Crystalline
2.2 oz EDT Sp
0.5 oz EDT Sp $ 90.00
Your Price : _____

Bvlgari
Omnia Green Jade & Crystalline
0.84 oz EDT Sp Omnia Green Jade
0.84 oz EDT Sp Crystalline
    Satin Pouch $ 75.00
Your Price : _____

Cabotine
Cabotine de Gres
6.76 oz Body Lotion
6.76 oz Bath & Shower Gel
3.4 oz EDT Sp $ 85.00
Your Price : _____

Cacharel
Amor Amor
6.7 oz Body Lotion
3.4 oz EDT Sp $ 90.00
Your Price : _____

Calvin Klein
CK Be
8.5 oz Skin Moisturizer
6.7 oz EDT Sp $ 70.00
Your Price : _____

Calvin Klein
CK Shock
6.7 oz EDT Sp
3.4 oz Body Lotion $ 70.00
Your Price : _____

Calvin Klein
Down Town
3.4 oz Body Lotion
3.4 oz Shower Gel
3.0 oz EDT Sp $ 84.00
Your Price : _____

Calvin Klein
Escape
6.7 oz Body Lotion
3.4 oz EDP Sp $ 85.00
Your Price : _____

Calvin Klein
Eternity Aqua
3.4 oz EDT Sp
1.0 oz EDT Sp $ 80.00
Your Price : _____

Calvin Klein
Obsession
6.7 oz Silkening Body Lotion
3.4 oz EDP Sp
0.5 oz EDP Sp $ 90.00
Your Price : _____

Carolina Herrera
212 NYC
6.75 oz Body Lotion
3.4 oz EDT Sp $ 105.00
Your Price : _____

Carolina Herrera
212 Sexy
6.75 oz Body Lotion
3.4 oz EDT Sp $ 105.00
Your Price : _____

Carolina Herrera
212 VIP
3.4 oz Body Lotion
2.7 oz EDP Sp $ 105.00
Your Price : _____

Carolina Herrera
Carolina Herrera
3.4 oz Body Lotion
3.4 oz EDP Sp $ 110.00
Your Price : _____

Carolina Herrera
CH
3.4 oz Body Lotion
1.7 oz EDT Sp $ 112.00
Your Price : _____

Cartier
Baiser Vole
3.3 oz EDP Sp
3.3 oz Shower Gel
1.6 oz Body Lotion $ 155.00
Your Price : _____

Cartier
Delices de Cartier
1.6 oz Body Milk
1.6 oz EDP Sp
0.16 oz EDP Sp $ 105.00
Your Price : _____

Chloe
Chloe Narcisse
6.8 oz Body Lotion
3.3 oz EDT Sp $ 80.00
Your Price : _____

Coach
Love
5.0 oz Body Lotion
1.7 oz EDP Sp $ 76.00
Your Price : _____

Curve
Curve Crush
3.4 oz EDT Sp
2.5 oz Body Lotion
2.5 oz Bath & Shower Gel
0.5 oz EDT Sp $ 72.00
Your Price : _____

DKNY
Be Delicious
3.4 oz Body Lotion
3.4 oz EDP Sp
0.25 oz EDP Sp $ 98.00
Your Price : _____

DKNY
Golden Night Out
3.4 oz Body Lotion DKNY Key Chain
1.7 oz EDP Sp
0.24 oz EDP Sp $ 85.00
Your Price : _____

Dolce & Gabbana
Dolce & Gabbana Pour Femme
3.3 oz EDP Sp
3.3 oz Body Lotion
0.2 oz EDP Fragrance Pen $ 120.00
Your Price : _____

Dolce & Gabbana
The One Collection
2.5 oz EDP Sp Rose The One
0.2 oz EDP Sp The One
0.2 oz EDP Sp L'eau The One
     $ 95.00
Your Price : _____

Donna Karan
Cashmere Mist
3.4 oz Body Lotion
1.7 oz EDP Sp $ 118.00
Your Price : _____

Donna Karan
Cashmere Mist
3.4 oz EDP Sp
2.5 oz Body Cream
2.5 oz Body Cleansing Lotion
     Cosmetic Bag $ 118.00
Your Price : _____

Ed Hardy
Born Wild
3.4 oz EDP Sp
3.0 oz Body Lotion
3.0 oz Shower Gel
0.25 oz EDP Sp $ 80.00
Your Price : _____

Ed Hardy
Deluxe Collection
1.0 oz EDP Sp Born Wild
1.0 oz EDP Sp Ed Hardy
1.0 oz EDP Sp Hearts & Daggers
     $ 80.00
Your Price : _____

Ed Hardy
Ed Hardy
3.4 oz EDP Sp
3.0 oz Body Lotion
3.0 oz Shower Gel Laggage Tag
0.25 oz EDP Sp $ 80.00
Your Price : _____

Ed Hardy
Hearts & Daggers
3.4 oz EDP Sp
3.0 oz Body Lotion
3.0 oz Shower Gel Laggage Tag
0.25 oz EDP Sp $ 80.00
Your Price : _____

Elizabeth Arden
5th Avenue
4.2 oz EDP Sp
3.3 oz Body Lotion
0.12 oz Parfum $ 65.00
Your Price : _____

Elizabeth Arden
Green Tea
3.3 oz EDP Sp
3.3 oz Body Lotion
3.3 oz Shower Gel $ 60.00
Your Price : _____

Elizabeth Arden
Provocative Woman
3.3 oz EDP Sp
3.3 oz Body Lotion $ 65.00
Your Price : _____

Elizabeth Arden
Red Door
3.3 oz EDP Sp
3.3 oz Body Lotion
3.3 oz Bath & Shower Gel
0.33 oz EDT Sp $ 89.00
Your Price : _____

Elizabeth Taylor
Diamonds and Emeralds
3.3 oz Body Lotion
3.3 oz EDT Sp $ 75.00
Your Price : _____

Elizabeth Taylor
Diamonds and Rubies
3.3 oz Body Lotion
3.3 oz EDT Sp $ 75.00
Your Price : _____

Elizabeth Taylor
Diamonds and Sapphires
3.3 oz Body Lotion
3.3 oz EDT Sp $ 75.00
Your Price : _____

Elizabeth Taylor
White Diamonds
3.3 oz EDT Sp
1.7 oz Body Wash
1.7 oz Body Lotion
0.33 oz EDT Sp $ 100.00
Your Price : _____

Ellen Tracy
Ellen Tracy
3.4 oz EDP Sp
3.4 oz Body Lotion
3.4 oz Shower Gel $ 78.00
Your Price : _____

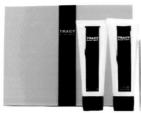

Ellen Tracy
Tracy
3.4 oz Body Lotion
3.4 oz Shower Gel
2.5 oz EDP Sp $ 80.00
Your Price : _____

Eva Longoria
Eva
3.4 oz EDP Sp
3.0 oz Shower Gel
0.25 oz EDP Rollerball
0.25 or EDP Sp $ 90.00
Your Price : _____

Givenchy
Amarige
3.3 oz EDT Sp
2.5 oz Silk Body Veil
2.5 oz Bath Gel $ 110.00
Your Price : _____

Halston
Halston
6.8 oz Body Lotion
3.4 oz Cologne Spray $ 82.00
Your Price : _____

Jennifer Lopez
Glow
6.7 oz Body Lotion
3.4 oz EDP Sp $ 90.00
Your Price : _____

Jennifer Lopez
Live
6.7 oz Body Lotion
3.4 oz EDP Sp $ 90.00
Your Price : _____

Jennifer Lopez
Live Luxe
6.7 oz Body Lotion
3.4 oz EDP Sp $ 90.00
Your Price : _____

Jennifer Lopez
Still
6.7 oz Body Lotion
3.4 oz EDP Sp $ 90.00
Your Price : _____

Jimmy Choo
Flash
3.3 oz Body Lotion
3.3 oz Shower Gel
3.3 oz EDP Sp $ 90.00
Your Price : _____

Juicy Couture
Juicy Couture
3.4 oz EDP Sp
3.4 oz Shower Gel
3.4 oz Shower Gel $ 99.00
Your Price : _____

Juicy Couture
Viva La Juicy
4.2 oz Body Lotion
4.2 oz Shower Gel
3.4 oz EDP Sp $ 100.00
Your Price : _____

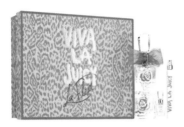

Juicy Couture
Viva La Juicy La Fleur
5.0 oz EDT Sp
0.33 oz EDT Sp
0.17 oz EDT Rollerball $ 96.00
Your Price : _____

Justin Bieber
Girlfriend
3.4 oz Body Lotion
3.4 oz Body Wash
3.4 oz EDP Sp $ 65.00
Your Price : _____

Justin Bieber
The Key
3.4 oz Body Lotion
3.4 oz Body Wash
3.4 oz EDP Sp $ 65.00
Your Price : _____

Kenzo
Flower
3.4 oz EDP Sp
1.7 oz Milky Shower Cream
1.7 oz Body Milk $ 118.00
Your Price : _____

Kim Kardashian
Gold
3.4 oz Body Lotion
3.4 oz Body Wash
3.4 oz EDP Sp $ 65.00
Your Price : _____

Kim Kardashian
Kim Kardashian
3.4 oz Body Lotion
3.4 oz EDP Sp $ 70.00
Your Price : _____

Lacoste
Eau de Lacoste
5.0 oz Body Lotion
3.0 oz EDP Sp $ 100.00
Your Price : _____

Lacoste
Touch of Pink
5.0 oz Body Lotion
3.3 oz EDT Sp $ 75.00
Your Price : _____

Lady Gaga
Fame
6.7 oz Body Lotion
3.4 oz EDP Sp
0.34 oz EDP Roller Ball $ 70.00
Your Price : _____

Liz Claiborne
Lizsport
3.4 oz Body Lotion
3.4 oz Shower Gel
3.4 oz EDT Sp $ 72.00
Your Price : _____

Liz Claiborne
Mambo
3.4 oz Body Lotion
3.4 oz Shower Gel
3.4 oz EDP Sp $ 72.00
Your Price : _____

Marc Jacobs
Dot
5.1 oz Body Lotion
3.4 oz EDP Sp
0.14 oz EDP Splash $ 100.00
Your Price : _____

Marc Jacobs
Honey
5.0 oz Body Lotion
3.4 oz EDP Sp $ 100.00
Your Price : _____

Marc Jacobs
Oh, Lola!
5.1 oz Body Lotion
3.4 oz EDP Sp
0.13 oz EDP $ 120.00
Your Price : _____

Narciso Rodriguez
Essence
3.3 oz Body Lotion
1.6 oz EDP Sp $ 125.00
Your Price : _____

Nicki Minaj
Pink Friday
3.4 oz Body Lotion
3.4 oz Shower Gel
3.4 oz EDP Sp $ 70.00
Your Price : _____

Paco Rabanne
Lady Milion
3.4 oz Body Lotion
2.7 oz EDP Sp $ 108.00
Your Price : _____

Paco Rabanne
Ultraviolet
3.4 oz Body Lotion
2.7 oz EDP Sp $ 75.00
Your Price : _____

Paloma Picasso
Paloma Picasso
6.7 oz Body Lotion
1.7 oz EDP Sp $ 85.00
Your Price : _____

Paris Hilton
Can Can
3.4 oz EDP Sp
3.0 oz Bath & Shower Gel
3.0 oz Body Lotion
0.34 oz EDP Sp $ 80.00
Your Price : _____

Paris Hilton
Fairy Dust
3.4 oz EDP Sp
3.0 oz Bath & Shower Gel
3.0 oz Body Lotion
0.34 oz EDP Sp $ 80.00
Your Price : _____

Paris Hilton
Heiress
3.4 oz EDP Sp
3.0 oz Bath & Shower Gel
3.0 oz Body Lotion
0.34 oz EDP Sp $ 80.00
Your Price : _____

Paris Hilton
Just Me
3.4 oz EDP Sp
3.0 oz Bath & Shower Gel
3.0 oz Body Lotion
0.34 oz EDP Sp $ 80.00
Your Price : _____

Paris Hilton
Paris Hilton
3.4 oz EDP Sp
3.0 oz Bath & Shower Gel
3.0 oz Body Lotion
0.34 oz EDP Sp $ 80.00
Your Price : _____

Paris Hilton
Variety
0.5 oz EDP Sp Can Can
0.5 oz EDP Sp Tease
0.5 oz EDP Sp Paris Hilton
0.5 oz EDP Sp Dazzle
0.5 oz EDP Sp Heiress $ 30.00
Your Price : _____

Perry Ellis
360 Blue
3.4 oz EDP Sp
3.0 oz Body Lotion
3.0 oz Shower Gel
0.25 oz EDP Sp $ 70.00
Your Price : _____

Perry Ellis
360 For Women
1.0 oz EDT Sp 360
1.0 oz EDP Sp 360 Red
1.0 oz EDP Sp 360 Reserve $ 40.00
Your Price : _____

Perry Ellis 360 Purple
3.4 oz EDP Sp
3.0 oz Body Lotion
3.0 oz Shower Gel
0.25 oz EDP Sp $ 70.00
Your Price : _____

Perry Ellis
Love
3.4 oz EDP Sp
3.0 oz Body Lotion
3.0 oz Shower Gel $ 70.00
Your Price : _____

Perry Ellis
Perry Ellis Women
3.4 oz EDP Sp
3.0 oz Body Lotion
3.0 oz Shower Gel $ 70.00
Your Price : _____

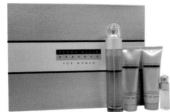

Perry Ellis
Reserve
3.4 oz EDP Sp
3.0 oz Body Lotion
3.0 oz Bath & Shower Gel
0.25 oz EDP Sp $ 70.00
Your Price : _____

Prada
Milano Infusion D'Iris
3.4 oz Body Lotion
1.7 oz EDP Sp $ 95.00
Your Price : _____

Prada
Prada L'Eau Ambree
3.4 oz Body Lotion
2.7 oz EDP Sp $ 110.00
Your Price : _____

Queen Latifah
Queen
3.4 oz EDP Sp
3.0 oz Body Butter
3.0 oz Body Lotion $ 70.00
Your Price : _____

Ralph Lauren
Romance
1.7 oz EDP Sp
1.0 oz EDP Sp $ 88.00
Your Price : _____

Realties
Realties
6.7 oz Shower Gel
6.7 oz Body Lotion
3.4 oz EDP Sp $ 72.00
Your Price : _____

Realties
Sweet Desire
6.7 oz Body Lotion
3.4 oz EDP Sp
0.25 oz Solid Perfume $ 90.00
Your Price : _____

Selena Gomez
Selena Gomez
4.0 oz Body Lotion
4.0 oz Shower Gel
3.4 oz EDP Sp
0.33 oz EDP Rollerball $ 75.00
Your Price : _____

Sisley Paris
Eau du Soir
8.4 oz Bath & Shower Gel
3.3 oz EDP Sp $ 250.00
Your Price : _____

Taylor Swift
Wonderstruk
3.4 oz Bath Gel
3.4 oz Body Lotion
3.4 oz EDP Sp $ 70.00
Your Price : _____

Thierry Muggler
Alien
3.4 oz Body Lotion
2.0 oz EDP Sp $ 120.00
Your Price : _____

Thierry Muggler
Angel
3.5 oz Body Lotion
1.0 oz Shower Gel
0.8 oz EDP Sp $ 100.00
Your Price : _____

Thierry Muggler
Angel
3.5 oz Body Lotion
1.7 oz EDP Sp $ 100.00
Your Price : _____

True Religion
Love Hope Denim
3.4 oz EDP Sp
3.0 oz Body Lotion
3.0 oz Bath & Shower Gel
0.25 oz EDP Sp $ 79.00
Your Price : _____

True Religion
True Religion
3.4 oz EDP Sp
3.0 oz Body Lotion
3.0 oz Bath & Shower Gel
0.25 oz EDP Sp $ 79.00
Your Price : _____

Usher
Usher
3.4 oz Butter Body Cream
3.4 oz EDP Sp $ 70.00
Your Price : _____

Vera Wang
Lovestruck
3.4 oz EDP Sp
2.5 oz Body Lotion
2.5 oz Shower Gel
0.33 oz Roller ball $ 85.00
Your Price : _____

Vera Wang
Princess
2.5 oz Satiny Body Lotion
2.5 oz Foamy Body Polish
1.7 oz EDT Sp
0.2 oz EDT Roller ball $ 70.00
Your Price : _____

Vera Wang
Vera Wang
3.4 oz EDP Sp
3.4 oz Body Lotion
3.4 oz Bath & Shower Cream
0.13 oz EDP $ 95.00
Your Price : _____

Versace
Bright Crystal
1.7 oz Bath & Shower Gel
1.7 oz Body Lotion
1.7 oz EDT Sp $ 78.00
Your Price : _____

Versace
Bright Crystal
3.4 oz Body Lotion Cosmetic Bag
3.0 oz EDT Sp $ 90.00
Your Price : _____

Versace
Crystal Noir
3.4 oz Body Lotion Cosmetic Bag
3.0 oz EDT Sp $ 90.00
Your Price : _____

Versace
Vanitas
3.4 oz Body Lotion
3.4 oz EDP Sp $ 135.00
Your Price : _____

Versace
Versus
3.4 oz Body Lotion
1.7 oz EDP Sp $ 90.00
Your Price : _____

Versace
Yellow Diamond
1.7 oz Shower Gel
1.7 oz Body Lotion
1.7 oz EDP Sp $ 78.00
Your Price : _____

Vince Camuto
Vince Camuto
3.4 oz EDP Sp
2.5 oz Body Lotion
2.5 oz Bath & Shower Gel $ 90.00
Your Price : _____

Vince Camuto
Fiori
3.4 oz EDP Sp
2.5 oz Body Lotion
2.5 oz Shower Gel $90.00
Your Price :___

Yves Saint Laurent
Opium
6.6 oz Body Moisturizer
3.0 oz EDT Sp $ 110.00
Your Price : _____

Yves Saint Laurent
Parisienne
1.6 oz Body Lotion
1.6 oz Shower Gel
1.6 oz EDP Sp $ 70.00
Your Price : _____

Yves Saint Laurent
Black Opium
1.6 oz EDP Sp
0.06 oz Masacara
Eyepencil $96.00
Your Price:___

Barbie
1.7 oz EDT Sp $35.00
Your Price : _____

Barbie
3.3 oz EDT Sp $ 35.00
Your Price : _____

Betty Boop
3.3 oz EDT Sp $ 40.00
Your Price : _____

Betty Boop
Princess
3.4 oz EDT Sp $ 40.00
Your Price : _____

BFC INC
Together Forever
3.3 oz EDT Sp $ 35.00
Your Price : _____

Bratz
Cloe
1.7 oz EDT Sp $ 30.00
Your Price : _____

Bratz
Jade
1.7 oz EDT Sp $ 30.00
Your Price : _____

Bratz
Sasha
1.7 oz EDT Sp $ 30.00
Your Price : _____

Bratz
Yasmin
1.7 oz EDT Sp $ 30.00
Your Price : _____

Daisy Duck
3.3 oz EDT Sp $ 35.00
Your Price : _____

Dora
Adorable
3.3 oz EDT Sp $ 35.00
Your Price : _____

Dora
Starry Night
3.3 oz EDT Sp $ 35.00
Your Price : _____

Frozen
3.3 oz EDT Sp $45.00
Your Price : _____

Fairies
3.3 oz EDT Sp $ 35.00
Your Price : _____

Hannah Montana
1.7 oz EDT Sp $ 25.00
Your Price : _____

Hannah Montana
Gotta Rock!
3.3 oz EDT Sp $ 35.00
Your Price : _____

Tangled Rapunzel
3.4 oz EDT Sp $45.00
Your Price : _____

Hello Kitty
3.4 oz EDT Sp $45.00
Your Price : _____

Hello Kitty
Dark Love
1.6 oz EDT Sp $ 45.00
Your Price : _____

Hello Kitty
Funny Love
1.6 oz EDT Sp $ 45.00
Your Price : _____

Hello Kitty
Sweet Love
1.6 oz EDT Sp $ 45.00
Your Price : _____

I Clary
Click
3.3 oz EDT Sp $ 40.00
Your Price : _____

Madagascar 2
2.5 oz EDT Sp $ 35.00
Your Price : _____

Minnie Mouse
1.7 oz EDT Sp $ 25.00
Your Price : _____
3.3 oz EDT Sp $ 35.00
Your Price : _____

I Clary
Sweet
3.3 oz EDT Sp $ 40.00
Your Price : _____

Kung Fu Panda
2.5 oz EDT Sp $ 30.00
Your Price : _____

Princess
Ariel
1.7 oz EDT Sp $ 25.00
Your Price : _____
3.3 oz EDT Sp $ 35.00
Your Price : _____

Princess
Sofia The First
3.4 oz EDP Sp $45.00
Your Price : _____

Princess
Belle
1.7 oz EDT Sp $ 25.00
Your Price : _____
3.3 oz EDT Sp $ 35.00
Your Price : _____

Princess
Cinderella
1.7 oz EDT Sp $ 25.00
Your Price : _____
3.3 oz EDT Sp $ 35.00
Your Price : _____

Princess
Sleeping Beauty
1.7 oz EDT Sp $ 25.00
Your Price : _____
3.3 oz EDT Sp $ 35.00
Your Price : _____

Princess
Snow White
1.7 oz EDT Sp $ 25.00
Your Price : _____
3.3 oz EDT Sp $ 35.00
Your Price : _____

Shrek - 2
2.5 oz EDT Sp $ 45.00
Your Price : _____

Shrek The Third
Princess Fiona
2.5 oz EDT Sp $ 45.00
Your Price : _____

Spongebob Squarepants
3.3 oz EDT Sp $ 35.00
Your Price : _____

Spongebob Squarepants
Sea Scents
3.3 oz EDT Sp $ 35.00
Your Price : _____

Strawberry Shortcake
3.3 oz EDT Sp $ 35.00
Your Price : _____

The Simpsons
3.3 oz EDT Sp $ 40.00
Your Price : _____

Tweet Tweet
3.3 oz EDT Sp $ 35.00
Your Price : _____

Tweety
3.3 oz EDT Sp $ 35.00
Your Price : _____

UNITED STATES ARMY
EST. 1775

Angry Birds
King Pig
1.7 oz EDT Sp $ 35.00
Your Price : _____

Angry Birds
Red Bird
1.7 oz EDT Sp $ 35.00
Your Price : _____

Angry Birds
Rio
3.4 oz EDT Sp $ 40.00
Your Price : _____

Angry Birds
Yellow Bird
1.7 oz EDT Sp $ 35.00
Your Price : _____

Avengers
Assemble
3.3 oz EDT Sp $ 30.00
Your Price : _____

Bee Movie
Bee Movie
3.3 oz EDT Sp $ 30.00
Your Price : _____

Cars
Cars 2
3.3 oz EDT Sp $ 30.00
Your Price : _____

Cars
Neon Endurance Cup
3.4 oz EDT Sp $ 30.00
Your Price : _____

G.I. Joe
The Rise of Cobra
3.3 oz EDT Sp $ 30.00
Your Price : _____

Go Diego Go
Go Diego Go
3.3 oz EDT Sp $ 30.00
Your Price : _____

Justice League
Batman
3.3 oz EDT Sp $ 30.00
Your Price : _____

Justice League
Green Lantern
3.3 oz EDT Sp $ 30.00
Your Price : _____

Justice League
Justice League
3.4 oz EDT Sp $ 30.00
Your Price : _____

Justice League
Superman
3.3 oz EDT Sp $ 30.00
Your Price : _____

Justice League
The Flash
3.3 oz EDT Sp $ 30.00
Your Price : _____

Kung Fu Panda
Kung Fu Panda
2.5 oz EDT Sp $ 30.00
Your Price : _____

Looney tunes
Bugs Bunny
3.3 oz EDT Sp $ 30.00
Your Price : _____

Looney Tunes
Daffy Duck
3.3 oz EDT Sp $ 30.00
Your Price : _____

Looney Tunes
Looney Tunes
3.3 oz EDT Sp $ 30.00
Your Price : _____

Marvel
Hulk
3.3 oz EDT Sp $ 30.00
Your Price : _____

Marvel
Iron Man
3.3 oz EDT Sp $ 30.00
Your Price : _____

Mickey Mouse
Mickey Mouse
1.7 oz EDT Sp $ 25.00
Your Price : _____
3.3 oz EDT Sp $ 35.00
Your Price : _____

Minions
Minions
3.3 oz EDT Sp $ 40.00
Your Price : _____

Ninja Turtles
Donatello
3.4 oz EDT Sp $ 40.00
Your Price : _____

Ninja Turtles
Leonardo
3.4 oz EDT Sp $ 40.00
Your Price : _____

Ninja Turtles
Michelangelo
3.4 oz EDT Sp $ 40.00
Your Price : _____

Ninja Turtles
Raphael
3.4 oz EDT Sp $ 40.00
Your Price : _____

Spiderman
The Amazing
3.3 oz EDT Sp $ 30.00
Your Price : _____

Spiderman
Ultimate
3.4 oz EDT Sp $ 30.00
Your Price : _____

Shrek
The Third
2.5 oz EDT Sp $ 30.00
Your Price : _____

Spongebob Squarepants
For Boy's
3.3 oz EDT Sp $ 30.00
Your Price : _____

Spongebob Squarepants
Patrick 3D
3.4 oz EDT Sp $ 45.00
Your Price : _____

Spongebob Squarepants
Sea Scents
3.3 oz EDT Sp $ 30.00
Your Price : _____

Spongebob Squarepants
Spongebob Squarepants 3D
3.4 oz EDT Sp $ 45.00
Your Price : _____

Spongebob Squarepants
Squidward 3D
3.4 oz EDT Sp $ 45.00
Your Price : _____

The Simpsons
The Simpsons
3.3 oz EDT Sp $ 30.00
Your Price : _____

Toy Story
Toy Story
3.3 oz EDT Sp $ 30.00
Your Price : _____

Transformers
Bumble Bee
3.3 oz EDT Sp $ 30.00
Your Price : _____

Transformers
Optimus Prime
3.3 oz EDT Sp $ 30.00
Your Price : _____

Winnie The Pooh
Winnie The Pooh
1.7 oz EDT Sp $ 25.00
Your Price : _____

Adidas
Intense Touch
3.4 oz EDT Sp $40.00
Your Price : _____

Adidas
Deep Energy
3.4 oz EDT Sp $ 40.00
Your Price : _____

Adidas
Dynamic Pulse
3.4 oz EDT Sp $ 40.00
Your Price : _____

Adidas
Pure Game
3.4 oz EDT Sp $ 40.00
Your Price : _____

Adidas
Fresh Impact
3.4 oz EDT Sp $ 40.00
Your Price : _____

Adidas
Game Spirit
3.4 oz EDT Sp $ 40.00
Your Price : _____

Adidas
Ice Dive
3.4 oz EDT Sp $ 40.00
Your Price : _____

Adidas
Extreme Power
3.4 oz EDT Sp $ 40.00
Your Price : _____

Adidas
Get Ready
3.4 oz EDT Sp $ 40.00
Your Price : _____

Adidas
Blue Challenge
3.4 oz EDT Sp $ 40.00
Your Price : _____

Adidas
Sport Fever
3.4 oz EDT Sp $ 40.00
Your Price : _____

Adidas
Sports Field
3.4 oz EDT Sp $ 40.00
Your Price : _____

Adidas
Team Force
3.4 oz EDT Sp $ 40.00
Your Price : _____

Adidas
Team Five
3.4 oz EDT Sp $ 40.00
Your Price : _____

Adidas
Victory League
3.4 oz EDT Sp $ 40.00
Your Price : _____

Alfred Dunhill
51.3 N
1.7 oz EDT Sp $ 49.00
Your Price : _____
3.4 oz EDT Sp $ 65.00
Your Price : _____

Alfred Dunhill
Black
1.7 oz EDT Sp $ 49.00
Your Price : _____
3.4 oz EDT Sp $ 65.00
Your Price : _____

Alfred Dunhill
Custom
3.3 oz EDT Sp $ 65.00
Your Price : _____

Alfred Dunhill
Desire
1.7 oz EDT Sp $ 49.00
Your Price : _____
3.4 oz EDT Sp $ 65.00
Your Price : _____

Alfred Dunhill
Desire Blue
1.7 oz EDT Sp $ 49.00
Your Price : _____
3.4 oz EDT Sp $ 65.00
Your Price : _____

Alfred Dunhill
Dunhill
1.7 oz EDT Sp $ 45.00
Your Price : _____
2.5 oz EDT Sp $ 60.00
Your Price : _____

Alfred Dunhill
Dunhill Edition
1.7 oz EDT Sp $ 49.00
Your Price : _____
3.4 oz EDT Sp $ 65.00
Your Price : _____

Alfred Dunhill
Fresh
1.7 oz EDT Sp $ 49.00
Your Price : _____
3.4 oz EDT Sp $ 65.00
Your Price : _____

Alfred Dunhill
London
1.7 oz EDT Sp $ 49.00
Your Price : _____
3.4 oz EDT Sp $ 65.00
Your Price : _____

Alfred Dunhill
Pure
1.7 oz EDT Sp $ 45.00
Your Price : _____
2.5 oz EDT Sp $ 60.00
Your Price : _____

Alfred Dunhill
Pursuit
1.6 oz EDT Sp $ 45.00
Your Price : _____
2.5 oz EDT Sp $ 60.00
Your Price : _____

Alfred Dunhill
Icon
1.7 oz EDP Sp $70.00
Your Price : _____
3.4 oz EDP Sp $95.00
Your Price : _____

Alfred Dunhill
Icon Elite
1.7 oz EDP Sp $70.00
Your Price : _____
3.4 oz EDP Sp $95.00
Your Price : _____

Alfred Sung
Hei
1.7 oz EDT Sp $ 52.00
Your Price : _____
3.4 oz EDT Sp $ 75.00
Your Price : _____

Alfred Sung
Paradise
1.7 oz EDT Sp $ 52.00
Your Price : _____
3.4 oz EDT Sp $ 75.00
Your Price : _____

Alfred Sung
Sung
1.7 oz EDT Sp $ 52.00
Your Price : _____
3.4 oz EDT Sp $ 75.00
Your Price : _____

Animale
Animale
1.7 oz EDT Sp $ 40.00
Your Price : _____
3.4 oz EDT Sp $ 60.00
Your Price : _____

Animale
Animale Animale
1.7 oz EDT Sp $ 40.00
Your Price : _____
3.4 oz EDT Sp $ 60.00
Your Price : _____

Animale
Animale Azul
1.7 oz EDT Sp $ 40.00
Your Price : _____
3.4 oz EDT Sp $ 60.00
Your Price : _____

Animale
Animale Black
1.7 oz EDT Sp $ 40.00
Your Price : _____
3.4 oz EDT Sp $ 60.00
Your Price : _____

Animale
Chaleur D' Animale
1.7 oz EDT Sp $ 40.00
Your Price : _____
3.4 oz EDT Sp $ 60.00
Your Price : _____

Animale
Sport
1.7 oz EDT Sp $40.00
Your Price : _____
3.4 oz EDT Sp $60.00
Your Price : _____

Annick Goutal
Duel
3.4 oz EDT Sp $ 120.00
Your Price : _____

Annick Goutal
Eau D' Hadrien
3.4 oz EDT Sp $ 120.00
Your Price : _____

Annick Goutal
Eau De Lavande
3.4 oz EDT Sp $ 120.00
Your Price : _____

Annick Goutal
Eau De Monsieur
3.4 oz EDT Sp $ 120.00
Your Price : _____

Annick Goutal
Eau De Sud
3.4 oz EDT Sp $ 120.00
Your Price : _____

Annick Goutal
Encens Flamboyant
3.4 oz EDT Sp $ 120.00
Your Price : _____

Annick Goutal
Hadrien Absolu
3.4 oz EDT Sp $ 120.00
Your Price : _____

Annick Goutal
Les Nuits D' Hadrien
3.4 oz EDT Sp $ 120.00
Your Price : _____

Annick Goutal
Mandragore
3.4 oz EDT Sp $ 120.00
Your Price : _____

Annick Goutal
Mandragore Pourpre
3.4 oz EDT Sp $ 120.00
Your Price : _____

Annick Goutal
Ninfeo Mio
3.4 oz EDT Sp $ 120.00
Your Price : _____

Antonio Banderas
The Golden Secret
1.7 oz EDT Sp $ 40.00
Your Price : _____
3.4 oz EDT Sp $ 60.00
Your Price : _____

Antonio Banderas
Seduction In Black
1.7 oz EDT Sp $ 40.00
Your Price : _____
3.4 oz EDT Sp $ 60.00
Your Price : _____
6.7 oz EDT Sp $ 75.00
Your Price : _____

Antonio Banderas
Mediterraneo
1.7 oz EDT Sp $ 40.00
Your Price : _____
3.4 oz EDT Sp $ 60.00
Your Price : _____

Antonio Banderas
Antonio
1.7 oz EDT Sp $ 40.00
Your Price : _____
3.4 oz EDT Sp $ 60.00
Your Price : _____

Antonio Banderas
Blue Seduction
1.7 oz EDT Sp $ 40.00
Your Price : _____
3.4 oz EDT Sp $ 60.00
Your Price : _____
6.7 oz EDT Sp $ 75.00
Your Price : _____

Antonio Banderas
Diavolo
1.7 oz EDT Sp $ 40.00
Your Price : _____
3.4 oz EDT Sp $ 60.00
Your Price : _____

Antonio Banderas
Spirit
1.7 oz EDT Sp $ 40.00
Your Price : _____

Antonio Banderas
The Secret
1.7 oz EDT Sp $40.00
Your Price : _____
3.4 oz EDT Sp $60.00
Your Price : _____

Antonio Banderas
The Secret Game
1.7 oz EDT Sp $ 40.00
Your Price : _____
3.4 oz EDT Sp $ 60.00
Your Price : _____

Antonio Banderas
King Of Seduction
1.7 oz EDT Sp $40.00
Your Price : _____
3.4 oz EDT Sp $60.00
Your Price : _____

Antonio Puig
Agua Brava
3.4 oz EDT Sp $ 55.00
Your Price : _____

Antonio Puig
Brave
3.4 oz EDT Sp $ 65.00
Your Price : _____

Antonio Puig
Aqua Quorum
1.7 oz EDT Sp $ 35.00
Your Price :
3.4 oz EDT Sp $ 55.00
Your Price :

Antonio Puig
Quorum
1.7 oz EDT Sp $ 40.00
Your Price :
3.4 oz EDT Sp $ 60.00
Your Price :

Antonio Puig
Quorum Silver
1.7 oz EDT Sp $ 40.00
Your Price :
3.4 oz EDT Sp $ 60.00
Your Price :

Anuuci
Anuuci
3.4 oz EDT Sp $ 65.00
Your Price :

Anuuci
Sport
3.4 oz EDT Sp $ 65.00
Your Price :

Aramis
900
1.7 oz EDT Sp $ 55.00
Your Price :
3.4 oz EDT Sp $ 79.00
Your Price :

Aramis
Always
1.7 oz EDT Sp $ 55.00
Your Price :
3.4 oz EDT Sp $ 79.00
Your Price :

Aramis
Aramis
2.0 oz EDT Sp $ 65.00
Your Price :
3.7 oz EDT Sp $ 80.00
Your Price :

Aramis
Cool
3.4 oz EDT Sp $ 79.00
Your Price :

Aramis
Cool Blend
3.4 oz EDT Sp $ 79.00
Your Price :

Aramis
Devin
3.4 oz EDT Sp $ 79.00
Your Price :

Aramis
Havana
3.4 oz EDT Sp $ 79.00
Your Price :

Aramis
J.H.L Blended
Cologne
3.4 oz EDT Sp $ 79.00
Your Price :

Aramis
Life
1.7 oz EDT Sp $ 55.00
Your Price :
3.4 oz EDT Sp $ 79.00
Your Price :

Aramis
New West Skinscent
1.7 oz EDT Sp $ 55.00
Your Price :
3.4 oz EDT Sp $ 79.00
Your Price :

Aramis
Tuscany Per Uomo
1.7 oz EDT Sp $ 55.00
Your Price :
3.4 oz EDT Sp $ 79.00
Your Price :

Azzaro
Azzaro
1.7 oz EDT Sp $ 65.00
Your Price :
3.4 oz EDT Sp $ 85.00
Your Price :
6.8 oz EDT Sp $ 110.00
Your Price :

Azzaro
Bright Visit
1.7 oz EDT Sp $ 55.00
Your Price :
3.4 oz EDT Sp $ 75.00
Your Price :

Azzaro
Chrome
1.7 oz EDT Sp $ 65.00
Your Price :
3.4 oz EDT Sp $ 85.00
Your Price :
6.8 oz EDT Sp $ 110.00
Your Price :

Azzaro
Chrome Legend
2.5 oz EDT Sp $ 55.00
Your Price :
4.2 oz EDT Sp $ 75.00
Your Price :

Azzaro
Chrome Sport
1.7 oz EDT Sp $ 50.00
Your Price : _____
3.4 oz EDT Sp $ 70.00
Your Price : _____

Azzaro
Chrome United
1.7 oz EDT Sp $ 60.00
Your Price : _____
3.4 oz EDT Sp $ 80.00
Your Price : _____
6.8 oz EDT Sp $ 103.00
Your Price : _____

Azzaro
Now
1.7 oz EDT Sp $ 55.00
Your Price : _____
3.4 oz EDT Sp $ 75.00
Your Price : _____

Azzaro
Onyx
1.7 oz EDT Sp $ 55.00
Your Price : _____
3.4 oz EDT Sp $ 75.00
Your Price : _____

Azzaro
Silver Black
1.7 oz EDT Sp $ 55.00
Your Price : _____
3.4 oz EDT Sp $ 75.00
Your Price : _____

Azzaro
Visit
1.7 oz EDT Sp $ 55.00
Your Price : _____
3.4 oz EDT Sp $ 75.00
Your Price : _____

Azzaro
Chrome Intense
3.7 oz EDT Sp $ 87.00
Your Price : _____

Azzaro
Chrome Pure
3.7 oz EDT Sp $ 85.00
Your Price : _____

Azzaro
Wanted
1.7 oz EDT Sp $65.00
Your Price : _____
3.4 oz EDT Sp $85.00
Your Price : _____

Banana Republic
Black Walnut
3.3 oz EDT Sp $ 60.00
Your Price : _____

Banana Republic
Cordovan
3.4 oz EDT Sp $ 75.00
Your Price : _____

Banana Republic
Classic
1.7 oz EDT Sp $ 55.00
Your Price : _____
4.2 oz EDT Sp $ 85.00
Your Price : _____

Banana Republic
Slate
1.7 oz EDT Sp $ 55.00
Your Price : _____
3.4 oz EDT Sp $ 75.00
Your Price : _____

Benetton
B-United
3.4 oz EDT Sp $ 52.00
Your Price : _____

Benetton
Colors
3.4 oz EDT Sp $ 52.00
Your Price : _____

Benetton
Cold
3.4 oz EDT Sp $ 52.00
Your Price : _____

Benetton
Sport Pure
3.4 oz EDT Sp $ 52.00
Your Price : _____

Benetton
Sport
3.4 oz EDT Sp $ 52.00
Your Price : _____

Benetton
United Colors
4.2 oz EDT Sp $ 59.00
Your Price : _____

Bijan
Bijan
1.7 oz EDT Sp $ 50.00
Your Price : _____
2.5 oz EDT Sp $ 70.00
Your Price : _____

Bijan
Black
1.7 oz EDT Sp $ 50.00
Your Price : _____
2.5 oz EDT Sp $ 70.00
Your Price : _____

Bijan
DNA
3.4 oz EDT Sp $ 75.00
Your Price : _____

Bijan
Nude
1.7 oz EDT Sp $ 50.00
Your Price : _____
2.5 oz EDT Sp $ 70.00
Your Price : _____

Bijan
Style
2.5 oz EDT Sp $ 58.00
Your Price : _____

Bijan
VIP
1.7 oz EDT Sp $ 50.00
Your Price : _____
2.5 oz EDT Sp $ 70.00
Your Price : _____

Bijan
Wicked
1.7 oz EDT Sp $ 50.00
Your Price : _____
2.5 oz EDT Sp $ 70.00
Your Price : _____

Bijan
With a Twist
1.7 oz EDT Sp $ 50.00
Your Price : _____
2.5 oz EDT Sp $ 70.00
Your Price : _____

Bob Mackie
Bob Mackie
3.4 oz EDT Sp $ 65.00
Your Price : _____

Bottega Veneta
Pour Homme
1.7 oz EDP Sp $ 95.00
Your Price : _____
3.0 oz EDP Sp $ 135.00
Your Price : _____

Bottega Veneta
Pour Homme
1.6 oz EDT Sp $ 85.00
Your Price : _____
3.0 oz EDT Sp $ 115.00
Your Price : _____

Boucheron
Boucheron
1.7 oz EDP Sp $ 90.00
Your Price : _____
3.3 oz EDP Sp $ 125.00
Your Price : _____
1.7 oz EDT Sp $ 65.00
Your Price : _____
3.3 oz EDT Sp $ 88.00
Your Price : _____

Boucheron
Jaipur
1.7 oz EDP Sp $ 90.00
Your Price : _____
3.3 oz EDP Sp $ 125.00
Your Price : _____
1.7 oz EDT Sp $ 65.00
Your Price : _____
3.3 oz EDT Sp $ 88.00
Your Price : _____

Burberry
Brit Rhythm
1.0 oz EDT Sp $ 50.00
Your Price : _____
1.7 oz EDT Sp $ 64.00
Your Price : _____
3.4 oz EDT Sp $ 80.00
Your Price : _____

Burberry
Brit Splash
3.4 oz EDT Sp $ 80.00
Your Price : _____

Burberry
Brit
1.7 oz EDT Sp $ 64.00
Your Price : _____
3.4 oz EDT Sp $ 80.00
Your Price : _____

Burberry
Burberry
1.0 oz EDT Sp $ 47.00
Your Price : _____
1.7 oz EDT Sp $ 60.00
Your Price : _____
3.4 oz EDT Sp $ 76.00
Your Price : _____

Burberry
London
1.0 oz EDT Sp $ 47.00
Your Price : _____
1.7 oz EDT Sp $ 60.00
Your Price : _____
3.4 oz EDT Sp $ 75.00
Your Price : _____

Burberry
Summer
3.3 oz EDT Sp $ 65.00
Your Price : _____

Burberry
The Beat
1.7 oz EDT Sp $ 60.00
Your Price : _____
3.4 oz EDT Sp $ 75.00
Your Price : _____

Burberry
Touch
1.0 oz EDT Sp $ 47.00
Your Price : _____
1.7 oz EDT Sp $ 60.00
Your Price : _____
3.4 oz EDT Sp $ 75.00
Your Price : _____

Burberry
Weekend
1.7 oz EDT Sp $ 47.00
Your Price : _____
1.7 oz EDT Sp $ 60.00
Your Price : _____
3.4 oz EDT Sp $ 75.00
Your Price : _____

Burberry
Brit Rhythm Intense
1.6 oz EDT Sp $ 70.00
Your Price : _____
3.0 oz EDT Sp $ 88.00
Your Price : _____

Burberry
Mr. Burberry
1.6 oz EDT Sp $ 68.00
Your Price : _____
3.3 oz EDT Sp $ 88.00
Your Price : _____
5.0 oz EDT Sp $ 115.00
Your Price : _____

Burberry
Mr. Burberry (EDP)
1.6 oz EDT Sp $ 75.00
Your Price : _____
3.3 oz EDT Sp $ 95.00
Your Price : _____
5.0 oz EDT Sp $ 128.00
Your Price : _____

Bvlgari
Aqva
1.7 oz EDT Sp $ 68.00
Your Price : _____
3.4 oz EDT Sp $ 88.00
Your Price : _____
5.0 oz EDT Sp $ 103.00
Your Price : _____

Bvlgari
Aqva Marine
1.7 oz EDT Sp $ 68.00
Your Price : _____
3.4 oz EDT Sp $ 88.00
Your Price : _____
5.0 oz EDT Sp $ 103.00
Your Price : _____

Bvlgari
Aqva Marine Toniq
1.7 oz EDT Sp $ 68.00
Your Price : _____
3.4 oz EDT Sp $ 88.00
Your Price : _____
5.0 oz EDT Sp $ 103.00
Your Price : _____

Bvlgari
Aqva Toniq
1.7 oz EDT Sp $ 68.00
Your Price : _____
3.4 oz EDT Sp $ 88.00
Your Price : _____
5.0 oz EDT Sp $ 103.00
Your Price : _____

Bvlgari
Black
2.5 oz EDT Sp $ 85.00
Your Price : _____

Bvlgari
Bvlgari Aqva Atlantique
1.7 oz EDT Sp $ 68.00
Your Price : _____
3.4 oz EDT Sp $ 88.00
Your Price : _____

Bvlgari
Blv
1.7 oz EDT Sp $ 68.00
Your Price : _____
3.4 oz EDT Sp $ 88.00
Your Price : _____

Bvlgari
BLV Notte
1.7 oz EDT Sp $ 62.00
Your Price : _____
3.4 oz EDT Sp $ 89.00
Your Price : _____

Bvlgari
Extreme
1.7 oz EDT Sp $ 62.00
Your Price : _____
3.4 oz EDT Sp $ 89.00
Your Price : _____

Bvlgari
Man
2.0 oz EDT Sp $ 70.00
Your Price : _____
3.4 oz EDT Sp $ 89.00
Your Price : _____
5.0 oz EDT Sp $ 106.00
Your Price : _____

Bvlgari
Man Extreme
2.0 oz EDT Sp $ 70.00
Your Price : _____
3.4 oz EDT Sp $ 89.00
Your Price : _____
5.0 oz EDT Sp $ 106.00
Your Price : _____

Bvlgari
Pour Homme
1.7 oz EDT Sp $ 65.00
Your Price : _____
3.4 oz EDT Sp $ 88.00
Your Price : _____

Bvlgari
Pour Homme Soir
1.0 oz EDT Sp $ 45.00
Your Price : _____
1.7 oz EDT Sp $ 65.00
Your Price : _____
3.4 oz EDT Sp $ 88.00
Your Price : _____

Bvlgari
Man In Black
2.0 oz EDP Sp $ 74.00
Your Price : _____
3.4 oz EDP Sp $ 94.00
Your Price : _____

Bvlgari
Man In Black Intense
1.7 oz EDT Sp $ 70.00
Your Price : _____
3.4 oz EDT Sp $ 89.00
Your Price : _____

Bvlgari
Man Extreme Intense
1.7 oz EDT Sp $ 70.00
Your Price : _____
3.4 oz EDT Sp $ 89.00
Your Price : _____

Caesars
Caesars
4.0 oz EDT Sp $ 50.00
Your Price :_____

Calvin Klein
CK One Shock
1.7 oz EDT Sp $ 40.00
Your Price :_____
3.4 oz EDT Sp $ 50.00
Your Price :_____
6.7 oz EDT Sp $ 64.00
Your Price :_____

Calvin Klein
Calvin
3.4 oz EDT Sp $ 76.00
Your Price :_____

Calvin Klein
Calvin Klein Man
1.7 oz EDT Sp $ 58.00
Your Price :_____
3.4 oz EDT Sp $ 76.00
Your Price :_____

Calvin Klein
CK Be
1.7 oz EDT Sp $ 40.00
Your Price :_____
3.4 oz EDT Sp $ 50.00
Your Price :_____
6.7 oz EDT Sp $ 65.00
Your Price :_____

Calvin Klein
CK Free
1.7 oz EDT Sp $ 50.00
Your Price :_____
3.4 oz EDT Sp $ 65.00
Your Price :_____

Calvin Klein
CK in 2U
1.7 oz EDT Sp $ 45.00
Your Price :_____
3.4 oz EDT Sp $ 55.00
Your Price :_____
5.0 oz EDT Sp $ 68.00
Your Price :_____

Calvin Klein
CK One
1.7 oz EDT Sp $ 49.00
Your Price :_____
3.4 oz EDT Sp $ 58.00
Your Price :_____
6.7 oz EDT Sp $ 72.00
Your Price :_____

Calvin Klein
CK One Summer
3.4 oz EDT Sp $ 54.00
Your Price :_____

Calvin Klein
Contradiction
1.7 oz EDT Sp $ 58.00
Your Price :_____
3.4 oz EDT Sp $ 76.00
Your Price :_____

Calvin Klein
Crave
1.3 oz EDT Sp $ 40.00
Your Price :_____
2.5 oz EDT Sp $ 60.00
Your Price :_____

Calvin Klein
Dark Obsession
4.0 oz EDT Sp $ 78.00
Your Price :_____

Calvin Klein
Escape
1.7 oz EDT Sp $ 58.00
Your Price :_____
3.4 oz EDT Sp $ 76.00
Your Price :_____

Calvin Klein
Eternity
1.7 oz EDT Sp $ 55.00
Your Price :_____
3.4 oz EDT Sp $ 78.00
Your Price :_____
6.7 oz EDT Sp $ 99.00
Your Price :_____

Calvin Klein
Eternity Aqua
1.7 oz EDT Sp $ 55.00
Your Price :_____
3.4 oz EDT Sp $ 78.00
Your Price :_____
6.7 oz EDT Sp $ 99.00
Your Price :_____

Calvin Klein
Eternity Summer
3.4 oz EDT Sp $ 75.00
Your Price :_____

Calvin Klein
Encounter
1.7 oz EDT Sp $ 55.00
Your Price :_____
3.4 oz EDT Sp $ 70.00
Your Price :_____

Calvin Klein
Euphoria
1.7 oz EDT Sp $ 62.00
Your Price :_____
3.4 oz EDT Sp $ 80.00
Your Price :_____

Calvin Klein
Euphoria Intense
1.7 oz EDT Sp $ 62.00
Your Price :_____
3.4 oz EDT Sp $ 80.00
Your Price :_____

Calvin Klein
Obsession
2.5 oz EDT Sp $ 62.00
Your Price :_____
4.0 oz EDT Sp $ 76.00
Your Price :_____
6.7 oz EDT Sp $ 99.00
Your Price :_____

Calvin Klein
Obsession Night
2.5 oz EDT Sp $ 62.00
Your Price : _____
4 oz EDT Sp $ 76.00
Your Price : _____

Calvin Klein
Reveal
3.4 oz EDT Sp $ 78.00
Your Price : _____

Calvin Klein
Euphoria Gold
1.7 oz EDT Sp $62.00
Your Price : _____
3.4 oz EDT Sp $80.00
Your Price : _____

Calvin Klein
Truth
1.7 oz EDT Sp $ 62.00
Your Price : _____
3.4 oz EDT Sp $ 76.00
Your Price : _____

Calvin Klein
CK One Red
3.4 oz EDT Sp $ 54.00
Your Price : _____

Calvin Klein
Eternity Now
1.0 oz EDT Sp $ 40.00
Your Price : _____
3.4 oz EDT Sp $ 78.00
Your Price : _____

Calvin Klein
Eternity Intense
1.7 oz EDT Sp $ 66.00
Your Price : _____
3.4 oz EDT Sp $ 84.00
Your Price : _____
6.7 oz EDT Sp $ 105.00
Your Price : _____

Carlo Corinto
Carlo Corinto
3.4 oz EDT Sp $ 59.00
Your Price : _____

Carlo Corinto
315
3.4 oz EDT Sp $ 59.00
Your Price : _____

Carlo Corinto
Rouge
3.4 oz EDT Sp $ 59.00
Your Price : _____

Carlo Corinto
Vetyver
3.4 oz EDT Sp $ 59.00
Your Price : _____

Carlo Corinto
Cool
3.4 oz EDT Sp $ 59.00
Your Price : _____

Carlos Santana
Carlos Santana
1.7 oz EDT Sp $ 62.00
Your Price : _____
3.4 oz EDT Sp $ 79.00
Your Price : _____

Carolina Herrera
212
1.7 oz EDT Sp $ 55.00
Your Price : _____
3.4 oz EDT Sp $ 86.00
Your Price : _____

Carolina Herrera
212 Glam
3.4 oz EDT Sp $ 75.00
Your Price : _____

Carolina Herrera
212 Summer
1.7 oz EDT Sp $ 55.00
Your Price : _____
3.4 oz EDT Sp $ 75.00
Your Price : _____

Carolina Herrera
212 Sexy
1.7 oz EDT Sp $ 55.00
Your Price : _____
3.4 oz EDT Sp $ 86.00
Your Price : _____

Carolina Herrera
212 VIP
1.7 oz EDT Sp $ 55.00
Your Price : _____
3.4 oz EDT Sp $ 86.00
Your Price : _____

Carolina Herrera
CH
1.7 oz EDT Sp $ 59.00
Your Price : _____
3.4 oz EDT Sp $ 85.00
Your Price : _____

Carolina Herrera
CH Prive
1.7 oz EDT Sp $ 59.00
Your Price : _____
3.4 oz EDT Sp $ 85.00
Your Price : _____

Carolina Herrera
CH Sport
1.7 oz EDT Sp $ 55.00
Your Price : _____
3.4 oz EDT Sp $ 80.00
Your Price : _____

Carolina Herrera
Chic
2.0 oz EDT Sp $ 45.00
Your Price : _____
3.4 oz EDT Sp $ 65.00
Your Price : _____

Carolina Herrera
Herrera
1.7 oz EDT Sp $ 68.00
Your Price : _____
3.4 oz EDT Sp $ 82.00
Your Price : _____

Carolina Herrera
Herrera Aqua
1.7 oz EDT Sp $ 59.00
Your Price : _____
3.4 oz EDT Sp $ 85.00
Your Price : _____

Cartier
Declaration
1.7 oz EDT Sp $ 77.00
Your Price : _____
3.3 oz EDT Sp $ 108.00
Your Price : _____
5.1 oz EDT Sp $ 138.00
Your Price : _____

Cartier
Declaration Bois Bleu
1.7 oz EDT Sp $ 77.00
Your Price : _____
3.4 oz EDT Sp $ 108.00
Your Price : _____
5.1 oz EDT Sp $ 138.00
Your Price : _____

Cartier
Declaration Essence
1.7 oz EDT Sp $ 80.00
Your Price : _____
3.3 oz EDT Sp $ 112.00
Your Price : _____

Cartier
Eau De Cartier
1.7 oz EDT Sp $ 68.00
Your Price : _____
3.4 oz EDT Sp $ 95.00
Your Price : _____
6.7 oz EDT Sp $ 127.00
Your Price : _____

Cartier
Must De Cartier
1.7 oz EDT Sp $ 90.00
Your Price : _____
3.4 oz EDT Sp $ 130.00
Your Price : _____

Cartier
Pasha De Cartier
1.7 oz EDT Sp $ 80.00
Your Price : _____
3.4 oz EDT Sp $ 108.00
Your Price : _____

Cartier
Declaration D'Un soir
1.7 oz EDT Sp $ 80.00
Your Price : _____
3.3 oz EDT Sp $ 108.00
Your Price : _____

Cartier
Roadster
1.7 oz EDT Sp $ 80.00
Your Price : _____
3.4 oz EDT Sp $ 108.00
Your Price : _____

Cartier
Santos De Cartier
1.7 oz EDT Sp $ 80.00
Your Price : _____
3.4 oz EDT Sp $ 108.00
Your Price : _____

Cartier
Pasha De Cartier Noire
3.3 oz EDT Sp $ 112.00
Your Price : _____
5.1 oz EDT Sp $ 142.00
Your Price : _____

Cartier
Roadster Sport
1.7 oz EDT Sp $ 80.00
Your Price : _____
3.3 oz EDT Sp $ 108.00
Your Price : _____

Carven
Vetiver
3.3 oz EDT Sp $ 75.00
Your Price : _____

Chanel
Allure Homme
1.7 oz EDT Sp $ 75.00
Your Price : _____
3.4 oz EDT Sp $ 95.00
Your Price : _____
5.0 oz EDT Sp $ 128.00
Your Price : _____

Chanel
Allure Homme sport
Eau Extreme
1.7 oz EDP Sp $ 90.00
Your Price : _____
3.4 oz EDP Sp $ 115.00
Your Price : _____
5.0 oz EDP Sp $ 150.00
Your Price : _____

Chanel
Allure Homme Edition
Blanche
1.7 oz EDP Sp $ 90.00
Your Price : _____
3.4 oz EDP Sp $ 115.00
Your Price : _____
5.0 oz EDP Sp $ 150.00
Your Price : _____

Chanel
Allure Homme Sport
1.7 oz EDT Sp $ 75.00
Your Price : _____
3.4 oz EDT Sp $ 95.00
Your Price : _____
5.0 oz EDT Sp $ 128.00
Your Price : _____

Chanel
Antaeus
1.7 oz EDT Sp $ 75.00
Your Price : _____
3.4 oz EDT Sp $ 95.00
Your Price : _____

Chanel
Bleu De Chanel (EDP)
1.7 oz EDP Sp $ 90.00
Your Price : _____
3.3 oz EDP Sp $ 115.00
Your Price : _____
5.0 oz EDP Sp $ 150.00
Your Price : _____

Chanel
Bleu De Chanel
1.7 oz EDT Sp $ 75.00
Your Price : _____
3.4 oz EDT Sp $ 95.00
Your Price : _____
5.0 oz EDT Sp $ 128.00
Your Price : _____
10.0 oz EDT Sp $ 225.00
Your Price : _____

Chanel
Egoiste
1.7 oz EDT Sp $ 75.00
Your Price : _____
3.4 oz EDT Sp $ 95.00
Your Price : _____

Chanel
Platinum Egoiste
1.7 oz EDT Sp $ 75.00
Your Price : _____
3.4 oz EDT Sp $ 95.00
Your Price : _____

Chanel
Pour Monsieur
1.7 oz EDT Sp $ 75.00
Your Price : _____
3.4 oz EDT Sp $ 95.00
Your Price : _____
2.5 oz EDP Sp $ 90.00
Your Price : _____

Cacharel
Amor Pour Homme
2.5 oz EDT Sp $ 55.00
Your Price : _____
4.2 oz EDT Sp $ 80.00
Your Price : _____

Christian Dior
Dior Homme
1.7 oz EDT Sp $ 60.00
Your Price : _____
3.4 oz EDT Sp $ 80.00
Your Price : _____

Christian Dior
Dior Homme Intense
1.7 oz EDP Sp $ 70.00
Your Price : _____
3.4 oz EDP Sp $ 90.00
Your Price : _____

Christian Dior
Dior Homme Sport
1.7 oz EDT Sp $ 60.00
Your Price : _____
2.4 oz EDT Sp $ 74.00
Your Price : _____
3.4 oz EDT Sp $ 80.00
Your Price : _____

Christian Dior
Dune
1.7 oz EDT Sp $ 70.00
Your Price : _____
3.4 oz EDT Sp $ 85.00
Your Price : _____

Christian Dior
Eau Sauvage
1.7 oz EDP Sp $ 70.00
Your Price : _____
3.4 oz EDP Sp $ 90.00
Your Price : _____

Christian Dior
Fahrenheit
1.7 oz EDT Sp $ 60.00
Your Price : _____
3.4 oz EDT Sp $ 92.00
Your Price : _____
6.8 oz EDT Sp $ 145.00
Your Price : _____

Christian Dior
Fahrenheit Absolute
1.7 oz EDT Sp $ 60.00
Your Price : _____
3.4 oz EDT Sp $ 90.00
Your Price : _____

Christian Dior
Aqua Fahrenheit
2.5 oz EDT Sp $ 60.00
Your Price : _____
4.2 oz EDT Sp $ 85.00
Your Price : _____

Christian Dior
Fahrenheit 32
3.4 oz EDT Sp $ 92.00
Your Price : _____

Christian Dior
Fahrenheit Summer
1.7 oz EDT Sp $ 70.00
Your Price : _____
4.2 oz EDT Sp $ 95.00
Your Price : _____

Christian Dior
Higher
1.7 oz EDT Sp $ 70.00
Your Price : _____
3.4 oz EDT Sp $ 85.00
Your Price : _____

Christian Dior
Higher Energy
1.7 oz EDT Sp $ 70.00
Your Price : _____
3.4 oz EDT Sp $ 85.00
Your Price : _____

Christian Dior
Eau Sauvage
1.7 oz EDT Sp $ 60.00
Your Price : _____
3.4 oz EDT Sp $ 80.00
Your Price : _____

Christian Dior
Dior Homme Cologne
2.5 oz EDT Sp $ 74.00
Your Price : _____
4.2 oz EDT Sp $ 94.00
Your Price : _____
6.7 oz EDT Sp $ 126.00
Your Price : _____

Christian Dior
Dior Homme Eau For Men
1.7 oz EDT Sp $ 72.00
Your Price : _____
3.4 oz EDT Sp $ 95.00
Your Price : _____
5.0 oz EDT Sp $ 120.00
Your Price : _____

Christian Dior
Sauvage
2.0 oz EDT Sp $ 74.00
Your Price : _____
3.4 oz EDT Sp $ 92.00
Your Price : _____
6.8 oz EDT Sp $ 145.00
Your Price : _____

Coty
Aspen
2.5 oz EDT Sp $ 30.00
Your Price : _____
4 oz EDT Sp $ 45.00
Your Price : _____

Creed
Erolfa Millesime
4.0 oz EDT Sp $ 330.00
Your Price : _____

Creed
Green Valley Millesime
4.0 oz EDT Sp $ 330.00
Your Price : _____

Creed
Himalaya Millesime
2.5 oz EDT Sp $ 275.00
Your Price : _____
4.0 oz EDT Sp $ 330.00
Your Price : _____

Creed
Millesime Imperial (Gold)
1.0 oz EDP Sp $ 215.00
Your Price : _____
2.5 oz EDP Sp $ 350.00
Your Price : _____
4.0 oz EDP Sp $ 395.00
Your Price : _____

Creed
Original Santal
2.5 oz EDP Sp $ 350.00
Your Price : _____
4.0 oz EDP Sp $ 425.00
Your Price : _____

Creed
Original Vetiver
2.5 oz EDP Sp $ 350.00
Your Price : _____
4.0 oz EDP Sp $ 425.00
Your Price : _____

Creed
Royal Water
2.5 oz EDP Sp $ 350.00
Your Price : _____
4.0 oz EDT Sp $ 425.00
Your Price : _____

Creed
Silver Mountain Water
1.7 oz EDP Sp $ 290.00
Your Price : _____
2.5 oz EDP Sp $ 350.00
Your Price : _____
3.4 oz EDP Sp $ 395.00
Your Price : _____
4.0 oz EDP Sp $ 425.00
Your Price : _____

Creed
Virgin Island Water
1.0 oz EDP Sp $ 215.00
Your Price : _____
2.5 oz EDP Sp $ 350.00
Your Price : _____
4.0 oz EDP Sp $ 425.00
Your Price : _____

Creed
Green Irish Tweed
1.7 oz EDP Sp $ 290.00
Your Price : _____
2.5 oz EDP Sp $ 350.00
Your Price : _____
4.0 oz EDP Sp $ 425.00
Your Price : _____

Creed
Tabarome
2.5 oz EDP Sp $ 275.00
Your Price : _____
4.0 oz EDP Sp $ 330.00
Your Price : _____

Creed
Royal Oud
2.5 oz EDP Sp $ 430.00
Your Price : _____
4.0 oz EDP Sp $ 540.00
Your Price : _____

Creed
Aventus
1.0 oz EDP Sp $ 230.00
Your Price : _____
1.7 oz EDP Sp $ 315.00
Your Price : _____
3.4 oz EDP Sp $ 425.00
Your Price : _____
4.0 oz EDP Sp $ 455.00
Your Price : _____

Dana
British Sterling
1.7 oz EDT Sp $ 35.00
Your Price : _____
3.4 oz EDT Sp $ 50.00
Your Price : _____

Dana
English Leather
1.7 oz EDT Sp $ 35.00
Your Price : _____
3.4 oz EDT Sp $ 50.00
Your Price : _____

Davidoff
Adventure
1.7 oz EDT Sp $ 50.00
Your Price : _____
3.4 oz EDT Sp $ 65.00
Your Price : _____

Davidoff
Adventure Amazonia
3.4 oz EDT Sp $ 80.00
Your Price : _____

Davidoff
Cool Water
2.5 oz EDT Sp $ 55.00
Your Price : _____
4.2 oz EDT Sp $ 70.00
Your Price : _____

Davidoff
Cool Water Frozen
2.5 oz EDT Sp $ 45.00
Your Price : _____
4.2 oz EDT Sp $ 60.00
Your Price : _____

Davidoff
Cool Water Game
1.7 oz EDT Sp $ 50.00
Your Price : _____
3.4 oz EDT Sp $ 65.00
Your Price : _____

Davidoff
Cool Water Summer Fizz
2.5 oz EDT Sp $ 45.00
Your Price : _____
4.2 oz EDT Sp $ 60.00
Your Price : _____

Davidoff
Echo
1.7 oz EDT Sp $ 50.00
Your Price : _____
3.4 oz EDT Sp $ 65.00
Your Price : _____

Davidoff
Goodlife
2.5 oz EDT Sp $ 50.00
Your Price : _____
4.2 oz EDT Sp $ 65.00
Your Price : _____

Davidoff
Hotwater
2.0 oz EDT Sp $ 45.00
Your Price : _____
3.7 oz EDT Sp $ 60.00
Your Price : _____

Davidoff
Silver Shadow
1.7 oz EDT Sp $ 50.00
Your Price : _____
3.4 oz EDT Sp $ 65.00
Your Price : _____

Davidoff
Zino Davidoff
1.7 oz EDT Sp $ 50.00
Your Price : _____
3.4 oz EDT Sp $ 65.00
Your Price : _____

Davidoff
The Game
2.0 oz EDT Sp $ 50.00
Your Price : _____
3.4 oz EDT Sp $ 60.00
Your Price : _____

Davidoff
The Game Intense
2.0 oz EDT Sp $ 50.00
Your Price : _____
3.4 oz EDT Sp $ 60.00
Your Price : _____

Deray
Attitude Man
3.4 oz EDT Sp $ 55.00
Your Price : _____

Deray
Blue Attitude
3.4 oz EDT Sp $ 55.00
Your Price : _____

Deray
White Attitude
3.4 oz EDT Sp $ 55.00
Your Price : _____

Deray
Silver Attitude
3.4 oz EDT Sp $ 55.00
Your Price : _____

Diesel
Fuel For Life
1.6 oz EDT Sp $ 57.00
Your Price : _____
2.5 oz EDT Sp $ 67.00
Your Price : _____

Diesel
Only The Brave
1.6 oz EDT Sp $ 57.00
Your Price : _____
2.5 oz EDT Sp $ 67.50
Your Price : _____
4.2 oz EDT Sp $ 85.00
Your Price : _____

Diesel
Zero Plus
2.5 oz EDT Sp $ 50.00
Your Price : _____

Diesel
Plus Plus
2.5 oz EDT Sp $ 50.00
Your Price : _____

Diesel
Only The Brave Wild
1.6 oz EDT Sp $ 57.00
Your Price : _____
2.5 oz EDT Sp $ 68.00
Your Price : _____

Dolce & Gabbana
Light Blue
2.5 oz EDT Sp $ 67.00
Your Price : _____
4.2 oz EDT Sp $ 86.00
Your Price : _____
6.7 oz EDT Sp $ 115.00
Your Price : _____

Dolce & Gabbana
Light Blue Living Stromboli
1.3 oz EDT Sp $ 48.00
Your Price : _____
2.5 oz EDT Sp $ 60.00
Your Price : _____
4.2 oz EDT Sp $ 75.00
Your Price : _____

Dolce & Gabbana
Pour Homme
2.5 oz EDT Sp $ 67.00
Your Price : _____
4.2 oz EDT Sp $ 86.00
Your Price : _____
6.7 oz EDT Sp $ 117.00
Your Price : _____

Dolce & Gabbana
The One
1.6 oz EDT Sp $ 67.00
Your Price : _____
3.3 oz EDT Sp $ 86.00
Your Price : _____
5.0 oz EDT Sp $ 115.00
Your Price : _____

Dolce & Gabbana
The One Gentleman
1.6 oz EDT Sp $ 67.00
Your Price : _____
3.3 oz EDT Sp $ 86.00
Your Price : _____
5.0 oz EDT Sp $ 115.00
Your Price : _____

Dolce & Gabbana
The One Sport
1.6 oz EDT Sp $ 67.00
Your Price : _____
3.3 oz EDT Sp $ 86.00
Your Price : _____
5.0 oz EDT Sp $ 115.00
Your Price : _____

Dolce & Gabbana
Light Blue Intense
1.6 oz EDP Sp $ 68.00
Your Price : _____
3.3 oz EDP Sp $ 86.00
Your Price : _____
6.7 oz EDP Sp $ 125.00
Your Price : _____

Dolce & Gabbana
The One (EDP)
1.7 oz EDP Sp $ 72.00
Your Price : _____
3.4 oz EDP Sp $ 92.00
Your Price : _____
5.0 oz EDP Sp $ 125.00
Your Price : _____

Dolce & Gabbana
Intenso
2.5 oz EDP Sp $ 70.00
Your Price : _____
3.4 oz EDP Sp $ 89.00
Your Price : _____
6.7 oz EDP Sp $ 122.00
Your Price : _____

Dolce & Gabbana
Masculine
1.7 oz EDT Sp $ 65.00
Your Price : _____
3.4 oz EDT Sp $ 89.00
Your Price : _____

Donna Karan
Be Delicious
1.7 oz EDT Sp $ 65.00
Your Price : _____
3.4 oz EDT Sp $ 89.00
Your Price : _____

Donna Karan
Red Delicious Man
1.7 oz EDT Sp $ 65.00
Your Price : _____
3.4 oz EDT Sp $ 89.00
Your Price : _____

Elizabeth Taylor
Passion
4.0 oz EDT Sp $ 55.00
Your Price : _____

Erox
Realm
1.7 oz EDT Sp $ 50.00
Your Price : _____
3.4 oz EDT Sp $ 82.00
Your Price : _____

Escada
Moon Sparkle
1.7 oz EDT Sp $ 45.00
Your Price : _____
3.4 oz EDT Sp $ 67.00
Your Price : _____

Escada
Sentiment
1.7 oz EDT Sp $ 45.00
Your Price : _____
3.4 oz EDT Sp $ 67.00
Your Price : _____

Escada
Sunset Heat
1.7 oz EDT Sp $ 45.00
Your Price : _____
3.4 oz EDT Sp $ 67.00
Your Price : _____

Estee Lauder
Beyond Paradise
1.7 oz EDT Sp $ 45.00
Your Price : _____
3.4 oz EDT Sp $ 67.00
Your Price : _____

Estee Lauder
Intuition
1.7 oz EDT Sp $ 59.00
Your Price : _____
3.3 oz EDT Sp $ 82.00
Your Price : _____

Estee Lauder
Pleasures
1.7 oz EDT Sp $ 59.00
Your Price : _____
3.3 oz EDT Sp $ 82.00
Your Price : _____

Estee Lauder
Pleasures Intense
1.7 oz EDT Sp $ 59.00
Your Price : _____
3.3 oz EDT Sp $ 82.00
Your Price : _____

Fendi
Fan Di Fendi Assoluto
1.7 oz EDP Sp $ 60.00
Your Price : _____

Fendi
Fendi Uomo
1.7 oz EDT Sp $ 55.00
Your Price : _____
3.4 oz EDT Sp $ 75.00
Your Price : _____

Fendi
Fan Di Fendi
1.7 oz EDT Sp $ 60.00
Your Price : _____
3.4 oz EDT Sp $ 75.00
Your Price : _____

Fendi
Fan Di Fendi Acqua
1.7 oz EDT Sp $ 60.00
Your Price : _____
3.4 oz EDT Sp $ 75.00
Your Price : _____

Ferrari
Extreme
2.5 oz EDT Sp $ 40.00
Your Price : _____
4.2 oz EDT Sp $ 55.00
Your Price : _____

Ferrari
UOMO
3.3 oz EDT Sp $ 60.00
Your Price : _____

Ferrari
Passion
1.7 oz EDT Sp $ 45.00
Your Price : _____
3.3 oz EDT Sp $ 60.00
Your Price : _____

Ferrari
Red
2.5 oz EDT Sp $ 45.00
Your Price : _____
4.2 oz EDT Sp $ 60.00
Your Price : _____

Ferrari
Scuderia Racing Red
2.5 oz EDT Sp $ 45.00
Your Price : _____
4.2 oz EDT Sp $ 60.00
Your Price : _____

Ferrari
Scuderia Black
4.2 oz EDT Sp $ 65.00
Your Price : _____

Ferrari
Leather Essence
3.3 oz EDP Sp $ 55.00
Your Price : _____

Franck Olivier
Passion
3.4 oz EDT Sp $ 50.00
Your Price : _____

Fred Hayman
273 Indigo
2.5 oz EDT Sp $ 45.00
Your Price : _____

Fred Hayman
273
2.5 oz EDT Sp $ 45.00
Your Price : _____

Fred Hayman
273 Red
1.7 oz EDT Sp $ 40.00
Your Price : _____
2.5 oz EDT Sp $ 55.00
Your Price : _____

Fred Hayman
Hollywood
1.7 oz EDT Sp $ 40.00
Your Price : _____
2.5 oz EDT Sp $ 65.00
Your Price : _____

Fred Hayman
Touch
1.7 oz EDT Sp $ 40.00
Your Price : _____
3.4 oz EDT Sp $ 65.00
Your Price : _____

Fred Hayman
Touch With Love
3.4 oz EDT Sp $ 65.00
Your Price : _____

French Connection
Fcuk
1.7 oz EDP Sp $ 40.00
Your Price : _____
3.4 oz EDP Sp $ 65.00
Your Price : _____

Fubu
Plush
1.7 oz EDP Sp $ 50.00
Your Price : _____

Geoffrey Beene
Bowling Green
4 oz EDP Sp $ 75.00
Your Price : _____

Geoffrey Beene
Eau De Grey Flannel
2 oz EDT Sp $ 49.00
Your Price : _____
4 oz EDT Sp $ 75.00
Your Price : _____

Geoffrey Beene
Grey Flannel
2 oz EDT Sp $ 49.00
Your Price : _____
4 oz EDT Sp $ 75.00
Your Price : _____

Gilles Cantuel
Arsenal Blue
3.4 oz EDP Sp $ 64.00
Your Price : _____

Giorgio Armani
Armani Code Ultimate
1.7 oz EDT Sp $ 70.00
Your Price : _____
2.5 oz EDT Sp $ 88.00
Your Price : _____

Giorgio Armani
Armani Code Sport
1.0 oz EDT Sp $ 40.00
Your Price : _____
1.7 oz EDT Sp $ 68.00
Your Price : _____
2.5 oz EDT Sp $ 82.00
Your Price : _____
4.2 oz EDT Sp $ 94.00
Your Price : _____

Giorgio Armani
Armani Eau De Nuit
1.7 oz EDT Sp $ 78.00
Your Price : _____
3.4 oz EDT Sp $ 110.00
Your Price : _____

Giorgio Armani
Acqua Di Gio
1.7 oz EDT Sp $ 68.00
Your Price : _____
3.4 oz EDT Sp $ 85.00
Your Price : _____
6.7 oz EDT Sp $ 118.00
Your Price : _____
10.1 oz EDT Sp $ 138.00
Your Price : _____

Giorgio Armani
Armani
1.7 oz EDT Sp $ 78.00
Your Price : _____
3.4 oz EDT Sp $ 110.00
Your Price : _____

Giorgio Armani
Attitude
1.7 oz EDT Sp $ 55.00
Your Price : _____
2.5 oz EDT Sp $ 75.00
Your Price : _____

Giorgio Armani
Acqua Di Gio Essenza
1.3 oz EDP Sp $ 80.00
Your Price : _____
2.5 oz EDP Sp $ 110.00
Your Price : _____
6.8 oz EDP Sp $ 172.00
Your Price : _____

Giorgio Armani
Armani Code
1.0 oz EDT Sp $ 40.00
Your Price : _____
1.7 oz EDT Sp $ 60.00
Your Price : _____
2.5 oz EDT Sp $ 82.00
Your Price : _____
4.2 oz EDT Sp $ 94.00
Your Price : _____

Giorgio Armani
City Glam
1.7 oz EDT Sp $ 60.00
Your Price : _____
3.4 oz EDT Sp $ 75.00
Your Price : _____

Giorgio Armani
Emporio Armani
1.7 oz EDT Sp $ 60.00
Your Price : _____
3.4 oz EDT Sp $ 75.00
Your Price : _____

Giorgio Armani
Emporio Armani
Diamonds
1.7 oz EDT Sp $ 60.00
Your Price : _____
2.5 oz EDT Sp $ 79.00
Your Price : _____

Giorgio Armani
Emporio Armani
Night
1.7 oz EDT Sp $ 60.00
Your Price : _____
3.4 oz EDT Sp $ 75.00
Your Price : _____

Giorgio Armani
Emporio Armani Remix
1.7 oz EDT Sp $ 55.00
Your Price : _____
3.4 oz EDT Sp $ 70.00
Your Price : _____

Giorgio Armani
Emporio White
1.7 oz EDT Sp $ 55.00
Your Price : _____
3.4 oz EDT Sp $ 70.00
Your Price : _____

Giorgio Armani
Armani Mania
1.7 oz EDT Sp $ 65.00
Your Price : _____
3.4 oz EDT Sp $ 79.00
Your Price : _____

Giorgio Armani
Acqua Di Gio Profumo
2.5 oz EDP Sp $ 95.00
Your Price : _____
4.2 oz EDP Sp $ 130.00
Your Price : _____
6.1 oz EDP Sp $ 150.00
Your Price : _____

Giorgio Armani
Armani Code Ice
2.5 oz EDT Sp $ 75.00
Your Price : _____

Giorgio Armani
Armani Code Turquoise
2.5 oz EDT Sp $ 75.00
Your Price : _____

Giorgio Armani
Armani Code Colonia
2.5 oz EDT Sp $ 82.00
Your Price : _____
4.2 oz EDT Sp $ 94.00
Your Price : _____

Giorgio Armani
Armani Code Profumo
1.0 oz EDT Sp $ 72.00
Your Price : _____
2.0 oz EDT Sp $ 90.00
Your Price : _____
3.7 oz EDT Sp $ 110.00
Your Price : _____
6.7 oz EDT Sp $ 135.00
Your Price : _____

Giorgio Beverly Hills
Red
1.7 oz EDT Sp $ 40.00
Your Price : _____
3.4 oz EDT Sp $ 55.00
Your Price : _____

Giorgio Beverly Hills
Wings
1.7 oz EDT Sp $ 55.00
Your Price : _____
3.4 oz EDT Sp $ 70.00
Your Price : _____

Giorgio Beverly Hills
Giorgio
1.7 oz EDT Sp $ 55.00
Your Price : _____
3.4 oz EDT Sp $ 70.00
Your Price : _____

Giorgio Valenti
One O One
3.3 oz EDT Sp $ 60.00
Your Price : _____

Giorgio Valenti
P.U.R.E. Million
3.3 oz EDT Sp $ 60.00
Your Price : _____

Giorgio Valenti
Rose Noire
3.4 oz EDT Sp $ 80.00
Your Price : _____

Giorgio Valenti
Rose Noire Black
3.4 oz EDT Sp $ 80.00
Your Price : _____

Givenchy
Gentleman
1.7 oz EDT Sp $ 60.00
Your Price : _____
3.4 oz EDT Sp $ 89.00
Your Price : _____

Givenchy
Pour Homme
1.7 oz EDT Sp $ 65.00
Your Price : _____
3.4 oz EDT Sp $ 89.00
Your Price : _____

Givenchy
Blue Label
1.7 oz EDT Sp $ 65.00
Your Price : _____
3.4 oz EDT Sp $ 89.00
Your Price : _____

Givenchy
Greenenergy
1.7 oz EDT Sp $ 60.00
Your Price : _____
3.4 oz EDT Sp $ 80.00
Your Price : _____

Givenchy
Insense Ultramarine
1.7 oz EDT Sp $ 60.00
Your Price : _____
3.4 oz EDT Sp $ 80.00
Your Price : _____

Givenchy
Monsieur Givenchy
3.4 oz EDT Sp $ 80.00
Your Price : _____

Givenchy
Gentlemen Only
1.7 oz EDT Sp $ 65.00
Your Price : _____
3.4 oz EDT Sp $ 89.00
Your Price : _____
5.1 oz EDT Sp $ 108.00
Your Price : _____

Estelle Ewen
IN BLACK pour homme
3.4 oz EDT Sp $ 72.00

Estelle Ewen
BLANC D'ORIENT
3.4 oz EDT Sp $ 75.00

Estelle Ewen
IN BLUE pour homme
3.4 oz EDT Sp $72.00

Estelle Ewen
IN PLAY pour homme
3.4 oz EDT Sp $ 72.00

Estelle Ewen
IN pour homme
3.4 oz EDT Sp $ 72.00

Estelle Ewen
IN RED pour homme
3.4 oz EDT Sp $ 72.00

Estelle Ewen
IN WHITE pour homme
3.4 oz EDT Sp $ 72.00

Estelle Ewen
L'ORIENTAL men
3.4 oz EDT Sp $ 80.00

Estelle Ewen
L'ORIENTAL BLUE EDITION men
3.4 oz EDT Sp $ 80.00

Estelle Ewen
L'ORIENTAL ICON
3.4 oz EDT Sp $ 112.00

Estelle Ewen
L'ORIENTAL OUD Sahara
3.4 oz EDT Sp $ 80.00

Estelle Ewen
L'ORIENTAL NUIT ROYALE men
3.4 oz EDT Sp $ 80.00

Estelle Ewen
L'ORIENTAL TERRE ROUGE men
3.4 oz EDT Sp $ 80.00

Estelle Ewen
L'ORIENTAL WHITE EDITON men
3.4 oz EDT Sp $ 80.00

Estelle Ewen
L'ORIENTAL DOUBLE WHITE
3.4 oz EDT Sp $ 80.00

Estelle Ewen
NOIR D'ORIENT
3.4 oz EDT Sp $ 123.00

Estelle Ewen
L'ORIENTAL YELLOW EDITION men
3.4 oz EDT Sp $ 80.00

Estelle Ewen
BLUE CODE for men
3.4 oz EDT Sp $ 80.00

Gemina B.
CONFIDENTIAL
3.0 oz EDT Sp $ 135.00

Gemina B.
CONFIDENTIAL MAN
3.0 oz EDT Sp $ 135.00

Glenn Perri
DARKSIDER men
3.4 oz EDT Sp $ 75.00

Glenn Perri
PROUD men
3.4 oz EDT Sp $ 48.00

Glenn Perri
PROUD GAME men
3.4 oz EDT Sp $ 88.00

Glenn Perri
PROUD SPORT men
3.4 oz EDT Sp $ 88.00

Glenn Perri
UNPREDICTABLE ADVENTURE
3.4 oz EDT Sp $ 98.00

Glenn Perri
UNPREDICTABLE DESIRE
3.4 oz EDT Sp $ 98.00

Glenn Perri
UNPREDICTABLE FOR MEN
3.4 oz EDT Sp $ 98.00

Glenn Perri
UNPREDICTABLE INTENSE
3.4 oz EDT Sp $ 58.00

Glenn Perri
UNPREDICTABLE MEN EXTREME
3.4 oz EDT Sp $ 98.00

Glenn Perri
UNPREDICTABLE NIGHT
3.4 oz EDT Sp $ 98.00

Glenn Perri
UNPREDICTABLE NOIR
3.4 oz EDT Sp $ 149.00

Glenn Perri
UNPREDICTABLE POUR HOMME
3.4 oz EDT Sp $ 98.00

Glenn Perri
UNPREDICTABLE SPORT
3.4 oz EDT Sp $98.00

Glenn Perri
UNBELIEVABLE BLU
3.4 oz EDT Sp $ 98.00

Glenn Perri
UNBELIEVABLE EXTREME
3.4 oz EDT Sp $ 149.00

Glenn Perri
UNFORGETTABLE PURE WHITE
3.4 oz EDT Sp $ 123.00

Glenn Perri
UNBELIEVABLE MEN
3.4 oz EDT Sp $ 98.00

Glenn Perri
UNBELIEVABLE BLU INTENSE
3.4 oz EDT Sp $ 149.00

Glenn Perri
UNEXPECTED MEN
3.4 oz EDT Sp $ 95.00

Glenn Perri
UNFORGETTABLE PURE BLACK
3.4 oz EDT Sp $ 123.00

Givenchy
Pi
1.7 oz EDT Sp $ 65.00
Your Price : _____
3.4 oz EDT Sp $ 89.00
Your Price : _____
5.1 oz EDT Sp $ 108.00
Your Price : _____

Givenchy
Pi Fraiche
1.7 oz EDT Sp $ 60.00
Your Price : _____
3.4 oz EDT Sp $ 80.00
Your Price : _____

Givenchy
Pi Neo
1.7 oz EDT Sp $ 65.00
Your Price : _____
3.4 oz EDT Sp $ 89.00
Your Price : _____

Givenchy
Play
1.7 oz EDT Sp $ 60.00
Your Price : _____
3.3 oz EDT Sp $ 79.00
Your Price : _____
5.0 oz EDT Sp $ 108.00
Your Price : _____

Givenchy
Play Intense
1.7 oz EDT Sp $ 65.00
Your Price : _____
3.3 oz EDT Sp $ 89.00
Your Price : _____

Givenchy
Very Irresistible
Fresh Attitude
3.4 oz EDT Sp $ 80.00
Your Price : _____

Givenchy
Very Irresistible Man
1.7 oz EDT Sp $ 55.00
Your Price : _____
3.4 oz EDT Sp $ 80.00
Your Price : _____

Givenchy
Xeryus
1.6 oz EDT Sp $ 60.00
Your Price : _____
3.4 oz EDT Sp $ 80.00
Your Price : _____

Givenchy
Xeryus Rouge
1.6 oz EDT Sp $ 65.00
Your Price : _____
3.4 oz EDT Sp $ 89.00
Your Price : _____

Givenchy
Gentleman Only Casual Chic
3.3 oz EDT Sp $ 89.00
Your Price : _____

Givenchy
Gentleman Only Intense
1.7 oz EDT Sp $ 71.00
Your Price : _____
3.3 oz EDT Sp $ 93.00
Your Price : _____
5.0 oz EDT Sp $ 115.00
Your Price : _____

Givenchy
Play Sport
3.3 oz EDT Sp $ 77.00
Your Price : _____

Gucci
Made to Measure
1.7 oz EDT Sp $ 75.00
Your Price : _____
3.0 oz EDT Sp $ 92.00
Your Price : _____
5.0 oz EDT Sp $ 125.00
Your Price : _____

Gucci
Envy
3.4 oz EDT Sp $ 85.00
Your Price : _____

Gucci
Gucci
1.7 oz EDT Sp $ 69.00
Your Price : _____
3.0 oz EDT Sp $ 88.00
Your Price : _____

Gucci
Guilty
1.6 oz EDT Sp $ 69.00
Your Price : _____
3.0 oz EDT Sp $ 88.00
Your Price : _____

Gucci
Pour Homme
1.7 oz EDT Sp $ 55.00
Your Price : _____
3.3 oz EDT Sp $ 88.00
Your Price : _____

Gucci
Pour Homme II
1.7 oz EDT Sp $ 55.00
Your Price : _____
3.3 oz EDT Sp $ 88.00
Your Price : _____

Gucci
Gucci Sport
1.7 oz EDT Sp $ 68.00
Your Price : _____
3.0 oz EDT Sp $ 88.00
Your Price : _____

Gucci
Guilty Intense
1.6 oz EDT Sp $ 72.00
Your Price : _____
3.0 oz EDT Sp $ 95.00
Your Price : _____

Gucci
Guilty Black
1.6 oz EDT Sp $ 69.00
Your Price : _____
3.0 oz EDT Sp $ 85.00
Your Price : _____

Gucci
Guilty Absolute
3.0 oz EDP Sp $ 99.00
Your Price : _____
5.0 oz EDP Sp $ 125.00
Your Price : _____

Gucci
Guilty Eau
1.6 oz EDT Sp $ 69.00
Your Price : _____
3.0 oz EDT Sp $ 88.00
Your Price : _____

Guerlain
Vetiver Guerlain
1.7 oz EDT Sp $ 50.00
Your Price : _____
3.4 oz EDT Sp $ 65.00
Your Price : _____

Guerlain
Habit Rouge
3.4 oz EDT Sp $ 75.00
Your Price : _____

Guerlain
L' Instant De Guerlain
4.2 oz EDT Sp $ 85.00
Your Price : _____

Guess
Man
1.7 oz EDT Sp $ 40.00
Your Price : _____
2.5 oz EDT Sp $ 55.00
Your Price : _____

Guess
Guess Suede
1.7 oz EDT Sp $ 40.00
Your Price : _____
2.5 oz EDT Sp $ 55.00
Your Price : _____

Guess
Marciano
3.4 oz EDT Sp $ 55.00
Your Price : _____

Guess
Night
1.7 oz EDT Sp $ 48.00
Your Price : _____
3.4 oz EDT Sp $ 65.00
Your Price : _____

Guess
Seductive Homme Blue
1.7 oz EDT Sp $ 48.00
Your Price : _____
3.4 oz EDT Sp $ 65.00
Your Price : _____

Guess
Seductive Homme
1.7 oz EDT Sp $ 48.00
Your Price : _____
3.4 oz EDT Sp $ 65.00
Your Price : _____

Guess
Night Acces
1.7 oz EDT Sp $ 48.00
Your Price : _____
3.4 oz EDT Sp $ 65.00
Your Price : _____

Guy Laroche
Drakkar Essence
1.7 oz EDT Sp $ 45.00
Your Price : _____
3.4 oz EDT Sp $ 65.00
Your Price : _____
6.7 oz EDT Sp $ 80.00
Your Price : _____

Guy Laroche
Drakkar Noir
1.7 oz EDT Sp $ 45.00
Your Price : _____
3.4 oz EDT Sp $ 65.00
Your Price : _____
6.7 oz EDT Sp $ 80.00
Your Price : _____

Guy Laroche
Drakkar Noir
Dynamik
1.7 oz EDT Sp $ 45.00
Your Price : _____
3.4 oz EDT Sp $ 60.00
Your Price : _____

Halston
1-12
4.2 oz EDT Sp $ 60.00
Your Price : _____

Halston
Z-14
2.5 oz EDT Sp $ 55.00
Your Price : _____
4.2 oz EDT Sp $ 65.00
Your Price : _____

Halston
Catalyst
3.4 oz EDT Sp $ 55.00
Your Price : _____

Hermes
Equipage
1.7 oz EDT Sp $ 69.00
Your Price : _____
3.4 oz EDT Sp $ 90.00
Your Price : _____

Hermes
Aroma D'Orange
Verte
3.3 oz EDT Sp $ 90.00
Your Price : _____

Hermes
Eau D'Hermes
3.4 oz EDT Sp $ 90.00
Your Price : _____

Hermes
Eau D' Gentiane Blanche
3.3 oz COL Sp $ 129.00
Your Price : _____

Hermes
Rocabar
1.7 oz EDT Sp $ 69.00
Your Price : _____
3.4 oz EDT Sp $ 138.00
Your Price : _____

Hermes
Terre D' hermes
1.6 oz EDT Sp $ 86.00
Your Price : _____
3.3 oz EDT Sp $ 119.00
Your Price : _____
6.7 oz EDT Sp $ 165.00
Your Price : _____

Hermes
Terre D'Hermes
2.5 oz EDP Sp $ 130.00
Your Price : _____
6.7 oz EDP Sp $ 220.00
Your Price : _____

Hermes
Voyage D'hermes
1.2 oz EDT Sp $ 98.00
Your Price : _____
3.3 oz EDT Sp $ 137.00
Your Price : _____

Hugo Boss
Boss Elements Aqua
1.7 oz EDT Sp $ 50.00
Your Price : _____
3.3 oz EDT Sp $ 65.00
Your Price : _____

Hugo Boss
Baldessarini
1.7 oz EDT Sp $ 59.00
Your Price : _____
3.4 oz EDT Sp $ 74.00
Your Price : _____

Hugo Boss
Baldessarini Del Mar
1.7 oz EDT Sp $ 59.00
Your Price : _____
3.4 oz EDT Sp $ 74.00
Your Price : _____

Hugo Boss
Boss Number One
1.7 oz EDT Sp $ 59.00
Your Price : _____
4.2 oz EDT Sp $ 74.00
Your Price : _____

Hugo Boss
Boss Bottled
1.7 oz EDT Sp $ 50.00
Your Price : _____
3.3 oz EDT Sp $ 79.00
Your Price : _____
6.7 oz EDT Sp $ 109.00
Your Price : _____

Hugo Boss
Boss Bottled Intense
3.3 oz EDT Sp $ 82.00
Your Price : _____

Hugo Boss
Boss Bottled Tonic
3.3 oz EDT Sp $ 86.00
Your Price : _____
6.7 oz EDT Sp $ 119.00
Your Price : _____

Hugo Boss
Boss Bottled Unlimited
3.3 oz EDT Sp $ 79.00
Your Price : _____

Hugo Boss
Boss The Scent
1.7 oz EDT Sp $ 69.00
Your Price : _____
3.4 oz EDT Sp $ 85.00
Your Price : _____
6.7 oz EDT Sp $ 119.00
Your Price : _____

Hugo Boss
Boss Bottled Night
1.7 oz EDT Sp $ 50.00
Your Price : _____
3.3 oz EDT Sp $ 79.00
Your Price : _____
6.7 oz EDT Sp $ 109.00
Your Price : _____

Hugo Boss
Boss in Motion Orange
1.3 oz EDT Sp $ 45.00
Your Price : _____
3.0 oz EDT Sp $ 65.00
Your Price : _____

Hugo Boss
Boss Elements
1.7 oz EDT Sp $ 50.00
Your Price : _____
3.3 oz EDT Sp $ 65.00
Your Price : _____

Hugo Boss
Hugo Man (Green Box)
2.5 oz EDT Sp $ 61.00
Your Price : _____
4.2 oz EDT Sp $ 76.00
Your Price : _____
6.7 oz EDT Sp $ 102.00
Your Price : _____

Hugo Boss
Hugo Dark Blue
2.5 oz EDT Sp $ 55.00
Your Price : _____
4.2 oz EDT Sp $ 75.00
Your Price : _____

Hugo Boss
Hugo Energize
2.5 oz EDT Sp $ 55.00
Your Price : _____
4.2 oz EDT Sp $ 75.00
Your Price : _____

Hugo Boss
Hugo Element
2.0 oz EDT Sp $ 40.00
Your Price : _____
3.0 oz EDT Sp $ 65.00
Your Price : _____

Hugo Boss
Hugo Red
2.5 oz EDT Sp $ 61.00
Your Price : _____
4.2 oz EDT Sp $ 76.00
Your Price : _____
6.7 oz EDT Sp $ 102.00
Your Price : _____

Hugo Boss
Hugo Just Different
2.5 oz EDT Sp $ 61.00
Your Price : _____
4.2 oz EDT Sp $ 76.00
Your Price : _____
6.7 oz EDT Sp $ 102.00
Your Price : _____

Hugo Boss
Boss Orange Man
2.0 oz EDT Sp $ 50.00
Your Price : _____
3.3 oz EDT Sp $ 65.00
Your Price : _____

Hugo Boss
Boss Pure
1.7 oz EDT Sp $ 50.00
Your Price : _____
2.5 oz EDT Sp $ 70.00
Your Price : _____

Hugo Boss
Boss Selection
1.6 oz EDT Sp $ 50.00
Your Price : _____
3.0 oz EDT Sp $ 67.00
Your Price : _____

Hugo Boss
Boss Soul
1.6 oz EDT Sp $ 55.00
Your Price : _____
3.0 oz EDT Sp $ 70.00
Your Price : _____

Hugo Boss
Boss Bottled Sport
1.6 oz EDT Sp $ 50.00
Your Price : _____
3.3 oz EDT Sp $ 75.00
Your Price : _____

Hugo Boss
Hugo XY
2.0 oz EDT Sp $ 50.00
Your Price : _____
3.3 oz EDT Sp $ 65.00
Your Price : _____

Hummer
Hummer
2.5 oz EDT Sp $ 50.00
Your Price : _____
4.2 oz EDT Sp $ 65.00
Your Price : _____

Hummer
Hummer 2
2.5 oz EDT Sp $ 50.00
Your Price : _____
4.2 oz EDT Sp $ 65.00
Your Price : _____

Hummer
Black
2.5 oz EDT Sp $ 50.00
Your Price : _____
4.2 oz EDT Sp $ 65.00
Your Price : _____

ILana Jivago
Jivago 24k
1.7 oz EDT Sp $ 50.00
Your Price : _____
3.4 oz EDT Sp $ 65.00
Your Price : _____

ILana Jivago
Connect
1.7 oz EDT Sp $ 52.00
Your Price : _____
3.4 oz EDT Sp $ 75.00
Your Price : _____

Issey Miyake
Intense
2.5 oz EDT Sp $ 65.00
Your Price : _____
4.2 oz EDT Sp $ 85.00
Your Price : _____

Issey Miyake
L'eau Bleue D' Issey
2.5 oz EDT Sp $ 70.00
Your Price : _____
4.2 oz EDT Sp $ 90.00
Your Price : _____

Issey Miyake
L'Eau D'Issey Pour Homme
2.5 oz EDT Sp $ 70.00
Your Price : _____
4.2 oz EDT Sp $ 90.00
Your Price : _____

Issey Miyake
L'eau D'Issey
1.3 oz EDT Sp $ 53.00
Your Price : _____
2.5 oz EDT Sp $ 70.00
Your Price : _____
4.2 oz EDT Sp $ 92.00
Your Price : _____
6.7 oz EDT Sp $ 114.00
Your Price : _____

Issey Miyake
Nuit D'Issey
2.5 oz EDT Sp $ 70.00
Your Price : _____
4.2 oz EDT Sp $ 92.00
Your Price : _____
6.7 oz EDT Sp $ 114.00
Your Price : _____

Issey Miyake
Sport
1.6 oz EDT Sp $ 64.00
Your Price : _____
3.3 oz EDT Sp $ 85.00
Your Price : _____
6.7 oz EDT Sp $ 112.00
Your Price : _____

Jacomo
Deep Blue
3.4 oz EDT Sp $ 70.00
Your Price : _____

Jacomo
Jacomo De Jacomo
3.4 oz EDT Sp $ 70.00
Your Price : _____

Jacomo
Jacomo De Jacomo Rouge
3.4 oz EDT Sp $ 70.00
Your Price : _____

Jacomo
Jacomo De Jacomo Silver
3.4 oz EDT Sp $ 70.00
Your Price : _____

Jacomo
Paradox
3.4 oz EDT Sp $ 70.00
Your Price : _____

Jacomo
Paradox Blue
3.4 oz EDT Sp $ 70.00
Your Price : _____

Jacomo
Paradox Green
3.4 oz EDT Sp $ 70.00
Your Price : _____

Jacques Bogart
Bogart
2.5 oz EDP Sp $ 60.00
Your Price : _____
4.2 oz EDT Sp $ 82.00
Your Price : _____

Jacques Bogart
Chevignon
2.5 oz EDP Sp $ 60.00
Your Price : _____
3.4 oz EDP Sp $ 82.00
Your Price : _____
4.2 oz EDT Sp $ 92.00
Your Price : _____

Jacques Bogart
Eau Fresh De Jacques
1.6 oz EDT Sp $ 60.00
Your Price : _____

Jacques Bogart
One Man Show
3.4 oz EDT Sp $ 55.00
Your Price : _____

Jacques Evard
Remittance
3.4 oz EDT Sp $ 55.00
Your Price : _____

Jacques Fath
Yang
1.6 oz EDT Sp $ 60.00
Your Price : _____

Jaguar
Classic
3.4 oz EDT Sp $ 69.00
Your Price : _____

Jaguar
Classic Black
3.4 oz EDT Sp $ 69.00
Your Price : _____

Jaguar
Extreme
3.4 oz EDT Sp $ 69.00
Your Price : _____

Jaguar
Fresh
3.4 oz EDT Sp $ 69.00
Your Price : _____

Jaguar
Classic Red
3.4 oz EDT Sp $ 69.00
Your Price : _____

Jaguar
For Men
3.4 oz EDT Sp $ 69.00
Your Price : _____

Jaguar
Performance
3.4 oz EDT Sp $ 69.00
Your Price : _____

Jaguar
Performance Intense
3.4 oz EDT Sp $ 58.00
Your Price : _____

Jaguar
Prestige
3.4 oz EDT Sp $ 69.00
Your Price : _____

Jaguar
Pure Instinct
3.4 oz EDT Sp $ 69.00
Your Price : _____

Jaguar
Vision
3.4 oz EDT Sp $ 69.00
Your Price : _____

Jean Paul Gaultier
Le Male
2.5 oz EDT Sp $ 71.00
Your Price : _____
4.2 oz EDT Sp $ 92.00
Your Price : _____
6.7 oz EDT Sp $ 116.00
Your Price : _____

Jean Paul Gaultier
Le Beau Male
2.5 oz EDT Sp $ 60.00
Your Price : _____
4.2 oz EDT Sp $ 80.00
Your Price : _____

Jean Paul Gaultier
Fleur Du Male
2.5 oz EDT Sp $ 60.00
Your Price : _____
4.2 oz EDT Sp $ 80.00
Your Price : _____

Jean Paul Gaultier
Summer Fragrance
4.2 oz EDT Sp $ 75.00
Your Price : _____

Jean Paul Gaultier
Le Male Terrible
1.3 oz EDT Sp $ 48.00
Your Price : _____
2.5 oz EDT Sp $ 64.00
Your Price : _____
4.2 oz EDT Sp $ 85.00
Your Price : _____

Jean Paul Gaultier
Le Male In Love
4.2 oz EDT Sp $ 80.00
Your Price : _____

Jean Paul Gaultier
Kokorico
1.7 oz EDT Sp $ 60.00
Your Price : _____
3.4 oz EDT Sp $ 80.00
Your Price : _____

Jean Paul Gaultier
Kokorico by Night
1.7 oz EDT Sp $ 60.00
Your Price : _____
3.4 oz EDT Sp $ 80.00
Your Price : _____

Jesus Del Pozo
Halloween Man
4.2 oz EDT Sp $ 60.00
Your Price : _____

Jesus Del Pozo
Quasar
4.2 oz EDT Sp $ 58.00
Your Price : _____

Jil Sander
Sport
2.5 oz EDT Sp $ 55.00
Your Price : _____
4.2 oz EDT Sp $ 75.00
Your Price : _____

Jil Sander
Sander
2.5 oz EDT Sp $ 55.00
Your Price : _____
4.2 oz EDT Sp $ 75.00
Your Price : _____

Jil Sander
Man
3.0 oz EDT Sp $ 75.00
Your Price : _____

Jimmy Choo
Jimmy Choo Man Ice
1.7 oz EDT Sp $ 68.00
Your Price : _____
3.3 oz EDT Sp $ 88.00
Your Price : _____

Jimmy Choo
Jimmy Choo Man
1.7 oz EDT Sp $ 68.00
Your Price : _____
3.3 oz EDT Sp $ 88.00
Your Price : _____
6.7 oz EDT Sp $ 110.00
Your Price : _____

Jimmy Choo
Jimmy Choo Man Intense
3.3 oz EDT Sp $ 92.00
Your Price : _____

John Mac Steed
Original Blue Tartan
3.3 oz EDT Sp $ 48.00
Your Price : _____

John Mac Steed
Original Green Tartan
3.3 oz EDT Sp $ 48.00
Your Price : _____

John Mac Steed
Original Red Tartan
3.3 oz EDT Sp $ 48.00
Your Price : _____

John Mac Steed
Safari Camel
3.3 oz EDT Sp $ 48.00
Your Price : _____

John Mac Steed
Safari White
3.3 oz EDT Sp $ 48.00
Your Price : _____

John Varvatos
John Varvatos
2.5 oz EDT Sp $ 69.00
Your Price : _____
4.2 oz EDT Sp $ 89.00
Your Price : _____
6.7 oz EDT Sp $ 105.00
Your Price : _____

John Varvatos
Vintage
2.5 oz EDT Sp $ 69.00
Your Price : _____
4.2 oz EDT Sp $ 89.00
Your Price : _____
6.7 oz EDT Sp $ 105.00
Your Price : _____

John Varvatos
Artisan
2.5 oz EDT Sp $ 69.00
Your Price : _____
4.2 oz EDT Sp $ 89.00
Your Price : _____
6.7 oz EDT Sp $ 105.00
Your Price : _____

John Varvatos
Artisan Black
2.5 oz EDT Sp $ 69.00
Your Price : _____
4.2 oz EDT Sp $ 89.00
Your Price : _____
6.7 oz EDT Sp $ 105.00
Your Price : _____

John Varvatos
Artisan Aqua
2.5 oz EDT Sp $ 69.00
Your Price : _____
4.2 oz EDT Sp $ 89.00
Your Price : _____

John Varvatos
Dark Rebel
2.5 oz EDT Sp $ 69.00
Your Price : _____
4.2 oz EDT Sp $ 89.00
Your Price : _____

John Varvatos
Star USA
1.7 oz EDT Sp $ 55.00
Your Price : _____
3.4 oz EDT Sp $ 70.00
Your Price : _____

Joop
Nightflight
2.5 oz EDT Sp $ 50.00
Your Price : _____
4.2 oz EDT Sp $ 70.00
Your Price : _____

Joop
Joop Homme
2.5 oz EDT Sp $ 50.00
Your Price : _____
4.2 oz EDT Sp $ 70.00
Your Price : _____
6.7 oz EDT Sp $ 90.00
Your Price : _____

Joop
Go
1.7 oz EDT Sp $ 45.00
Your Price : _____
3.4 oz EDT Sp $ 60.00
Your Price : _____

Joop
Jump
1.7 oz EDT Sp $ 45.00
Your Price : _____
3.3 oz EDT Sp $ 60.00
Your Price : _____

Joop
Splash Summer Ticket
3.8 oz EDT Sp $ 70.00
Your Price : _____

Joop
Hot contact
4.2 oz EDT Sp $ 75.00
Your Price : _____

Joop
Go Hot Contact
4.2 oz EDT Sp $ 75.00
Your Price : _____

Jovan
Black Musk
3.0 oz EDC Sp $ 40.00
Your Price : _____

Jovan
White Musk
3.0 oz EDC Sp $ 40.00
Your Price : _____

Jovan
Musk
3.0 oz EDC Sp $ 45.00
Your Price : _____

Jovan
Sex Appeal
3.0 oz EDC Sp $ 45.00
Your Price : _____

Juicy Couture
Dirty English
1.7 oz EDT Sp $ 45.00
Your Price : _____
3.4 oz EDT Sp $ 60.00
Your Price : _____

Karl Lagerfeld
Classic
2.0 oz EDT Sp $ 50.00
Your Price : _____
4.2 oz EDT Sp $ 75.00
Your Price : _____

Karl Lagerfeld
Photo
2.0 oz EDT Sp $ 50.00
Your Price : _____
4.2 oz EDT Sp $ 75.00
Your Price : _____

Karl Lagerfeld
Jako
2.0 oz EDT Sp $ 50.00
Your Price : _____
4.2 oz EDT Sp $ 75.00
Your Price : _____

Kenneth Cole
Vintage Black
1.7 oz EDT Sp $ 50.00
Your Price : _____
3.4 oz EDT Sp $ 70.00
Your Price : _____

Kenneth Cole
Black
1.7 oz EDT Sp $ 50.00
Your Price : _____
3.4 oz EDT Sp $ 78.00
Your Price : _____

Kenneth Cole
Connected
2.5 oz EDT Sp $ 55.00
Your Price : _____
4.2 oz EDT Sp $ 70.00
Your Price : _____

Kenneth Cole
Mankind
1.7 oz EDT Sp $ 60.00
Your Price : _____
3.4 oz EDT Sp $ 80.00
Your Price : _____
6.7 oz EDT Sp $ 100.00
Your Price : _____

Kenneth Cole
Mankind Hero
1.7 oz EDT Sp $ 60.00
Your Price : _____
3.4 oz EDT Sp $ 80.00
Your Price : _____

Kenneth Cole
Mankind Ultimate
1.7 oz EDT Sp $ 60.00
Your Price : _____
3.4 oz EDT Sp $ 80.00
Your Price : _____

Kenneth Cole
Reaction
1.7 oz EDT Sp $ 50.00
Your Price : _____
3.4 oz EDT Sp $ 65.00
Your Price : _____

Kenneth Cole
Reaction T-Shirt
1.7 oz EDT Sp $ 50.00
Your Price : _____
3.4 oz EDT Sp $ 65.00
Your Price : _____

Kenneth Cole
Reaction Thermal
3.4 oz EDT Sp $ 77.00
Your Price : _____

Kenneth Cole
RSVP
1.7 oz EDT Sp $ 55.00
Your Price : _____
3.4 oz EDT Sp $ 77.00
Your Price : _____

Kenneth Cole
Signature
1.7 oz EDT Sp $ 55.00
Your Price : _____
3.4 oz EDT Sp $ 77.00
Your Price : _____

Kenzo
Pour Homme
1.7 oz EDT Sp $ 63.00
Your Price : _____
3.4 oz EDT Sp $ 86.00
Your Price : _____

Kenzo
Homme Sport
1.7 oz EDT Sp $ 63.00
Your Price : _____
3.4 oz EDT Sp $ 85.00
Your Price : _____

Kenzo
Homme Woody
1.7 oz EDT Sp $ 61.00
Your Price : _____
3.4 oz EDT Sp $ 85.00
Your Price : _____

Kenzo
Homme Night
1.7 oz EDT Sp $ 63.00
Your Price : _____
3.4 oz EDT Sp $ 85.00
Your Price : _____

Kenzo
Kenzo L'eau Par Kenzo
1.7 oz EDT Sp $ 61.00
Your Price : _____
3.4 oz EDT Sp $ 75.00
Your Price : _____

Kenzo
Jungle
3.4 oz EDT Sp $ 75.00
Your Price : _____

Kenzo
Kenzo Power
4.2 oz EDT Sp $ 75.00
Your Price : _____

Kenzo
Kenzo Tokyo
1.7 oz EDT Sp $ 55.00
Your Price : _____
3.4 oz EDT Sp $ 75.00
Your Price : _____

Kristel Saint Martin
Parfum D'Or Homme
3.4 oz EDT Sp $ 55.00
Your Price : _____

Kristel Saint Martin
K S M
3.4 oz EDT Sp $ 55.00
Your Price : _____

Krizia
Krizia Time
1.7 oz EDT Sp $ 30.00
Your Price : _____
3.4 oz EDT Sp $ 45.00
Your Price : _____

Krizia
Krizia
3.4 oz EDT Sp $ 55.00
Your Price : _____

Lacoste
L!ve
1.3 oz EDT Sp $ 45.00
Your Price : _____
3.3 oz EDT Sp $ 70.00
Your Price : _____

Lacoste
L.12.12 Jaune (Yellow)
1.6 oz EDT Sp $ 59.00
Your Price : _____
3.3 oz EDT Sp $ 74.00
Your Price : _____

Lacoste
Booster
2.5 oz EDT Sp $ 45.00
Your Price : _____
4.2 oz EDT Sp $ 70.00
Your Price : _____

Lacoste
Pour Homme
1.7 oz EDT Sp $ 55.00
Your Price : _____
3.4 oz EDT Sp $ 70.00
Your Price : _____

Lacoste
Cool Play
2.5 oz EDT Sp $ 45.00
Your Price : _____
4.2 oz EDT Sp $ 70.00
Your Price : _____

Lacoste
Challenge
1.6 oz EDT Sp $ 45.00
Your Price : _____
2.5 oz EDT Sp $ 55.00
Your Price : _____
3.0 oz EDT Sp $ 65.00
Your Price : _____

Lacoste
Elegance
1.6 oz EDT Sp $ 45.00
Your Price : _____
3.0 oz EDT Sp $ 70.00
Your Price : _____

Lacoste
Essential
2.5 oz EDT Sp $ 62.00
Your Price : _____
4.2 oz EDT Sp $ 75.00
Your Price : _____

Lacoste
Hot Play
2.5 oz EDT Sp $ 45.00
Your Price : _____
4.2 oz EDT Sp $ 70.00
Your Price : _____

Lacoste
Essential Sport
2.5 oz EDT Sp $ 62.00
Your Price : _____
4.2 oz EDT Sp $ 75.00
Your Price : _____

Lacoste
Style in Play
1.6 oz EDT Sp $ 45.00
Your Price : _____
2.5 oz EDT Sp $ 55.00
Your Price : _____
4.2 oz EDT Sp $ 70.00
Your Price : _____

Lacoste
L.12.12 Blanc (White)
1.0 oz EDT Sp $ 40.00
Your Price : _____
3.3 oz EDT Sp $ 74.00
Your Price : _____
5.9 oz EDT Sp $ 92.00
Your Price : _____

Lacoste
L.12.12 Noir (Black)
1.0 oz EDT Sp $ 40.00
Your Price : _____
3.3 oz EDT Sp $ 74.00
Your Price : _____
5.9 oz EDT Sp $ 92.00
Your Price : __

Lacoste
L.12.12 Rouge (Red)
1.0 oz EDT Sp $ 40.00
Your Price : _____
3.3 oz EDT Sp $ 74.00
Your Price : _____
5.9 oz EDT Sp $ 92.00
Your Price : __

Lacoste
L.12.12 Bleu (Blue)
1.0 oz EDT Sp $ 40.00
Your Price : _____
3.3 oz EDT Sp $ 74.00
Your Price : _____
5.9 oz EDT Sp $ 92.00
Your Price : __

Lacoste
L.12.12 Vert (Green)
1.0 oz EDT Sp $ 40.00
Your Price : _____
3.3 oz EDT Sp $ 74.00
Your Price : _____
5.9 oz EDT Sp $ 92.00
Your Price : __

Lacoste Original
Lacoste
3.4 oz EDT Sp $ 58.00
Your Price : _____

Lacoste
L'Homme
1.7 oz EDT Sp $ 62.00
Your Price : _____
3.4 oz EDT Sp $ 78.00
Your Price : _____

Lalique
Pour Homme (Lion)
2.5 oz EDP Sp $ 115.00
Your Price : _____
4.2 oz EDP Sp $ 135.00
Your Price : _____

Lalique
Pour Homme (Lion)
2.5 oz EDT Sp $ 97.00
Your Price : _____
4.2 oz EDT Sp $ 125.00
Your Price : _____

Lalique
Pour Homme (Equus)
2.5 oz EDP Sp $ 115.00
Your Price : _____
4.2 oz EDP Sp $ 135.00
Your Price : _____

Lalique
Pour Homme (Equus)
2.5 oz EDT Sp $ 97.00
Your Price : _____
4.2 oz EDT Sp $ 125.00
Your Price : _____

Lalique
White
2.5 oz EDT Sp $ 101.00
Your Price : _____
4.2 oz EDT Sp $ 125.00
Your Price : _____

Lalique
L'Insomis
1.7 oz EDT Sp $ 95.00
Your Price : _____
3.3 oz EDT Sp $ 125.00
Your Price : _____

Lalique
Hommage A L'Homme Voyageur
1.7 oz EDT Sp $ 92.00
Your Price : _____
3.3 oz EDT Sp $ 125.00
Your Price : _____

Lancome
Hypnose Homme
1.7 oz EDT Sp $ 50.00
Your Price : _____
2.5 oz EDT Sp $ 70.00
Your Price : _____

Lancome
Miracle Homme
1.7 oz EDT Sp $ 50.00
Your Price : _____
3.4 oz EDT Sp $ 70.00
Your Price : _____

Lancome
Miracle L' Aquatonic
1.7 oz EDT Sp $ 50.00
Your Price : _____
4.2 oz EDT Sp $ 72.00
Your Price : _____

Lancome
Sagamore
1.7 oz EDT Sp $ 50.00
Your Price :
3.3 oz EDT Sp $ 72.00
Your Price :

Lanvin
Arpege Pour Homme
1.7 oz EDT Sp $ 55.00
Your Price :
3.4 oz EDT Sp $ 70.00
Your Price :

Lanvin
L' Homme
1.7 oz EDT Sp $ 55.00
Your Price :
3.4 oz EDT Sp $ 70.00
Your Price :

Lanvin
Avant Garde
1.7 oz EDT Sp $ 55.00
Your Price :
3.4 oz EDT Sp $ 70.00
Your Price :

Lanvin
Lanvin for Men
1.7 oz EDT Sp $ 55.00
Your Price :
3.4 oz EDT Sp $ 70.00
Your Price :

Lanvin
L' Homme Sport
1.7 oz EDT Sp $ 50.00
Your Price :
3.4 oz EDT Sp $ 70.00
Your Price :

Lanvin
Oxygene
1.7 oz EDT Sp $ 55.00
Your Price :
3.4 oz EDT Sp $ 75.00
Your Price :

Lanvin
Vetyver
1.7 oz EDT Sp $ 50.00
Your Price :
3.4 oz EDT Sp $ 65.00
Your Price :

Lapidus
Pour Homme
3.3 oz EDT Sp $ 50.00
Your Price :

Laura Biagiotti
Roma Uomo
4.2 oz EDT Sp $ 60.00
Your Price :

Liz Claiborne
Appeal
1.0 oz EDT Sp $ 30.00
Your Price :
2.5 oz EDT Sp $ 45.00
Your Price :

Liz Claiborne
Curve Connect
4.2oz EDT Sp $ 54.00
Your Price :

Liz Claiborne
Spark
1.7 oz EDT Sp $ 55.00
Your Price :
3.4 oz EDT Sp $ 70.00
Your Price :

Liz Claiborne
Bora Bora
1.7 oz EDT Sp $ 45.00
Your Price :
3.4 oz EDT Sp $ 60.00
Your Price :

Liz Claiborne
Bora Bora Exotic
3.4 oz EDT Sp $ 55.00
Your Price :

Liz Claiborne
Claiborne
3.4 oz EDT Sp $ 55.00
Your Price :

Liz Claiborne
Sport
1.7 oz EDT Sp $ 45.00
Your Price :
3.4 oz EDT Sp $ 60.00
Your Price :

Liz Claiborne
Curve
2.5 oz EDT Sp $ 35.00
Your Price :
4.2 oz EDT Sp $ 54.00
Your Price :
6.7 oz EDT Sp $ 70.00
Your Price :

Liz Claiborne
Curve Chill
2.5 oz EDT Sp $ 35.00
Your Price :
4.2 oz EDT Sp $ 54.00
Your Price :

Liz Claiborne
Curve Crush
2.5 oz EDT Sp $ 35.00
Your Price :
4.2 oz EDT Sp $ 54.00
Your Price :
6.7 oz EDT Sp $ 70.00
Your Price :

Liz Claiborne
Curve Kicks
2.5 oz EDT Sp $ 35.00
Your Price : _____
4.2 oz EDT Sp $ 54.00
Your Price : _____

Liz Claiborne
Curve Soul
1.7 oz EDT Sp $ 45.00
Your Price : _____
3.4 oz EDT Sp $ 60.00
Your Price : _____

Liz Claiborne
Curve Wave
2.5 oz EDT Sp $ 35.00
Your Price : _____
4.2 oz EDT Sp $ 54.00
Your Price : _____

Liz Claiborne
Curve Black
4.2 oz EDT Sp $ 54.00
Your Price : _____

Liz Claiborne
Curve Sport
4.2 oz EDT Sp $ 54.00
Your Price : _____

Liz Claiborne
Lucky Number 6
1.7 oz EDT Sp $ 45.00
Your Price : _____
3.4 oz EDT Sp $ 60.00
Your Price : _____

Liz Claiborne
Lucky You
1.7 oz EDT Sp $ 45.00
Your Price : _____
3.4 oz EDT Sp $ 60.00
Your Price : _____

Liz Claiborne
Mambo
1.7 oz EDT Sp $ 45.00
Your Price : _____
3.4 oz EDT Sp $ 60.00
Your Price : _____

Liz Claiborne
Realities
1.7 oz EDT Sp $ 45.00
Your Price : _____
3.4 oz EDT Sp $ 60.00
Your Price : _____

Liz Claiborne
Realities Graphite Blue
1.7 oz EDT Sp $ 45.00
Your Price : _____
3.4 oz EDT Sp $ 60.00
Your Price : _____

Lolita Lempicka
Au Masculin
1.7 oz EDT Sp $ 48.00
Your Price : _____
3.4 oz EDT Sp $ 65.00
Your Price : _____

Lolita Lempicka
Au Masculin Fraicheur
1.7 oz EDT Sp $ 45.00
Your Price : _____
3.4 oz EDT Sp $ 60.00
Your Price : _____

Lomani
Pour Homme
3.4 oz EDT Sp $ 30.00
Your Price : _____

Lomani
Code
3.3 oz EDT Sp $ 30.00
Your Price : _____

Lomani
Best
3.3 oz EDT Sp $ 30.00
Your Price : _____

Lomani
Ignition
3.3 oz EDT Sp $ 40.00
Your Price : _____

Lomani
Mister Lomani
3.3 oz EDT Sp $ 30.00
Your Price : _____

Lomani
AB Spirit
3.3 oz EDT Sp $ 35.00
Your Price : _____

Lomani
Amitabh Bachchan
3.3 oz EDT Sp $ 35.00
Your Price : _____

Lomani
Spirit Millionaire
3.4 oz EDT Sp $ 55.00
Your Price : _____

Marc Ecko
3.4 oz EDT Sp $ 50.00
Your Price : _____

Marc Ecko
Blue
3.4 oz EDT Sp $ 50.00
Your Price : _____

Marc Ecko
Green
3.4 oz EDT Sp $ 50.00
Your Price : _____

Marc Ecko
UNLTD.
3.4 oz EDT Sp $ 50.00
Your Price : _____

Marc Ecko
UNLTD. The Exhibit
3.4 oz EDT Sp $ 50.00
Your Price : _____

Marc Jacobs
Marc Jacobs
2.5 oz EDT Sp $ 55.00
Your Price : _____
4.2 oz EDT Sp $ 70.00
Your Price : _____

Marc Jacobs
Bang
1.7 oz EDT Sp $ 55.00
Your Price : _____
3.4 oz EDT Sp $ 70.00
Your Price : _____

Marc Jacobs
Bang Bang
1.7 oz EDT Sp $ 55.00
Your Price : _____
3.4 oz EDT Sp $ 70.00
Your Price : _____

Marilyn Miglin
Pheromone
3.4 oz EDT Sp $ 59.00
Your Price : _____

Michael Jordan
Flight
3.4 oz EDT Sp $ 48.00
Your Price : _____

Michael Jordan
Flight Sport
3.4 oz EDT Sp $ 48.00
Your Price : _____

Michael Jordan
23
3.4 oz EDT Sp $ 48.00
Your Price : _____

Michael Jordan
3.4 oz EDT Sp $ 48.00
Your Price : _____

Michael Jordan
Jordan by Michael
3.4 oz EDT Sp $ 48.00
Your Price : _____

Michael Jordan
Legend
3.4 oz EDT Sp $ 45.00
Your Price : _____

Michael Kors
Michael Kors
2.5 oz EDT Sp $ 50.00
Your Price : _____
4.2 oz EDT Sp $ 75.00
Your Price : _____

Michael Kors
Extreme Blue
1.4 oz EDT Sp $ 50.00
Your Price : _____
2.3 oz EDT Sp $ 65.00
Your Price : _____
4.0 oz EDT Sp $ 80.00
Your Price : _____

Michael Kors
Extreme Night
1.4 oz EDT Sp $ 50.00
Your Price : _____
2.3 oz EDT Sp $ 65.00
Your Price : _____
4.0 oz EDT Sp $ 80.00
Your Price : _____

Michel Germain
Sexual Pour Homme
2.5 oz EDT Sp $ 55.00
Your Price : _____
4.2 oz EDT Sp $ 75.00
Your Price : _____

Michel Germain
Sexual Sugar Daddy
2.5 oz EDT Sp $ 60.00
Your Price : _____

Michel Germain
Sexual Nights
2.5 oz EDT Sp $ 55.00
Your Price : _____
4.2 oz EDT Sp $ 75.00
Your Price : _____

Michel Germain
Sexual Secret Man
2.5 oz EDT Sp $ 55.00
Your Price : _____
4.2 oz EDT Sp $ 75.00
Your Price : _____

Michel Germain
Sexual Fresh
2.5 oz EDT Sp $ 55.00
Your Price : _____
4.2 oz EDT Sp $ 75.00
Your Price : _____

Michel Germain
Sexual Noir
2.5 oz EDT Sp $ 55.00
Your Price : _____
4.2 oz EDT Sp $ 75.00
Your Price : _____

Michel Germain
Sexual Steel
2.5 oz EDT Sp $ 55.00
Your Price : _____
4.2 oz EDT Sp $ 75.00
Your Price : _____

Michel Germain
Deauville Pour Homme
2.5 oz EDT Sp $ 60.00
Your Price : _____

Mont Blanc
Legend
1.7 oz EDT Sp $ 68.00
Your Price : _____
3.3 oz EDT Sp $ 88.00
Your Price : _____
5.0 oz EDT Sp $ 105.00
Your Price : _____
6.7 oz EDT Sp $ 110.00
Your Price : _____

Mont Blanc
Legend Special Edition
(Blue Box)
3.3 oz EDT Sp $ 70.00
Your Price : _____

Mont Blanc
Legend Intense
1.7 oz EDT Sp $ 60.00
Your Price : _____
3.3 oz EDT Sp $ 92.00
Your Price : _____

Mont Blanc
Exceptionnel
1.7 oz EDT Sp $ 50.00
Your Price : _____
2.5 oz EDT Sp $ 65.00
Your Price : _____

Mont Blanc
Individuelle
1.7 oz EDT Sp $ 50.00
Your Price : _____
2.5 oz EDT Sp $ 65.00
Your Price : _____

Mont Blanc
Presence Cool
1.7 oz EDT Sp $ 50.00
Your Price : _____
2.5 oz EDT Sp $ 65.00
Your Price : _____

Mont Blanc
Presence
1.7 oz EDT Sp $ 50.00
Your Price : _____
2.5 oz EDT Sp $ 65.00
Your Price : _____

Mont Blanc
Starwalker
1.7 oz EDT Sp $ 50.00
Your Price : _____
2.5 oz EDT Sp $ 65.00
Your Price : _____

Mont Blanc
Legend Special Edition
3.3 oz EDT Sp $ 70.00
Your Price : _____

Mont Blanc
Emblem
1.7 oz EDT Sp $ 68.00
Your Price : _____
3.3 oz EDT Sp $ 88.00
Your Price : _____

Mont Blanc
Emblem
1.7 oz EDT Sp $ 70.00
Your Price : _____
3.3 oz EDT Sp $ 90.00
Your Price : _____

Mont Blanc
Legend Spirit
1.7 oz EDT Sp $ 68.00
Your Price : _____
3.3 oz EDT Sp $ 88.00
Your Price : _____
6.7 oz EDT Sp $ 110.00
Your Price : _____

Moschino
Uomo
2.5 oz EDT Sp $ 45.00
Your Price : _____
4.2 oz EDT Sp $ 60.00
Your Price : _____

Moschino
Friends
2.5 oz EDT Sp $ 45.00
Your Price : _____
4.2 oz EDT Sp $ 60.00
Your Price : _____

Moschino
Forever
1.7 oz EDT Sp $ 55.00
Your Price : _____
3.4 oz EDT Sp $ 70.00
Your Price : _____

Moschino
Forever Sailing
1.7 oz EDT Sp $ 55.00
Your Price : _____
3.4 oz EDT Sp $ 70.00
Your Price : _____

Narciso Rodriguez
For Him
1.6 oz EDT Sp $ 50.00
Your Price : _____
3.3 oz EDT Sp $ 89.00
Your Price : _____

Narciso Rodriguez
Bleu Noir
3.3 oz EDT Sp $ 89.00
Your Price : _____

Nautica
Nautica
1.7 oz EDT Sp $ 40.00
Your Price : _____
3.4 oz EDT Sp $ 55.00
Your Price : _____

Nautica
Blue
3.4 oz EDT Sp $ 50.00
Your Price : _____

Nautica
Competition
2.5 oz EDT Sp $ 40.00
Your Price : _____
4.2 oz EDT Sp $ 55.00
Your Price : _____

Nautica
Island Voyage
1.7 oz EDT Sp $ 40.00
Your Price : _____
3.4 oz EDT Sp $ 55.00
Your Price : _____

Nautica
Latitude Longitude
1.7 oz EDT Sp $ 45.00
Your Price : _____
3.4 oz EDT Sp $ 60.00
Your Price : _____

Nautica
Oceans
1.7 oz EDT Sp $ 40.00
Your Price : _____
3.4 oz EDT Sp $ 55.00
Your Price : _____

Nautica
Pure
1.7 oz EDT Sp $ 40.00
Your Price : _____
3.4 oz EDT Sp $ 55.00
Your Price : _____

Nautica
Sunset Voyage
1.7 oz EDT Sp $ 40.00
Your Price : _____
3.4 oz EDT Sp $ 55.00
Your Price : _____

Nautica
Voyage
1.7 oz EDT Sp $ 40.00
Your Price : _____
3.4 oz EDT Sp $ 55.00
Your Price : _____

Nautica
Voyage N-83
1.7 oz EDT Sp $ 34.99
Your Price : _____
3.4 oz EDT Sp $ 62.50
Your Price : _____

Nautica
Voyage Sport
1.7 oz EDT Sp $ 34.99
Your Price : _____
3.4 oz EDT Sp $ 62.50
Your Price : _____

Nautica
Voyage Summer
3.4 oz EDT Sp $ 65.00
Your Price : _____

Nautica
White Sail
1.7 oz EDT Sp $ 40.00
Your Price : _____
3.4 oz EDT Sp $ 55.00
Your Price : _____

Nautica
Classic
1.7 oz EDT Sp $ 35.00
Your Price : _____
3.4 oz EDT Sp $ 50.00
Your Price : _____

Nautica
Competition (Blue Box)
2.4 oz EDT Sp $ 40.00
Your Price : _____
4.2 oz EDT Sp $ 55.00
Your Price : _____

Nautica
Aqua Rush
1.7 oz EDT Sp $ 45.00
Your Price : _____
3.4 oz EDT Sp $ 60.00
Your Price : _____

Johan B.
CLUB for men
3.4 oz EDT Sp $ 90.00

Johan B.
CLUB GENTLEMAN
3.4 oz EDT Sp $ 90.00

Johan B.
CLUB V.I.P.
3.4 oz EDT Sp $ 90.00

Johan B.
ELEGANT DIPLOMATE
3.4 oz EDT Sp $ 98.00

Johan B.
ELEGANT GENTLEMAN
3.4 oz EDT Sp $ 92.00

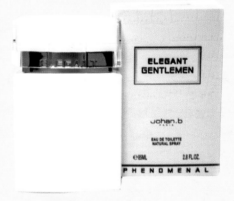

Johan B.
ELEGANT Gentlemen Phenomenal
3.4 oz EDT Sp $ 125.00

Karen Low
BLUE NIGHT
3.4 oz EDT Sp $ 72.00

Karen Low
CODE 37 men
3.4 oz EDT Sp $ 80.00

Karen Low
CODE 37 SPORT
3.4 oz EDT Sp $ 48.00

Karen Low
INDESCENCE BLACK
3.4 oz EDT Sp $ 72.00

Karen Low
KL BLACK
3.4 oz EDT Sp $ 48.00

Karen Low
KL CONNECT
3.4 oz EDT Sp $ 48.00

Karen Low
XCHANGE
3.4 oz EDT Sp $ 68.00

Karen Low
HOPE for men
3.4 oz EDT Sp $72.00

Karen Low
XCHANGE COOL
3.4 oz EDT Sp $ 68.00

Karen Low
XCHANGE UNLIMITED WHITE
3.4 oz EDT Sp $ 48.00

Karen Low
XCHANGE WONDERMAN
3.4 oz EDT Sp $ 72.00

Karen Low
XCHANGE DARK NIGHT
3.4 oz EDT Sp $ 70.00

Karen Low
XCHANGE UNLIMITED
3.4 oz EDT Sp $ 70.00

Karen Low
XCHANGE UNLIMITED GOLD
3.4 oz EDT Sp $ 69.00

Viviane Vendelle
World Extension END-OFF
3.4 oz EDT Sp $ 78.00

Nautica
Aqua Rush Gold
1.7 oz EDT Sp $ 45.00
Your Price : _____
3.4 oz EDT Sp $ 60.00
Your Price : _____

Nautica
Life
1.7 oz EDT Sp $ 34.99
Your Price : _____
3.4 oz EDT Sp $ 62.50
Your Price : _____

Nina Ricci
Memoire D' homme
2 oz EDT Sp $ 60.00
Your Price : _____
3.4 oz EDT Sp $ 75.00
Your Price : _____

Nina Ricci
Ricci Club
3.4 oz EDT Sp $ 75.00
Your Price : _____

Nina Ricci
Signoricci
3.4 oz EDT Sp $ 75.00
Your Price : _____

Ocean Pacific
Endless
1.7 oz EDT Sp $ 35.00
Your Price : _____
2.5 oz EDT Sp $ 53.00
Your Price : _____

Ocean Pacific
Ocean Pacific
1.7 oz EDT Sp $ 35.00
Your Price : _____
2.5 oz EDT Sp $ 53.00
Your Price : _____

Ocean Pacific
Op Juice
1.7 oz EDT Sp $ 35.00
Your Price : _____
2.5 oz EDT Sp $ 53.00
Your Price : _____

Ocean Pacific
Op Juice Blend
1.7 oz EDT Sp $ 35.00
Your Price : _____
2.5 oz EDT Sp $ 53.00
Your Price : _____

Oleg Cassini
Cassini
1.7 oz EDT Sp $ 35.00
Your Price : _____
3.4 oz EDT Sp $ 62.00
Your Price : _____

Oleg Cassini
Reporter
1.7 oz EDT Sp $ 35.00
Your Price : _____
3.4 oz EDT Sp $ 62.00
Your Price : _____

Orlane
Derrick Black
3.4 oz EDT Sp $ 65.00
Your Price : _____

Oscar De La Renta
Oscar
1.6 oz EDT Sp $ 40.00
Your Price : _____
3.4 oz EDT Sp $ 55.00
Your Price : _____

Oscar De La Renta
Oscar Pour Lui
1.6 oz EDT Sp $ 40.00
Your Price : _____
3.0 oz EDT Sp $ 55.00
Your Price : _____

Paco Rabanne
Pour Homme
1.7 oz EDT Sp $ 50.00
Your Price : _____
3.4 oz EDT Sp $ 74.00
Your Price : _____
6.7 oz EDT Sp $ 92.00
Your Price : _____

Paco Rabanne
Energy
3.4 oz EDT Sp $ 60.00
Your Price : _____

Paco Rabanne
Invictus
1.7 oz EDT Sp $ 66.00
Your Price : _____
3.4 oz EDT Sp $ 86.00
Your Price : _____
5.1 oz EDT Sp $ 110.00
Your Price : _____

Paco Rabanne
Invictus Intense
1.7 oz EDT Sp $ 70.00
Your Price : _____
3.4 oz EDT Sp $ 93.00
Your Price : _____

Paco Rabanne
Invictus Aqua
1.7 oz EDT Sp $ 64.00
Your Price : _____
3.4 oz EDT Sp $ 84.00
Your Price : _____

Paco Rabanne
One Million Prive
3.4 oz EDP Sp $ 90.00
Your Price : _____

Paco Rabanne
One Million
1.7 oz EDT Sp $ 66.00
Your Price : _____
3.4 oz EDT Sp $ 86.00
Your Price : _____
6.7 oz EDT Sp $ 114.00
Your Price : _____

Paco Rabanne
One Million Cologne
4.2 oz EDT Sp $ 86.00
Your Price : _____

Paco Rabanne
One Million Intense
1.7 oz EDT Sp $ 65.00
Your Price : _____
3.4 oz EDT Sp $ 85.00
Your Price : _____

Paco Rabanne
XS Sensual Skin Summer
1.7 oz EDT Sp $ 45.00
Your Price : _____
3.4 oz EDT Sp $ 55.00
Your Price : _____

Paco Rabanne
Black XS
1.7 oz EDT Sp $ 45.00
Your Price : _____
3.4 oz EDT Sp $ 60.00
Your Price : _____

Paco Rabanne
Black XS L'Exces
1.7 oz EDT Sp $ 50.00
Your Price : _____
3.4 oz EDT Sp $ 75.00
Your Price : _____

Paco Rabanne
Unisex
3.4 oz EDT Sp $ 55.00
Your Price : _____

Paco Rabanne
Sport
1.7 oz EDT Sp $ 47.00
Your Price : _____
3.4 oz EDT Sp $ 60.00
Your Price : _____

Paco Rabanne
Tenere
3.4 oz EDT Sp $ 60.00
Your Price : _____

Paco Rabanne
Ultra Red
1.7 oz EDT Sp $ 40.00
Your Price : _____
3.4 oz EDT Sp $ 55.00
Your Price : _____

Paco Rabanne
Ultraviolet
1.7 oz EDT Sp $ 45.00
Your Price : _____
3.4 oz EDT Sp $ 60.00
Your Price : _____

Paco Rabanne
XS
1.7 oz EDT Sp $ 45.00
Your Price : _____
3.4 oz EDT Sp $ 60.00
Your Price : _____

Paloma Picasso
Minotaure
2.5 oz EDT Sp $ 60.00
Your Price : _____
4.2 oz EDT Sp $ 90.00
Your Price : _____

Paris Hilton
Men
1.7 oz EDT Sp $ 45.00
Your Price : _____
3.4 oz EDT Sp $ 60.00
Your Price : _____

Paris Hilton
Heir
1.7 oz EDT Sp $ 40.00
Your Price : _____
3.4 oz EDT Sp $ 55.00
Your Price : _____

Paris Hilton
Just Me
1.7 oz EDT Sp $ 40.00
Your Price : _____
3.4 oz EDT Sp $ 55.00
Your Price : _____

Parisvally
Aura Parisvally
1.7 oz EDT Sp $ 45.00
Your Price : _____
3.4 oz EDT Sp $ 70.00
Your Price : _____

Parlux
Bellagio
3.4 oz EDT Sp $ 50.00
Your Price : _____

Paul Sebastian
Casual
1.7 oz EDT Sp $ 35.00
Your Price : _____
3.4 oz EDT Sp $ 55.00
Your Price : _____

Paul Sebastian
Design
1.7 oz EDT Sp $ 37.00
Your Price : _____
3.4 oz EDT Sp $ 55.00
Your Price : _____

Paul Sebastian
PS
2.0 oz EDC Sp $ 39.00
Your Price : _____
4.0 oz EDC Sp $ 54.00
Your Price : _____
8.0 oz EDC Sp $ 76.00
Your Price : _____

Paul Smith
Paul Smith
1.7 oz EDT Sp $ 55.00
Your Price : _____
3.4 oz EDT Sp $ 72.00
Your Price : _____

Paul Smith
Paul Smith Extreme
1.7 oz EDT Sp $ 55.00
Your Price : _____
3.4 oz EDT Sp $ 72.00
Your Price : _____

Paul Smith
Paul Smith London
1.7 oz EDT Sp $ 55.00
Your Price : _____
3.4 oz EDT Sp $ 72.00
Your Price : _____

Perfumers Workshop
Samba
3.4 oz EDT Sp $ 60.00
Your Price : _____

Perfumers Workshop
Samba French Kiss
3.4 oz EDT Sp $ 60.00
Your Price : _____

Perfumers Workshop
Samba Heat
3.3 oz EDT Sp $ 60.00
Your Price : _____

Perry Ellis
Perry Ellis
1.7 oz EDT Sp $ 45.00
Your Price : _____
3.4 oz EDT Sp $ 60.00
Your Price : _____

Perry Ellis
360 Green
1.7 oz EDT Sp $ 40.00
Your Price : _____
3.4 oz EDT Sp $ 55.00
Your Price : _____

Perry Ellis
Spirited
1.7 oz EDT Sp $ 40.00
Your Price : _____
3.4 oz EDT Sp $ 60.00
Your Price : _____

Perry Ellis
Aqua
1.7 oz EDT Sp $ 40.00
Your Price : _____
3.4 oz EDT Sp $ 60.00
Your Price : _____

Perry Ellis
Platinum Label
1.7 oz EDT Sp $ 45.00
Your Price : _____
3.4 oz EDT Sp $ 60.00
Your Price : _____

Perry Ellis
18 Intense
1.7 oz EDT Sp $ 40.00
Your Price : _____
3.4 oz EDT Sp $ 55.00
Your Price : _____

Perry Ellis
18
1.7 oz EDT Sp $ 40.00
Your Price : _____
3.4 oz EDT Sp $ 55.00
Your Price : _____

Perry Ellis
America
1.7 oz EDT Sp $ 40.00
Your Price : _____
3.4 oz EDT Sp $ 55.00
Your Price : _____

Perry Ellis
Perry
1.7 oz EDT Sp $ 40.00
Your Price : _____
3.4 oz EDT Sp $ 55.00
Your Price : _____

Perry Ellis
Perry for HIM
1.7 oz EDT Sp $ 40.00
Your Price : _____
3.4 oz EDT Sp $ 55.00
Your Price : _____

Perry Ellis
360
1.7 oz EDT Sp $ 40.00
Your Price : _____
3.4 oz EDT Sp $ 55.00
Your Price : _____

Perry Ellis
360 Black
1.7 oz EDT Sp $ 40.00
Your Price : _____
3.4 oz EDT Sp $ 55.00
Your Price : _____

Perry Ellis
360 Blue
1.7 oz EDT Sp $ 40.00
Your Price : _____
3.4 oz EDT Sp $ 55.00
Your Price : _____

Perry Ellis
360 Red
1.7 oz EDT Sp $ 40.00
Your Price : _____
3.4 oz EDT Sp $ 55.00
Your Price : _____

Perry Ellis
360 White
1.7 oz EDT Sp $ 40.00
Your Price : _____
3.4 oz EDT Sp $ 55.00
Your Price : _____

Perry Ellis
M
1.7 oz EDT Sp $ 40.00
Your Price : _____
3.4 oz EDT Sp $ 55.00
Your Price : _____

Perry Ellis
Night
1.7 oz EDT Sp $ 45.00
Your Price : _____
3.4 oz EDT Sp $ 60.00
Your Price : _____

Perry Ellis
360 Collection
3.4 oz EDT Sp $ 65.00
Your Price : _____

Perry Ellis
Portfolio
3.4 oz EDT Sp $ 60.00
Your Price : _____

Perry Ellis
Portfolio Elite
1.7 oz EDP Sp $ 45.00
Your Price : _____
3.4 oz EDT Sp $ 60.00
Your Price : _____

Perry Ellis
Portfolio Green
1.7 oz EDP Sp $ 45.00
Your Price : _____
3.4 oz EDT Sp $ 60.00
Your Price : _____

Perry Ellis
Reserve
3.4 oz EDT Sp $ 55.00
Your Price : _____

Perry Ellis
Pour Homme
3.4 oz EDT Sp $ 65.00
Your Price : _____

Perry Ellis
Cobalt
3.4 oz EDT Sp $ 65.00
Your Price : _____

Perry Ellis
Portfolio Red
1.7 oz EDT Sp $ 45.00
Your Price : _____
3.4 oz EDT Sp $ 60.00
Your Price : _____

Perry Ellis
Portfolio Black
1.7 oz EDT Sp $ 45.00
Your Price : _____
3.4 oz EDT Sp $ 60.00
Your Price : _____

Perry Ellis
Men
3.4 oz EDT Sp $ 65.00
Your Price : _____

Perry Ellis
Red
3.4 oz EDT Sp $ 65.00
Your Price : _____

Perry Ellis
Citron
3.4 oz EDT Sp $ 65.00
Your Price : _____

Phat Farm
Phat Farm Premium
3.4 oz EDT Sp $ 73.00
Your Price : _____

Phillip Van Heusen
IZOD
3.4 oz EDT Sp $ 50.00
Your Price : _____

Pierre Cardin
Pierre Cardin
2.8 oz EDC Sp $ 45.00
Your Price : _____
8.0 oz EDC Splash $ 60.00
Your Price : _____

Pitbull
Ptbull
3.4 oz EDT Sp $ 58.00
Your Price : _____

PlayBoy
VIP
3.3 oz EDT Sp $ 45.00
Your Price : _____

PlayBoy
New York
3.3 oz EDT Sp $ 45.00
Your Price : _____

PlayBoy
London
3.3 oz EDT Sp $ 45.00
Your Price : _____

PlayBoy
Ibiza
3.3 oz EDT Sp $ 45.00
Your Price : _____

PlayBoy
Miami
3.3 oz EDT Sp $ 45.00
Your Price : _____

PlayBoy
Hollywood
3.3 oz EDT Sp $ 45.00
Your Price : _____

PlayBoy
Vegas
3.3 oz EDT Sp $ 45.00
Your Price : _____

PlayBoy
Malibu
3.3 oz EDT Sp $ 45.00
Your Price : _____

PlayBoy
Super Playboy
3.3 oz EDT Sp $ 45.00
Your Price : _____

Prada
Amber Pour Homme
1.7 oz EDT Sp $ 60.00
Your Price : _____
3.4 oz EDT Sp $ 80.00
Your Price : _____

Prada
Amber Pour Homme Intense
1.7 oz EDT Sp $ 60.00
Your Price : _____
3.4 oz EDT Sp $ 92.00
Your Price : _____

Prada
Luna Rossa
1.7 oz EDT Sp $ 66.00
Your Price : _____
3.4 oz EDT Sp $ 86.00
Your Price : _____
5.1 oz EDT Sp $ 105.00
Your Price : _____

Prada
Amber Pour Homme
1.7 oz EDT Sp $ 68.00
Your Price : _____
3.4 oz EDT Sp $ 88.00
Your Price : _____

Prada
Infusion D' Homme
1.7 oz EDT Sp $ 55.00
Your Price : _____
3.4 oz EDT Sp $ 75.00
Your Price : _____
6.75 oz EDT Sp $ 100.00
Your Price : _____

Prada
Infusion De Vetiver
1.7oz EDT Sp $ 70.00
Your Price : _____
3.4 oz EDT Sp $ 90.00
Your Price : _____

Prada
L'Homme
1.7 oz EDT Sp $ 78.00
Your Price : _____
3.4 oz EDT Sp $ 98.00
Your Price : _____

Prada
Lunna Rossa Carbon
1.7 oz EDT Sp $ 66.00
Your Price : _____
3.4 oz EDT Sp $ 86.00
Your Price : _____
5.1 oz EDT Sp $ 105.00
Your Price : _____

Prada
Lunna Rossa Sport
1.7 oz EDT Sp $ 68.00
Your Price : _____
3.4 oz EDT Sp $ 86.00
Your Price : _____

Prada
Luna Rossa Extreme
1.7 oz EDT Sp $ 68.00
Your Price : _____
3.4 oz EDT Sp $ 88.00
Your Price : _____

Prada
Luna Rossa Eau Sport
4.2 oz EDT Sp $ 86.00
Your Price : _____

Puma
Jam
1.3 oz EDT Sp $ 35.00
Your Price : _____
2.0 oz EDT Sp $ 45.00
Your Price : _____

Ralph Lauren
Big Pony # 1 Blue
2.5 oz EDT Sp $ 62.00
Your Price : _____
4.2 oz EDT Sp $ 70.00
Your Price : _____

Ralph Lauren
Big Pony # 2 Red
2.5 oz EDT Sp $ 62.00
Your Price : _____
4.2 oz EDT Sp $ 70.00
Your Price : _____

Ralph Lauren
Big Pony # 3 Green
2.5 oz EDT Sp $ 62.00
Your Price : _____
4.2 oz EDT Sp $ 70.00
Your Price : _____

Ralph Lauren
Big Pony # 4 Orange
2.5 oz EDT Sp $ 62.00
Your Price : _____
4.2 oz EDT Sp $ 70.00
Your Price : _____

Ralph Lauren
Polo Black
1.3 oz EDT Sp $ 48.00
Your Price : _____
2.5 oz EDT Sp $ 68.00
Your Price : _____
4.2 oz EDT Sp $ 85.00
Your Price : _____
6.7 oz EDT Sp $ 105.00
Your Price : _____

Ralph Lauren
Polo Blue
1.3 oz EDT Sp $ 50.00
Your Price : _____
2.5 oz EDT Sp $ 68.00
Your Price : _____
4.2 oz EDT Sp $ 85.00
Your Price : _____
6.7 oz EDT Sp $ 102.00
Your Price : _____

Ralph Lauren
Polo Blue (EDP)
1.3 oz EDP Sp $ 55.00
Your Price : _____
2.5 oz EDP Sp $ 76.00
Your Price : _____
4.2 oz EDP Sp $ 98.00
Your Price : _____
6.7 oz EDP Sp $ 125.00
Your Price : _____

Ralph Lauren
Polo Double Black
1.3 oz EDT Sp $ 48.00
Your Price : _____
2.5 oz EDT Sp $ 68.00
Your Price : _____
4.2 oz EDT Sp $ 85.00
Your Price : _____

Ralph Lauren
Polo Explorer
1.3 oz EDT Sp $ 40.00
Your Price : _____
2.5 oz EDT Sp $ 55.00
Your Price : _____
4.2 oz EDT Sp $ 70.00
Your Price : _____

Ralph Lauren
Polo
2.0 oz EDT Sp $ 68.00
Your Price : _____
4.0 oz EDT Sp $ 85.00
Your Price : _____
8.0 oz EDT Sp $ 105.00
Your Price : _____

Ralph Lauren
Polo Oud Supreme
1.36 oz EDP Sp $ 74.00
Your Price : _____
4.2 oz EDP Sp $ 125.00
Your Price : _____

Ralph Lauren
Polo Red Extreme
1.35 oz EDP Sp $ 55.00
Your Price : _____
2.5 oz EDP Sp $ 75.00
Your Price : _____
4.2 oz EDP Sp $ 95.00
Your Price : _____

Ralph Lauren
Polo Red Intense
2.5 oz EDP Sp $ 74.00
Your Price : _____
4.2 oz EDP Sp $ 92.00
Your Price : _____
6.7 oz EDP Sp $ 112.00
Your Price : _____

Ralph Lauren
Polo Sport
2.5 oz EDT Sp $ 50.00
Your Price : _____
4.2 oz EDT Sp $ 65.00
Your Price : _____

Ralph Lauren
Purple Label
2.5 oz EDT Sp $ 65.00
Your Price : _____
4.2 oz EDT Sp $ 90.00
Your Price : _____

Ralph Lauren
Romance
1.7 oz EDT Sp $ 60.00
Your Price : _____
3.4 oz EDT Sp $ 75.00
Your Price : _____

Ralph Lauren
Romance Silver
1.7 oz EDP Sp $ 55.00
Your Price : _____
3.4 oz EDT Sp $ 70.00
Your Price : _____

Ralph Lauren
Safari
2.5 oz EDT Sp $ 62.00
Your Price : _____
4.2 oz EDT Sp $ 74.00
Your Price : _____

Ralph Lauren
Chaps
3.4 oz EDT Sp $ 50.00
Your Price : _____

Ralph Lauren
Polo Blue Sport
2.5 oz EDT Sp $ 60.00
Your Price : _____
4.2 oz EDT Sp $ 75.00
Your Price : _____

Ralph Lauren
Polo Red, White & Blue
2.5 oz EDT Sp $ 55.00
Your Price : _____
4.2 oz EDT Sp $ 70.00
Your Price : _____

Ralph Lauren
Polo Red
1.3 oz EDT Sp $ 50.00
Your Price : _____
2.5 oz EDT Sp $ 68.00
Your Price : _____
4.2 oz EDT Sp $ 85.00
Your Price : _____
6.7 oz EDT Sp $ 102.00
Your Price : _____

Remy Latour
Cigar
3.4 oz EDT Sp $ 60.00
Your Price : _____

Roberto Cavalli
Man
1.7 oz EDT Sp $ 40.00
Your Price : _____
3.4 oz EDT Sp $ 55.00
Your Price : _____

Roberto Cavalli
Black
1.7 oz EDT Sp $ 40.00
Your Price : _____
3.4 oz EDT Sp $ 55.00
Your Price : _____

Roberto Cavalli
Just Cavalli
1.7 oz EDT Sp $ 45.00
Your Price : _____
3.0 oz EDT Sp $ 60.00
Your Price : _____

Roberto Cavalli
Just Cavalli Him
2.0 oz EDT Sp $ 35.00
Your Price : _____

Roca Wear
9 IX
1.7 oz EDT Sp $ 40.00
Your Price : _____
3.4 oz EDT Sp $ 55.00
Your Price : _____

Roca Wear
X
1.7 oz EDT Sp $ 40.00
Your Price : _____
3.4 oz EDT Sp $ 55.00
Your Price : _____

Roca Wear
Evolution
1.7 oz EDT Sp $ 40.00
Your Price : _____
3.4 oz EDT Sp $ 55.00
Your Price : _____

Rochas
Man
1.7 oz EDT Sp $ 45.00
Your Price : _____
3.4 oz EDT Sp $ 60.00
Your Price : _____

Rochas
Eau De Rochas
1.7 oz EDT Sp $ 45.00
Your Price : _____
3.4 oz EDT Sp $ 60.00
Your Price : _____

Romero Britto
Britto Man
2.5 oz EDT Sp $ 45.00
Your Price : _____
4.2 oz EDT Sp $ 65.00
Your Price : _____

Salvador Dali
Laguna Homme
1.7 oz EDT Sp $ 40.00
Your Price : _____
3.4 oz EDT Sp $ 55.00
Your Price : _____

Salvador Dali
Aqua Verde
1.7 oz EDT Sp $ 40.00
Your Price : _____
3.4 oz EDT Sp $ 55.00
Your Price : _____

Salvatore Ferragamo
Pour Homme
1.7 oz EDT Sp $ 45.00
Your Price : _____
3.4 oz EDT Sp $ 60.00
Your Price : _____

Salvatore Ferragamo
F by Ferragamo
1.7 oz EDT Sp $ 50.00
Your Price : _____
3.4 oz EDT Sp $ 70.00
Your Price : _____

Salvatore Ferragamo
F by Ferragamo Black
1.7 oz EDT Sp $ 55.00
Your Price : _____
3.4 oz EDT Sp $ 75.00
Your Price : _____

Salvatore Ferragamo
F by Ferragamo Free Time
1.7 oz EDT Sp $ 55.00
Your Price : _____
3.4 oz EDT Sp $ 75.00
Your Price : _____

Salvatore Ferragamo
Acqua Essenziale Blu
1.7 oz EDT Sp $ 60.00
Your Price : _____
3.4 oz EDT Sp $ 80.00
Your Price : _____

Salvatore Ferragamo
Acqua Essenziale Colonia
1.7 oz EDT Sp $ 60.00
Your Price : _____
3.4 oz EDT Sp $ 80.00
Your Price : _____

Salvatore Ferragamo
Uomo
1.7 oz EDT Sp $ 70.00
Your Price : _____
3.4 oz EDT Sp $ 90.00
Your Price : _____

Salvatore Ferragamo
Uomo Casual Life
1.7 oz EDT Sp $ 70.00
Your Price : _____
3.4 oz EDT Sp $ 90.00
Your Price : _____

Salvatore Ferragamo
Acqua Essenziale
1.7 oz EDT Sp $ 60.00
Your Price : _____
3.4 oz EDT Sp $ 80.00
Your Price : _____

Salvatore Ferragamo
Incanto Pour Homme
1.7 oz EDT Sp $ 45.00
Your Price : _____
3.4 oz EDT Sp $ 60.00
Your Price : _____

Salvatore Ferragamo
Subtil Pour Homme
1.7 oz EDT Sp $ 45.00
Your Price : _____
3.4 oz EDT Sp $ 60.00
Your Price : _____

Sean John
Unforgivable
1.0 oz EDT Sp $ 45.00
Your Price : _____
2.5 oz EDT Sp $ 75.00
Your Price : _____
4.2 oz EDT Sp $ 95.00
Your Price : _____

Sean John
Unforgivable Night
2.5 oz EDT Sp $ 70.00
Your Price : _____
4.2 oz EDT Sp $ 90.00
Your Price : _____

Sean John
I Am King
1.7 oz EDT Sp $ 55.00
Your Price : _____
3.4 oz EDT Sp $ 75.00
Your Price : _____

Sean John
I Am King of the Night
1.7 oz EDT Sp $ 50.00
Your Price : _____
3.4 oz EDT Sp $ 70.00
Your Price : _____

Sean John
I Am King of Miami
1.7 oz EDT Sp $ 50.00
Your Price : _____
3.4 oz EDT Sp $ 70.00
Your Price : _____

Sean John
Sean John
3.4 oz EDT Sp $ 70.00
Your Price : _____

Sean John
3:AM
1.7 oz EDT Sp $ 75.00
Your Price : _____

Swiss Army
Classic
1.7 oz EDT Sp $ 50.00
Your Price : _____
3.4 oz EDT Sp $ 65.00
Your Price : _____

Swiss Army
Altitude
1.7 oz EDT Sp $ 50.00
Your Price : _____
3.4 oz EDT Sp $ 65.00
Your Price : _____

Swiss Army
Mountain Water
1.7 oz EDT Sp $ 45.00
Your Price : _____
3.4 oz EDT Sp $ 60.00
Your Price : _____

The Baron
4.5 oz EDC Sp $ 55.00
Your Price : _____

The Original Penguin
Penguin
3.4 oz EDT Sp $ 65.00
Your Price : _____

Thierry Mugler
A Men
1.7 oz EDT Sp $ 60.00
Your Price : _____
3.4 oz EDT Sp $ 90.00
Your Price : _____

Thierry Mugler
B Men
1.7 oz EDT Sp $ 60.00
Your Price : _____
3.4 oz EDT Sp $ 89.00
Your Price : _____

Thierry Mugler
Ice Men
1.7 oz EDT Sp $ 50.00
Your Price : _____
3.4 oz EDT Sp $ 70.00
Your Price : _____

Thierry Mugler
A Men Pure Malt
1.7 oz EDT Sp $ 60.00
Your Price : _____
3.4 oz EDT Sp $ 89.00
Your Price : _____

Thierry Mugler
A Men Pure Havane
1.7 oz EDT Sp $ 60.00
Your Price : _____
3.4 oz EDT Sp $ 90.00
Your Price : _____

Tom Ford
Tom Ford
1.7 oz EDT Sp $ 88.00
Your Price : _____
3.4 oz EDT Sp $ 118.00
Your Price : _____

Tom Ford
Noir
1.7 oz EDP Sp $ 110.00
Your Price : _____
3.4 oz EDP Sp $ 150.00
Your Price : _____

Tom Ford
Mandarino Di Amalfi
1.7 oz EDP Sp $ 230.00
Your Price : _____
3.4 oz EDP Sp $ 312.00
Your Price : _____
8.4 oz EDP Sp $ 595.00
Your Price : _____

Tom Ford
Grey Vetiver
1.7 oz EDP Sp $ 110.00
Your Price : _____
3.4 oz EDP Sp $ 150.00
Your Price : _____

Tom Ford
Costa Azzurra
1.7 oz EDP Sp $ 230.00
Your Price : _____
3.4 oz EDP Sp $ 312.00
Your Price : _____
8.4 oz EDP Sp $ 595.00
Your Price : _____

Tom Ford
Extreme
1.7 oz EDP Sp $ 120.00
Your Price : _____

Tom Ford
Patchouli Absolu
1.7 oz EDP Sp $ 230.00
Your Price : _____
3.4 oz EDP Sp $ 312.00
Your Price : _____
8.4 oz EDP Sp $ 595.00
Your Price : _____

Tom Ford
Noir Extreme
1.7 oz EDP Sp $ 110.00
Your Price : _____
3.4 oz EDP Sp $ 150.00
Your Price : _____

Tom Ford
Neroli Portofino
1.7 oz EDP Sp $ 230.00
Your Price : _____
3.4 oz EDP Sp $ 312.00
Your Price : _____
8.4 oz EDP Sp $ 595.00
Your Price : _____

Tom Ford
Mandarino Di Amalfi Acqua
1.7 oz EDT Sp $ 155.00
Your Price : _____
3.4 oz EDT Sp $ 212.00
Your Price : _____

Tom Ford
Neroli Portofino Acqua
1.7 oz EDT Sp $ 155.00
Your Price : _____
3.4 oz EDT Sp $ 212.00
Your Price : _____

Tom Ford
Oud Fleur
1.7 oz EDP Sp $ 230.00
Your Price : _____
3.4 oz EDP Sp $ 312.00
Your Price : _____
8.4 oz EDP Sp $ 595.00
Your Price : _____

Tom Ford
Jasmin Rouge
1.7 oz EDP Sp $ 230.00
Your Price : _____
3.4 oz EDP Sp $ 312.00
Your Price : _____
8.4 oz EDP Sp $ 595.00
Your Price : _____

Tom Ford
Cafe Rose
1.7 oz EDP Sp $ 230.00
Your Price : _____
3.4 oz EDP Sp $ 312.00
Your Price : _____
8.4 oz EDP Sp $ 595.00
Your Price : _____

Tom Ford
Tobacco Vanille
1.7 oz EDP Sp $ 230.00
Your Price : _____
3.4 oz EDP Sp $ 312.00
Your Price : _____
8.4 oz EDP Sp $ 595.00
Your Price : _____

Tom Ford
Noir
1.7 oz EDT Sp $ 80.00
Your Price : _____
3.4 oz EDT Sp $ 108.00
Your Price : _____

Tom Ford
Oud Wood
1.7 oz EDP Sp $ 230.00
Your Price : _____
3.4 oz EDP Sp $ 312.00
Your Price : _____
8.4 oz EDP Sp $ 595.00
Your Price : _____

Tommy Bahama
Tommy Bahama
1.7 oz EDT Sp $ 45.00
Your Price : _____
3.4 oz EDT Sp $ 60.00
Your Price : _____

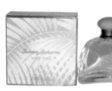

Tommy Bahama
Very Cool
1.7 oz EDT Sp $ 45.00
Your Price : _____
3.4 oz EDT Sp $ 60.00
Your Price : _____

Tommy Bahama
Tommy Bahama for Him
1.7 oz EDT Sp $ 62.00
Your Price : _____
3.4 oz EDT Sp $ 78.00
Your Price : _____

Tommy Bahama
Set Sail St. Barts
1.7 oz EDT Sp $ 45.00
Your Price : _____
3.4 oz EDT Sp $ 65.00
Your Price : _____

Tommy Bahama
Set Sail Martinique
1.7 oz EDT Sp $ 45.00
Your Price : _____
3.4 oz EDT Sp $ 65.00
Your Price : _____

Tommy Hilfiger
Tommy
1.7 oz EDT Sp $ 45.00
Your Price : _____
3.4 oz EDT Sp $ 57.00
Your Price : _____
6.7 oz EDT Sp $ 68.00
Your Price : _____

Tommy Hilfiger
Eau De Prep
1.7 oz EDT Sp $ 50.00
Your Price : _____
3.4 oz EDT Sp $ 65.00
Your Price : _____

Tommy Hilfiger
Jeans
1.7 oz EDT Sp $ 40.00
Your Price : _____
3.4 oz EDT Sp $ 55.00
Your Price : _____

Tommy Hilfiger
Hilfiger
1.7 oz EDT Sp $ 50.00
Your Price : _____
3.4 oz EDT Sp $ 65.00
Your Price : _____

Tommy Hilfiger
Freedom
1.7 oz EDT Sp $ 40.00
Your Price : _____
3.4 oz EDT Sp $ 55.00
Your Price : _____

Tommy Hilfiger
Tommy T
1.7 oz EDT Sp $ 40.00
Your Price : _____
3.4 oz EDT Sp $ 55.00
Your Price : _____

Tommy Hilfiger
Tommy 10
1.7 oz EDT Sp $ 40.00
Your Price : _____
3.4 oz EDT Sp $ 55.00
Your Price : _____

Tommy Hilfiger
Freedom (New)
1.7 oz EDT Sp $ 50.00
Your Price : _____
3.4 oz EDT Sp $ 65.00
Your Price : _____

Tommy Hilfiger
Freedom Sport
1.7 oz EDT Sp $ 50.00
Your Price : _____
3.4 oz EDT Sp $ 65.00
Your Price : _____

Tommy Hilfiger
Loud
2.5 oz EDT Sp $ 45.00
Your Price : _____

Tous
Man
1.7 oz EDT Sp $ 50.00
Your Price : _____
3.4 oz EDT Sp $ 65.00
Your Price : _____

Tous
Man Intense
1.7 oz EDT Sp $ 50.00
Your Price : _____
3.4 oz EDT Sp $ 65.00
Your Price : _____

Tous
Man Sport
1.7 oz EDT Sp $ 50.00
Your Price : _____
3.4 oz EDT Sp $ 65.00
Your Price : _____

Tous
Tous in Heaven
1.7 oz EDT Sp $ 50.00
Your Price : _____
3.4 oz EDT Sp $ 65.00
Your Price : _____

True Religion
1.7 oz EDT Sp $ 60.00
Your Price : _____
3.4 oz EDT Sp $ 80.00
Your Price : _____

True Religion
Drifter
1.7 oz EDT Sp $ 60.00
Your Price : _____
3.4 oz EDT Sp $ 80.00
Your Price : _____

Trussardi
UOMO
1.7 oz EDT Sp $ 70.00
Your Price : _____
3.4 oz EDT Sp $ 95.00
Your Price : _____

Trussardi
Jeans
1.7 oz EDT Sp $ 50.00
Your Price : _____
3.4 oz EDT Sp $ 75.00
Your Price : _____

Trussardi
Inside
1.7 oz EDT Sp $ 50.00
Your Price : _____
3.4 oz EDT Sp $ 75.00
Your Price : _____

Trussardi
My Land
1.7 oz EDT Sp $ 70.00
Your Price : _____
3.4 oz EDT Sp $ 95.00
Your Price : _____

Ungaro
Man
3.0 oz EDT Sp $ 65.00
Your Price : _____

Ungaro
Pour L' Homme III
1.7 oz EDT Sp $ 45.00
Your Price : _____
3.4 oz EDT Sp $ 60.00
Your Price : _____

Ungaro
Apparition
1.7 oz EDT Sp $ 45.00
Your Price : _____
3.4 oz EDT Sp $ 60.00
Your Price : _____

Ungaro
Apparition Intense
1.7 oz EDT Sp $ 45.00
Your Price : _____
3.4 oz EDT Sp $ 60.00
Your Price : _____

Usher
Usher
1.7 oz EDT Sp $ 40.00
Your Price : _____
3.4 oz EDT Sp $ 55.00
Your Price : _____

Usher
UR
1.7 oz EDT Sp $ 40.00
Your Price : _____
3.4 oz EDT Sp $ 55.00
Your Price : _____

Usher
VIP
3.4 oz EDT Sp $ 60.00
Your Price : _____

Valentino
Uomo
1.7 oz EDT Sp $ 78.00
Your Price : _____
3.4 oz EDT Sp $ 98.00
Your Price : _____
5.1 oz EDT Sp $ 122.00
Your Price : _____

Valentino
Uomo Acqua
3.4 oz EDT Sp $ 108.00
Your Price : _____

Valentino
Uomo Intense
1.7 oz EDP Sp $ 82.00
Your Price : _____
3.4 oz EDP Sp $ 102.00
Your Price : _____

Van Cleef & Arpels
Pour Homme
1.7 oz EDT Sp $ 45.00
Your Price : _____
3.4 oz EDT Sp $ 65.00
Your Price : _____

Van Cleef & Arpels
Tsar
1.7 oz EDT Sp $ 45.00
Your Price : _____
3.4 oz EDT Sp $ 65.00
Your Price : _____

Van Cleef & Arpels
Zanzibar
1.7 oz EDT Sp $ 45.00
Your Price : _____
3.4 oz EDT Sp $ 65.00
Your Price : _____

Vera Wang
Vera Wang
1.7 oz EDT Sp $ 55.00
Your Price : _____
3.4 oz EDT Sp $ 75.00
Your Price : _____

Versace
Eros
1.7 oz EDT Sp $ 65.00
Your Price : _____
3.4 oz EDT Sp $ 86.00
Your Price : _____
6.7 oz EDT Sp $ 110.00
Your Price : _____

Versace
Blue Jeans
2.5 oz EDT Sp $ 55.00
Your Price : _____

Versace
Baby Blue Jeans
1.7 oz EDT Sp $ 45.00
Your Price : _____

Versace
L' Homme
1.7 oz EDT Sp $ 50.00
Your Price : _____
3.4 oz EDT Sp $ 70.00
Your Price : _____

Versace
Pour Homme
1.7 oz EDT Sp $ 62.00
Your Price : _____
3.4 oz EDT Sp $ 82.00
Your Price : _____
6.7 oz EDT Sp $ 103.00
Your Price : _____

Versace
Man
1.7 oz EDT Sp $ 50.00
Your Price : _____
3.4 oz EDT Sp $ 70.00
Your Price : _____

Versace
Eau Fraiche
1.7 oz EDT Sp $ 61.00
Your Price : _____
3.4 oz EDT Sp $ 79.00
Your Price : _____
6.7 oz EDT Sp $ 101.00
Your Price : _____

Versace
Dreamer
1.7 oz EDT Sp $ 60.00
Your Price : _____
3.4 oz EDT Sp $ 76.00
Your Price : _____

Versace
Dylan Blue
1.7 oz EDT Sp $ 65.00
Your Price : _____
3.4 oz EDT Sp $ 86.00
Your Price : _____

Versace Oud Noir
Versace
3.4 oz EDP Sp $ 155.00
Your Price : _____

Viktor & Rolf
Antidote
1.3 oz EDT Sp $ 55.00
Your Price : _____
2.5 oz EDT Sp $ 75.00
Your Price : _____
4.2 oz EDT Sp $ 95.00
Your Price : _____

Viktor & Rolf
Spicebomb
1.7 oz EDT Sp $ 92.00
Your Price : _____
3.4 oz EDT Sp $ 112.00
Your Price : _____
5.0 oz EDT Sp $ 150.00
Your Price : _____

Victor & Rolf
Spicebomb Fresh
3.04 oz EDT Sp $ 98.00
Your Price : _____

Vince Camuto
Vince Camuto
1.7 oz EDT Sp $ 60.00
Your Price : _____
3.4 oz EDT Sp $ 77.00
Your Price : _____

Vince Camuto
Terra
1.6 oz EDT Sp $ 60.00
Your Price : _____
3.4 oz EDT Sp $ 77.00
Your Price : _____

Vince Camuto
Etereno
1.6 oz EDT Sp $ 60.00
Your Price : _____
3.4 oz EDT Sp $ 77.00
Your Price : _____

Vince Camuto
Solare
1.6 oz EDT Sp $ 60.00
Your Price : _____
3.4 oz EDT Sp $ 77.00
Your Price : _____

Vince Camuto
Homme
1.6 oz EDT Sp $ 60.00
Your Price : _____
3.4 oz EDT Sp $ 77.00
Your Price : _____

Vince Camuto
Oud
1.6 oz EDT Sp $ 60.00
Your Price : _____
3.4 oz EDT Sp $ 77.00
Your Price : _____

Yves Saint Laurent
Jazz
1.7 oz EDT Sp $ 50.00
Your Price : _____
2.7 oz EDT Sp $ 125.00
Your Price : _____
3.4 oz EDT Sp $ 65.00
Your Price : _____

Yves Saint Laurent
Live Jazz
1.7 oz EDT Sp $ 50.00
Your Price :
3.4 oz EDT Sp $ 65.00
Your Price :

Yves Saint Laurent
Kouros
1.7 oz EDT Sp $ 55.00
Your Price :
3.4 oz EDT Sp $ 75.00
Your Price :

Yves Saint Laurent
Kouros Summer
1.7 oz EDT Sp $ 45.00
Your Price :
3.4 oz EDT Sp $ 65.00
Your Price :

Yves Saint Laurent
Body Kouros
1.7 oz EDT Sp $ 45.00
Your Price :
3.4 oz EDT Sp $ 66.00
Your Price :

Yves Saint Laurent
L' Homme
2.0 oz EDT Sp $ 72.00
Your Price :
3.4 oz EDT Sp $ 92.00
Your Price :
6.7 oz EDT Sp $ 125.00
Your Price :

Yves Saint Laurent
L' Homme Parfum Intense
3.3 oz EDP Sp $ 104.00
Your Price :
6.7 oz EDP Sp $ 140.00
Your Price :

Yves Saint Laurent
La Nuit De L' Homme
2.0 oz EDT Sp $ 72.00
Your Price :
3.4 oz EDT Sp $ 92.00
Your Price :
6.7 oz EDT Sp $ 125.00
Your Price :

Yves Saint Laurent
La Nuit De L' Homme
Frozen Cologne
2.0 oz EDT Sp $ 55.00
Your Price :
3.4 oz EDT Sp $ 75.00
Your Price :

Yves Saint Laurent
L' Homme Libre
1.3 oz EDT Sp $ 54.00
Your Price :
2.0 oz EDT Sp $ 67.00
Your Price :
3.4 oz EDT Sp $ 87.00
Your Price :
6.7 oz EDT Sp $ 125.00
Your Price :

Yves Saint Laurent
L' Homme Libre Cologne
2.0 oz EDT Sp $ 55.00
Your Price :
3.4 oz EDT Sp $ 75.00
Your Price :

Yves Saint Laurent
Pour Homme
1.7 oz EDT Sp $ 45.00
Your Price :
3.4 oz EDT Sp $ 60.00
Your Price :

Yves Saint Laurent
Opium
1.7 oz EDT Sp $ 45.00
Your Price :
3.4 oz EDT Sp $ 60.00
Your Price :

Yves Saint Laurent
Rive Gauche
2.5 oz EDT Sp $ 50.00
Your Price :
4.2 oz EDT Sp $ 70.00
Your Price :

Yves Saint Laurent
M-7
2.5 oz EDT Sp $ 55.00
Your Price :
4.2 oz EDT Sp $ 75.00
Your Price :

Yves Saint Laurent
La Nuit De L'Homme Le Parfum
2.0 oz EDP Sp $ 65.00
Your Price :
3.4 oz EDP Sp $ 80.00
Your Price :

Yves Saint Laurent
La Nuit De L'Homme L'Intense
3.3 oz EDP Sp $ 104.00
Your Price :

Yves Saint Laurent
L'Homme Sport
1.3 oz EDT Sp $ 54.00
Your Price :
2.0 oz EDT Sp $ 67.00
Your Price :
3.4 oz EDT Sp $ 87.00
Your Price :
6.7 oz EDT Sp $ 98.00
Your Price :

Yves Saint Laurent
L'Homme Ultime
2.0 oz EDT Sp $ 80.00
Your Price :
3.4 oz EDT Sp $ 104.00
Your Price :
6.7 oz EDT Sp $ 140.00
Your Price :

Yves Saint Laurent
M-7 OUD ABSOLU
2.7 oz EDT Sp $ 125.00
Your Price :

Yves Saint Laurent
Y
2.7 oz EDT Sp $ 72.00
Your Price :
3.3 oz EDT Sp $ 94.00
Your Price :

Antonio Banderas
Seduction In Black
3.4 oz After Shave Splash
3.4 oz EDT Sp $62.00
Your Price : _____

Azzaro
Chrome Sport
3.4 oz EDT Sp
6.8 oz Shower Gel $75.00
Your Price : _____

Bvlgari
Man Extreme
3.4 oz EDT Sp
Bvlgari Signature Pouch
2.5 oz After Shave
2.5 oz Shower Gel $89.00
Your Price : _____

Calvin Klein
Eternity Aqua
3.4 oz EDT Sp
3.4 oz After Shave Balm
2.6 oz Deodorant $84.00
Your Price : _____

Calvin Klein
Eternity
3.4 oz EDT Sp
3.4 oz After Shave Balm
2.6 oz Deodorant $84.00
Your Price : _____

Calvin Klein
Eterenity
3.4 oz After Shave Splash
3.4 oz EDT Sp $82.00
Your Price : _____

Calvin Klein
Euphoria
3.4 oz After Shave Splash
3.4 oz EDT Sp $86.00
Your Price : _____

Calvin Klein
Euphoria
3.4 oz EDT Sp
3.4 oz After Shave Balm
2.6 oz Deodorant $86.00
Your Price : _____

Calvin Klein
Obsession
4.0 oz EDT Sp
3.4 oz After Shave Balm
2.6 oz Deodorant $84.00
Your Price : _____

Calvin Klein
Obsession
4.0 oz After Shave Splash
4.0 oz EDT Sp $84.00
Your Price : _____

Carolina Herrera
212 Men NYC
3.4 oz After Shave Balm
3.4 oz EDT Sp $91.00
Your Price : _____

Carolina Herrera
212 Men NYC
3.4 oz EDT Sp
2.1 oz Deodorant Stick $ 91.00
Your Price : _____

Carolina Herrera
212 Sexy Men
3.4 oz EDT Sp
2.1 oz Deodorant Stick $ 91.00
Your Price : _____

Carolina Herrera
212 VIP Men
3.4 oz EDT Bath & Shower Gel
3.4 oz EDT Sp $ 91.00
Your Price : _____

Carolina Herrera
CH
3.4 oz After Shave Balm
3.4 oz EDT Sp $ 95.00
Your Price : _____

Carolina Herrera
Herrera for Men
3.4 oz After Shave Balm
3.4 oz EDT Sp $ 85.00
Your Price : _____

Carolina Herrera
Herrera for Men
3.4 oz EDT Sp
2.1 oz Deodorant Stick $ 90.00
Your Price : _____

Cartier
Eau de Cartier
3.3 oz All Over Shampoo
3.3 oz EDT Sp $ 75.00
Your Price : _____

Cartier
pasha de Cartier
3.3 oz EDT Sp
2.5 oz Deodorant Stick $ 112.00
Your Price : _____

Davidoff
Cool Water
4.2 oz EDT Sp
2.5 oz Shower Gel
2.5 oz After Shave $ 72.00
Your Price : _____

Dolce & Gabbana
Pour Homme
4.2 oz EDT Sp
3.3 oz After Shave Balm
1.6 oz Shower Gel $90.00
Your Price : _____

Dolce & Gabbana
Light Blue
4.2 oz EDT Sp
3.3 oz After Shave Balm
1.6 oz Shower Gel $90.00
Your Price : _____

Dolce & Gabbana
Light Blue
4.2 oz EDT Sp
1.0 oz EDT Sp $94.00
Your Price : _____

Dolce & Gabbana
The One
3.3 oz EDT Sp
1.0 oz EDT Sp $94.00
Your Price : _____

Dolce & Gabbana
The One
3.3 oz EDT Sp
3.3 oz After Shave Balm
1.6 oz Shower Gel $90.00
Your Price : _____

Dunhill
Dunhill Desire
5.0 oz After Shave Balm
3.4 oz EDT Sp $ 80.00
Your Price : _____

Ed Hardy
Born Wild
3.4 oz EDT Sp
3.0 oz Hair & Body Wash Shampoo
2.75 Alcohol Free Deodorant
    Key Chain $ 80.00
Your Price : _____

Giorgio Armani
Acqua Di Gio
3.4 oz EDT Sp
2.6 oz Deodorant Stick $ 87.00
Your Price : _____

Giorgio Armani
Acqua Di Gio
3.4 oz EDT Sp
2.5 oz After Shave Balm
2.6 oz Deodorant $87.00
Your Price : _____

Giorgio Armani
Armani Code
2.5 oz EDT Sp
1.0 oz EDT Sp $88.00
Your Price : _____

Giorgio Armani
Armani Code
2.5 oz EDT Sp
2.5 oz After Shave Balm
2.6 oz Deodorant $85.00
Your Price : _____

Giorgio Armani
Acqua Di Gio
3.4 oz EDT Sp
1.0 oz EDT Sp $89.00
Your Price : _____

Givenchy
Gentlemen Only
3.3 oz Hair & Body Shower Gel
3.3 oz EDT Sp $ 90.00
Your Price :_____

Givenchy
Pour Homme Blue Label
3.4 oz EDT Sp
2.5 oz After Shave Balm
2.5 oz Shower Gel $92.00
Your Price :_____

Givenchy
Play Sport
6.7 oz Hair & Body Shower Gel
3.3 oz EDT Sp $ 80.00
Your Price :_____

Gucci
Guilty
3.0 oz EDT Sp
2.5 oz After Shave Balm
1.6 oz Shower Gel $93.00
Your Price :_____

Gucci
Gucci Pour Homme
3.0 oz EDT Sp
2.5 oz After Shave Balm
1.6 oz Shower Gel $93.00
Your Price :_____

Gucci
Gucci Pour Homme
3.0 oz After Shave Splash
3.0 oz EDT Sp $95.00
Your Price :_____

Guy Laroche
Drakkar Noir
3.4 oz EDT Sp
3.4 oz After Shave Balm
2.6 oz Deodorant $ 70.00
Your Price :_____

Hermes
Voyage D'Hermes
3.3 oz EDT Sp
1.0 oz Perfumed Body Lotion
1.0 oz Shaver Gel $ 115.00
Your Price :_____

Hugo Boss
Boss The Scent
2.4 oz Deodorant
1.6 oz Shower Gel
3.4 oz EDT Sp $90.00
Your Price :_____

Hugo Boss
Boss Bottled
2x1.6 oz Shower Gel
1.6 oz EDT Sp $ 80.00
Your Price :_____

Hugo Boss
Boss Orange
3.3 oz EDT Sp
1.6 oz After Shave Balm
1.6 oz Shower Gel $ 75.00
Your Price :_____

Hugo Boss
Hugo Man
5.0 oz EDT Sp
2.5 oz
1.6 oz Perfumed Shower Gel $ 90.00
Your Price :_____

Issey Miyake
L'eau d'Issey
4.2 oz EDT Sp
2.5 oz Shower Gel
0.5 oz EDT Sp $ 100.00
Your Price :_____

Jimmy Choo
Man
3.3 oz EDT Sp
3.3 oz After Shave Balm
2.5 oz Deodorant $92.00
Your Price :_____

Jimmy Choo
Man Ice
3.3 oz EDT Sp
3.3 oz After Shave Balm
3.3 oz Deodorant $92.00
Your Price :_____

John Varvatos
Artisan Black
4.2 oz EDT Sp
3.4 oz After Shave Gel $ 90.00
Your Price :_____

John Varvatos
U.S.A.
3.4 oz EDT Sp
3.4 oz Shower Gel
2.6 oz Deodorant Stick $ 72.00
Your Price :_____

Joop
Joop ! Homme
4.2 oz EDT Sp
2.5 oz After Shave $ 72.00
Your Price :_____

Juicy Couture
Dirty English
4.2 oz After Shave Lotion
3.4 oz EDT Sp
2.6 oz Deodorant Stick $ 78.00
Your Price :_____

Kenneth Cole
Black
3.4 oz EDT Sp
3.4 oz After Shave Balm
2.6 oz Deodorant $82.00
Your Price :_____

Kenneth Cole
Reaction
3.4 oz Hair & Body Wash
3.4 oz After Shave Gel
3.4 oz EDT Sp $ 78.00
Your Price :_____

Lacoste
Challenge
3.0 oz EDT Sp
1.0 oz EDT Sp $ 72.00
Your Price :_____

Lacoste
Eau De Lacoste Blanc
5.0 oz Shower Gel
3.3 oz EDT Sp $ 76.00
Your Price :_____

Lacoste
Eau De Lacoste Noir
5.0 oz Shower Gel
3.3 oz EDT Sp $76.00
Your Price :_____

Lacoste
Eau De Lacoste Vert
5.0 oz Shower Gel
3.3 oz EDT Sp $ 76.00
Your Price :_____

karl Lagerfeld
Lagerfeld
5.0 oz Shower Gel
3.3 oz EDT Sp $75.00
Your Price :_____

Liz Clairborne
Curve
4.2 oz EDT Sp
2.5 oz Hair & Body Wash
2.5 oz Skin Soother
0.5 oz Cologne Spray $ 60.00
Your Price :_____

Liz Claiborne
Bora Bora
3.4 oz Hair & Body Wash
3.4 oz Body Moisturizer
3.4 oz Cologne Spray $ 60.00
Your Price :_____

Liz Claiborne
Curve Crush
4.2 oz EDT Sp
2.5 oz Hair & Body Wash
2.5 oz Skin Soother
0.5 oz Cologne Spray $ 60.00
Your Price :_____

Lucky
Lucky Number 6
6.7 oz Exfoliating Shower Gel
3.4 oz EDT Sp $ 60.00
Your Price :_____

Mont Blanc
Presence
3.3 oz After Shave Balm
3.3 oz All over
2.5 oz EDT Sp $ 92.00
Your Price :_____

Mont Blanc
Legend Intense
3.3 oz After Shave Balm
3.3 oz Shwer Gel
3.3 oz EDT Sp $95.00
Your Price :_____

Mont Blanc
Legend Spirit
3.3 oz After Shave Balm
3.3 oz Shower Gel
3.3 oz EDT Sp $92.00
Your Price : _____

Mont Blanc
Legend
3.3 oz After Shave Balm
3.3 oz All over Shower Gel
3.3 oz EDT Sp $ 92.00
Your Price : _____

Paco Rabanne
One Million
3.4 oz EDT Sp
3.4 oz Shower Gel $88.00
Your Price : _____

Paco Rabanne
1 Million
3.4 oz EDT Sp
3.4 oz After Shave Lotion
2.2 oz Deodorant Stick $ 96.00
Your Price : _____

Paco Rabanne
Invictus
3.4 oz EDT Sp
2.5 oz After Shave Balm
2.5 Deodorant $91.00
Your Price : _____

Paco Rabanne
Black XS
3.3 oz EDT Sp
2.7 oz Deodorant Stick $ 65.00
Your Price : _____

Paco Rabanne
Pour Homme
3.4 oz EDT Sp
2.5 oz Deodorant Stick $ 76.00
Your Price : _____

Paco Rabanne
Ultraviolet Man
3.4 oz EDT Sp
2.5 oz Deodorant $ 70.00
Your Price : _____

Paco Rabanne
XS
3.4 oz EDT Sp
2.5 oz Deodorant Stick $ 62.00
Your Price : _____

Paris Hilton
Paris Hilton
3.4 oz EDT Sp
3.0 oz Hair & Body Wash
2.75 oz Deodorant Stick $ 70.00
Your Price : _____

Paul Sebastian
Design
3.4 oz Cologne Sp
3.4 oz After Shave $ 58.00
Your Price : _____

Paul Sebastian
Paul Sebastian
4.0 oz Cologne Sp
4.0 oz After Shave
2.5 oz Deodorant $ 59.00
Your Price : _____

Perry Ellis
360
3.4 oz EDT Sp
3.0 oz Shower Gel
2.75 oz Deodorant
0.25 oz EDT Sp $80.00
Your Price : _____

Perry Ellis
360 Black
3.4 oz EDT Sp
3.0 oz After Shave Balm
2.75 oz Deodorant Stick
0.25 oz EDT Sp $ 80.00
Your Price : _____

Perry Ellis
360 Green
3.4 oz EDT Sp
3.0 oz After Shave Balm
3.0 oz Shower Gel
0.25 oz EDT Sp $80.00
Your Price : _____

Perry Ellis
Perry Ellis 18
3.4 oz EDT Sp
3.0 oz After Shave Balm
3.0 oz Shower Gel
0.25 oz EDT Sp $80.00
Your Price : _____

Perry Ellis
360 Red
3.4 oz EDT Sp
3.0 oz After Shave Balm
2.75 oz Deodorant Stick
0.25 oz EDT Sp $ 90.00
Your Price :_____

Perry Ellis
Aqua
3.4 oz EDT Sp
3.0 oz After Shave Gel
3.0 oz Shower Gel
2.75 oz Deodorant $ 85.00
Your Price :_____

Perry Ellis
Perry Ellis 18 Intense
3.4 oz EDT Sp
3.0 oz After Shave Balm
2.75 oz Deodorant Stick
0.25 oz EDT Sp $ 80.00
Your Price :_____

Perry Ellis
Perry Ellis M
3.4 oz EDT Sp
3.0 oz After Shave Gel
2.75 oz Deodorant Stick
0.25 oz EDT Sp $ 80.00
Your Price :_____

Perry Ellis
Perry Man
3.4 oz EDT Sp
3.0 oz After Shave Gel
2.75 oz Deodorant Stick
0.25 oz EDT Sp $ 80.00
Your Price :_____

Perry Ellis
Portfolio
3.4 oz EDT Sp
3.0 oz Hair & Body Wash
3.0 oz After Shave Balm
0.25 oz EDT Sp $ 80.00
Your Price :_____

Perry Ellis
Reserve
3.4 oz EDT Sp
3.0 oz Shower Gel
3.0 oz After Shave Balm
0.25 oz EDT Sp $ 80.00
Your Price :_____

Prada
Luna Rossa
3.4 oz EDT Sp
3.4 oz Shower Gel $ 95.00
Your Price :_____

Ralph Lauren
Polo Black
4.2 oz EDT Sp
2.6 oz Deodorant $ 86.00
Your Price :_____

Ralph Lauren
Polo Blue
4.2 oz EDT Sp
2.6 oz Deodorant $ 86.00
Your Price :_____

RRalph Lauren
Polo
4.0 oz EDT Sp
2.1 oz Deodorant
1.36 oz EDT Sp $95.00
Your Price :_____

Ralph Lauren
Polo Red Intense
4.2 oz EDP Sp
2.6 oz Deodorant
1.36 oz EDP Sp $102.00
Your Price :_____

Ralph Lauren
Polo Red
4.2 oz EDT Sp
2.6 oz Deodorant
1.36 oz EDT Sp $95.00
Your Price :_____

Ralph Lauren
Polo Blue
4.2 oz EDT Sp
2.6 oz Deodorant
1.36 oz EDT Sp $95.00
Your Price :_____

Ralph Lauren
Polo Black
4.2 oz EDT Sp
2.6 oz Deodorant
1.36 oz EDT Sp $95.00
Your Price :_____

Sean John
I am King
2.5 oz After Shave Balm
1.7 oz EDT Sp $ 65.00
Your Price :_____

Versace
Eros
1.7 oz EDT Sp
1.7 oz Shower Gel
1.7 oz After Shave Balm $ 70.00
Your Price :_____

Versace
Eros
3.4 oz EDT Sp
3.4 oz After Shave
3.4 oz Shower Gel
0.3 oz EDT Sp $92.00
Your Price :_____

Versace
Eros
3.4 oz EDT Sp
3.4 oz Shower Gel $ 88.00
Your Price :_____

Versace
Man Eau Fraiche
3.4 oz EDT Sp
3.4 oz Perfumed Bath & Shower Gel $ 81.00
Your Price :_____

Versace
Man Eau Fraiche
1.7 oz EDT Sp
1.7 oz Perfumed Shower Gel
1.7 oz Perfumed Shampoo $ 66.00
Your Price :_____

Versace
Dylan Blue
3.4 oz EDT Sp
3.4 oz After Shave Balm
3.4 oz Shower Gel
0.3 oz EDT Sp $92.00
Your Price :_____

Versace
Eau Fraiche
3.4 oz EDT Sp
3.4 oz After Shave
3.4 oz Shower Gel
0.3 oz EDT Sp $85.00
Your Price :_____

Versace
Versace Pour Homme
3.4 oz EDT Sp
3.4 oz Hair & Body Shampoo $ 84.00
Your Price :_____

Versace
Versace Pour Homme
1.7 oz EDT Sp
1.7 oz Perfumed Shower Gel
1.7 oz Perfumed Shampoo $ 67.00
Your Price :_____

Versace
Pour Homme
3.4 oz EDT Sp
3.4 oz After Shave
3.4 oz Shower Gel
0.3 oz EDT Sp $88.00
Your Price :_____

Yves Saint Laurent
L'Homme
3.3 oz EDT Sp
2.6 oz Deodorant
1.6 oz Shower Gel $98.00
Your Price :_____

Yves Saint Laurent
Kouros
3.3 oz EDT Sp 80.00
Your Price :_____

Yves Saint Laurent
La Nuit de L'Homme
3.3 oz EDT Sp
3.3 oz Shawer Gel $ 96.00
Your Price :_____

Yves Saint Laurent
L'Homme Libre
3.3 oz EDT Sp
2.6 oz Deodorant
1.6 oz After Shave Gel $ 98.00
Your Price :_____

Yves Saint Laurent
L'Homme Sport
3.3 oz EDT Sp
2.6 oz Deodorant
1.6 oz Shower Gel $98.00
Your Price :_____

Vince Camuto
Vince Camuto
3.4 oz EDT Sp
5.0 oz After Shave Balm
0.5 oz EDT Sp $82.00
Your Price :_____